SPSS/PC+ Step By Step
A Simple Guide and Reference

All examples, instructions,
and datasets in this text
will work with both
SPSS Version 4.0 and
SPSS Version 5.0

SPSS/PC+ Step By Step
A Simple Guide and Reference

Darren George
Canadian Union College

Paul Mallery
University of California, Los Angeles

Wadsworth Publishing Company

I(T)P™ An International Thomson Publishing Company

Belmont • Albany • Bonn • Boston • Cincinnati • Detroit • London • Madrid • Melbourne
Mexico City • New York • Paris • San Francisco • Singapore • Tokyo • Toronto • Washington

Statistics Editor: Stan Loll
Editorial Assistant: Claire Masson
Production Editor: Carol Carreon Lombardi
Designer: Lisa Berman
Print Buyer: Diana Spence
Permissions Editor: Peggy Meehan
Copy Editor: George Dyke
Cover: The Visual Group
Printer: Malloy Lithographing, Inc.

ISBN 0-534-22068-1

Printed in the United States of America
1 2 3 4 5 6 7 8 9 10—01 00 99 98 97 96 95

For more information, contact Wadsworth Publishing Company:

Wadsworth Publishing Company
10 Davis Drive
Belmont, California 94002, USA

International Thomson Publishing Europe
Berkshire House 168-173
High Holborn
London, WC1V 7AA, England

Thomas Nelson Australia
102 Dodds Street
South Melbourne 3205
Victoria, Australia

Nelson Canada
1120 Birchmount Road
Scarborough, Ontario
Canada M1K 5G4

International Thomson Editores
Campos Eliseos 385, Piso 7
Col. Polanco
11560 México D.F. México

International Thomson Publishing GmbH
Königswinterer Strasse 418
53227 Bonn, Germany

International Thomson Publishing Asia
221 Henderson Road
#05-10 Henderson Building
Singapore 0315

International Thomson Publishing Japan
Hirakawacho Kyowa Building, 3F
2-2-1 Hirakawacho
Chiyoda-ku, Tokyo 102, Japan

Contents

Preface vii

Chapter 1   Overview of Statistics Step by Step for SPSS/PC+ 1

Chapter 2   How to Create a New Data File 8

Chapter 3   Editing a Data File 15

Chapter 4   Formatting the Data File 19

Chapter 5   The LIST, COMPUTE, IF, RECODE, SELECT IF, PROCESS IF, and SORT Commands: Managing Data 27

Chapter 6   The FREQUENCIES Command: Frequencies, Bar Charts, Histograms, Percentiles 39

Chapter 7   The DESCRIPTIVES Command: Measures of Central Tendency, Variability, Deviation from Normality, Size, and Stability 46

Chapter 8   The CROSSTABS Command: Crosstabulation and Chi-Square (χ^2) Tests of Independence 53

Chapter 9   The MEANS Command: Describing Subpopulation Differences 62

Chapter 10   The PLOT Command: Scatter Plots, Regression Plots, and Overlay Plots 67

Chapter 11   The CORRELATION Command: Correlations and the Correlation Matrix 75

Chapter 12   The T-TEST Command: Independent-Samples, Paired-Samples, and One-Sample Tests 83

Chapter 13   The ONEWAY Command: One-Way Analysis of Variance 92

Chapter 14   The ANOVA Command: Two-Way Analysis of Variance 100

Chapter 15   The ANOVA Command: Three-Way Analysis of Variance and the Influence of Covariates 107

Chapter 16   The MANOVA Command: Multivariate T Tests and Hotelling's T^2 120

Chapter 17   The MANOVA Command: Multivariate Analysis of Variance and Covariance 128

Chapter 18   The MANOVA Command: Multivariate Analysis of Variance with Repeated Measures and Within-Subjects Factors 139

Chapter 19   The REGRESSION Command: Simple Linear Regression and Curvilinear Regression 152

Chapter 20   The REGRESSION Command: Multiple Regression Analysis 163

Chapter 21   The FACTOR Command: Factor Analysis 175

Chapter 22   The CLUSTER Command: Cluster Analysis 189

Chapter 23   The DSCRIMINANT Command: Discriminant Analysis 202

Chapter 24   The RELIABILITY Command: Coefficient Alpha (α) and Split-Half Reliability 218

Chapter 25   The NLR Command: Nonlinear Regression 228

Chapter 26   The LOGISTIC REGRESSION Command: Logistic Regression Analysis 237

Chapter 27   The HILOGLINEAR Command: Hierarchical Log-Linear Models 246

Chapter 28   The LOGLINEAR Command: Nonhierarchical Log-Linear Models 258

Chapter 29   The PROBIT Command: Probit and Logit Analysis 266

Chapter 30   The NPAR Command: Nonparametric Tests 276

Data Disk 289

Glossary 293

References 308

Error Messages 311

Index 316

PREFACE

SPSS is a complicated program by any standards. The thousands of hours Paul and I have spent dealing with SPSS procedures has revealed just *how* complicated it is. Despite this complexity, however, SPSS is a powerful tool that is capable of conducting just about any type of data analysis used in the social sciences. While mathematics is generally thought to be the language of science, data analysis is the language of research. Research in many fields is critical for human progress, and as long as there is research, there will be the need to analyze data. The present book is designed to make data analysis more comprehendable and less toxic.

In our teaching at UCLA and other places, Paul and I have frequently encountered students so traumatized by the professor who cheerily says "Analyze these data on SPSS; get the manuals if you don't know how," that they dropped the course rather than continue the struggle. It is in response to this anguish that the present book was conceived. My background has been teaching high school mathematics, and my greatest pleasure in teaching was the challenge of making a process that was intrinsically complex as clear as possible. The ultimate goal in all our efforts with the present book has been to make SPSS procedures, above all else, clear.

As the book started to take shape, a second goal began to emerge. In addition to making SPSS procedures clear to the beginner, we wanted to create a tool that was an effective reference for anyone conducting data analysis. This involved the expansion of the original concept to include essentially all major statistical procedures that SPSS covers. The results of almost two years of effort you now hold in your hands.

While the first 15 chapters of the book would be understandable to many with very limited statistical background, the final 15 chapters involve procedures that progressively require a more secure statistical grounding. Those 15 chapters have provided our greatest challenge. At the beginning of each chapter we spend several pages describing the procedure that follows. But, how can one adequately describe factor analysis or discriminant analysis in five or six pages? The answer is simple: The procedures must be described at a common sense conceptual level that avoids excessive detail and excessive emphasis on computation. However, writing those introductions has not been at all simple. The chapter introductions are the most painstakingly worked sections of the entire book. Although we acknowledge the absence of much detail in our explanation of most procedures, we feel that we have done an adequate job at a project that few would even attempt. How successful have we been at achieving clarity in very limited space? You, the reader, will be our ultimate judge.

SPSS Inc. has produced three manuals to describe everything that their package of programs attempts to accomplish. These three volumes, more than 1000 pages of fine print documentation, are, if nothing else, comprehensive. Anything that SPSS is able to do is described in the manuals. For the experienced researcher, ownership of the manuals is required. We cannot cover in 300 pages what SPSS does in over 1000. However, we are convinced that 95% of analyses that are *ever* conducted in the social sciences could be accomplished with the information presented in our book. For the additional 5% we frequently refer the reader to the SPSS manuals when the level of specificity required extends beyond the scope of the present volume.

AUTHORS' BIOGRAPHICAL SKETCHES

Darren George is currently an assistant professor of Psychology at Canadian Union College (College Heights, AB, T0C 0Z0, 403-782-3381, Ext. 311), where he teaches personality and social psychology and research methods. He completed his M.A. in Experimental Psychology (1982) at California Sate University, Fullerton; taught high school mathematics for nine years (1980-1989) at Mark Keppel High School (Alhambra, CA) and Mountain View High School (El Monte, CA); then completed a Psychology Ph.D. at UCLA (1992) with emphases of personality psychology, social psychology, and measurement and psychometrics.

Paul Mallery is currently the Chair of the Psychology Department at La Sierra University (4700 Pierce Street, Riverside, CA, 92515, 909-785-2528), where he teaches social psychology, experimental methodology, and SPSS. He received his Ph.D. in Social Psychology from the University of California, Los Angeles (UCLA), with emphases in statistics and political psychology. Paul formerly worked as a computer specialist, both programming and teaching computer usage.

ACKNOWLEDGMENTS

As we look over the creative efforts of the past two years, Paul and I wish to acknowledge mostly people we have never met. The present manuscript has been reviewed by six different social science researchers, three different statisticians, and two detail editors at Wadsworth. Their efforts have helped to create a clear, consistent, accurate, and above all, a usable manual. Our gratitude is extended to: Grant Blank, University of Georgia; Ronald Bosch, University of Iowa; Hector Correa, GSPIA University of Pittsburgh; Richard J. Harris, University of Texas at San Antonio; Carl J. Huberty, University of Georgia; Ellen Koenigsberg, City University of New York at Baruch; Chao-Ying J. Peng, Indiana University; Lonnie Roy, University of Texas at Arlington; and Kay Um, Florida State University. We further wish to express appreciation to Stan Loll, Claire Masson, George Dyke, and Carol Carreon for their invaluable assistance in creating the present work. And then there's the standard (but no less appreciated) acknowledgment of our families and friends who endured us while we wrote this.

SPSS/PC+ Step By Step
A Simple Guide and Reference

Chapter 1

Overview of Statistics Step by Step for SPSS/PC+

This book is designed to give you the step-by-step instructions necessary to do almost any type of data analysis using SPSS/PC+ Version 4.0 for IBM or compatible computers. This software was created by S.P.S.S. (Statistical Package for the Social Sciences), a Chicago-based firm that has been developing and refining their package of statistical programs since the mid-1960s.

NECESSARY SKILLS FOR THE USER

You should have certain limited knowledge of statistics and a general acquaintance with the use of a computer. Each issue is addressed in the next two paragraphs.

Statistics: The user should have had at least a basic course in statistics or be in the process of taking such a course. While it is true that this book devotes the first two or three pages of each chapter to a description of the statistical procedure that follows, these descriptions are designed to refresh the reader's memory, *not* to instruct the novice. While it is certainly possible for the novice to follow the steps and get output (one author's 10-year-old son did a 2-way ANOVA with no prior instructions), we feel that a fundamental grounding in statistics is important for an understanding of which procedures to use and how to interpret the results. In addition, while the first 15 chapters should be understandable by individuals with limited statistical background, the final 15 chapters deal with much more complex and involved types of analyses. These chapters require substantial grounding in the statistical techniques involved.

Computer knowledge: Your knowledge of the computer may be quite limited. The following, however, are necessary: You must (1) have access to an IBM or compatible personal computer that has SPSS/PC+ Version 4.0 installed, (2) know how to turn the computer on, (3) have a working knowledge of the keys on the keyboard, and (4) know what the DOS prompt is. This book will take you the rest of the way. If you are working with a network of computers (many colleges and universities use networks) or have Windows installed, the way to *access* SPSS/PC+ may be different from the single step shown in the pages that follow. In Chapter 2 we address this concern.

OVERVIEW

This chapter introduces the major concepts discussed in this book, giving a brief overview of the book's organization and the basic tools that you will need in order to use it.

If you want to run a particular statistical procedure, have used SPSS/PC+ before, and already know which analysis you wish to conduct, then you should read the "Typographical Conventions" section in this chapter (pages 4-6) and then go to the chapter in the last portion of the book (Chapters 6 through 30) that will tell you exactly what you have to do in order to get the output you want.

If, however, you are new to SPSS/PC+, then this chapter will give you some important background information that will be useful whenever you use this book. The last section of this chapter ("Note for Experienced Users") should be read only by people with enough experience using SPSS/PC+ to understand phrases like *ASCII data* and *system file*.

THIS BOOK'S ORGANIZATION, CHAPTER BY CHAPTER

This book was created to describe the crucial concepts of analyzing data and doing statistical analysis of data. Three things are necessary in order to do statistics: (1) You must type data into the computer, (2) your data must be organized or *formatted* so SPSS can read it accurately, and (3) you must tell SPSS what type of analysis you wish to do.

After this introductory chapter, Chapters 2 and 3 deal with the first step—creating a data file. They are both short, simple chapters that tell you how to enter data and how to edit your data when you make mistakes (and you will!).

Chapters 4 and 5 deal with the second step—organizing or formatting data. Chapter 4 deals specifically with formatting data and labeling variables, while Chapter 5 (a longer and more involved chapter) deals with manipulation of data, such as creating new variables, reordering or restructuring your files, or selecting portions of data for analysis.

Chapters 6 through 30 then address step 3—analyzing your data or *running* statistics. It is important to note that each of these analysis chapters is self-contained. Even for the beginner, if he or she were instructed to do *t*-tests on certain data, Chapter 12 would give complete instructions for accomplishing that procedure. In the Step-by-Step portion, step 1 is always "create a data file or edit (if necessary) an already existing file," and the reader is then referred to Chapters 2 and 3 for instructions if needed. The second step is always "format your data . . ." and the reader is referred to Chapter 4. Then the steps that follow designate exactly how to conduct a *t*-test. We now briefly describe the topics covered in these final 25 chapters.

Chapters 6 through 11 describe the most fundamental data analysis methods available, including frequencies, bar charts, histograms, and percentiles (Chapter 6); descriptive statistics such as means, medians, modes, skewness, and ranges (Chapter 7); crosstabulations and chi-square tests of independence (Chapter 8); subpopulation means (Chapter 9); several different types of plots (Chapter 10); and correlations between variables (Chapter 11).

The next group of chapters (Chapter 12 through Chapter 18) explains ways of testing for differences between different subgroups within your data, through the use of *t*-tests (Chapter 12), ANOVAs (Chapters 13, 14, and 15), multivariate *T*-tests (Chapter 16), MANOVAs and MANCOVAs (Chapter 17), and MANOVAs with within-subject factors or repeated measures (Chapter 18).

Chapter 19 describes simple linear regression and regression with curvilinear trends, and Chapter 20 discusses the procedure for running multiple regression analyses. Following this, factor analysis (Chapter 21), cluster analysis (Chapter 22), discriminant analysis (Chapter 23), and reliability analysis (Chapter 24) are described.

The last six chapters deal with procedures that are only infrequently run in the social sciences, but they are described here because when they are needed they are indispensable. Chapter 25 describes nonlinear regression, and Chapter 26 describes logistic regression analysis. Chapters 27 and 28 describe hierarchical and nonhierarchical log-linear models, respectively. Chapter 29 discusses probit and logit analysis, and, finally, the most common nonparametric tests are discussed in Chapter 30.

AN INTRODUCTION TO THE EXAMPLE

A single example is used throughout the first 18 chapters of this book. As the material becomes more complex in the final 12 chapters, it has often been necessary to select different examples to reflect the particular procedures that are presented. Examples are useful because often, things that appear to be very confusing in the SPSS/PC+ documentation become quite clear when you see an example of how they are done. Although only the primary example is described here, there are a total of nine data sets that are used to demonstrate procedures throughout the book. A disk has been included with this manual that includes all nine data files with the same file names as used in the book. This disk can be of substantial benefit to you as you practice some of the processes presented here without the added burden of having to input the data. It is suggested that you make generous use of this disk by trying different procedures and then comparing your results with those included in the output section of each chapter.

The main example (the one used in the first 18 chapters) has been designed so that it may be used to demonstrate most of the statistical procedures presented here. Using only one example is of benefit to you because (a) you won't have to acquaint yourself with new examples while you are learning new SPSS/PC+ commands, and (b) you can actually experiment and practice on this one example without having to continually type in new data.

The example consists of a single data file, used by a teacher who teaches three sections of a class with approximately 35 students in each section. For each student, the following information is on file:

> ID number
> Name
> Gender
> Ethnicity
> Year in school
> Upper- or lower-division classperson
> Previous GPA
> Section
> Whether or not he or she came to review sessions
> Whether or not he or she did the extra credit
> The scores on five 10-point quizzes and one 75-point final

In Chapter 5 we describe how to create four new variables. In all presentations that follow, these four variables are included:

> The total number of points
> The final percent
> The final grade attained
> Whether the student passed or failed the course

The example data file (the entire data set is displayed at the end of Chapter 2) will be used as the example in the data entry and formatting chapters (Chapters 2 through 5). If you follow the procedures described in these chapters, you will have a working example data file that may be used through the first 18 chapters of this book. Yes, the same material is recorded on the included disk for purpose of analysis in later chapters, but it may be useful for you to practice data entry, formatting, and certain data manipulations with this data set. Of course, if you have your own data to work with, all the better.

One final note: All of the data in the grades file are totally fictional, so any findings exist only because we created them when we made the file.

TYPOGRAPHICAL CONVENTIONS

Since the details of what you need to type may sometimes be confusing, the following typographical conventions have been developed that will hopefully make everything clear:

The boxes: In all chapters what you *do* to accomplish a particular statistical analysis is included in page-width boxes.   What is written *after* each box is a brief description of what you just did and, in some instances, why it was done that way.   If you already know what you did or are not concerned about why you did it, you may simply do what is instructed in the box and ignore the material that follows.

Numbering: There are two types of numbering.   The first is the sequential numbering of the "to do" steps.

---

1) Step numbers: Each boxed step will have a number, like the "1)" at the beginning of this box.   Sometimes, you have the option of doing a step in more than one way; in these cases, there may be more than one version of a particular step.   Each will have its own step number (like 1a and 1b, for example), and each represents an alternative way of doing step 1.

The second type of numbering identifies particular lines within the box for explanation in the space following the box.

Sometimes, a box will contain several lines of information. When it does, each line	1
will usually be numbered, like this. --->	2
These line numbers will be referred to in the text to explain particular parts of the	3
information within the box.	4

LINE 2   The example above identifies with an arrow the second line number.   Beneath the box (right here) is where description about the second line takes place.

Command keys: Any key that gives the computer a command will be outlined within the page-width box.   What follows would be interpreted, "Press the **F7** key."

F7

Command keys that follow each other within the box should be pressed sequentially in the order indicated.   For instance, the following means, "Press the **F10** key, then press the **E**, then press the **RETURN** (also called **CARRIAGE RETURN** or **ENTER**) key."

F10   E   ↵

Finally, if two boxes are connected, press the two keys at the same time.   What follows means, "Hold down the **ALT** key and the **M** key at the same time."

ALT ⊣ M

Letters, numbers, words, punctuation: Some keys give the computer commands. The **ALT**, **M**, **E**, **F7** and others shown above are examples. Keys that do *not* give the computer commands such as numbers, letters, and punctuation that are used to make up words or sentences will be indicated by UPPERCASE letters in **BOLDFACE**. These should be typed into the computer exactly as they appear. In most instances, words will be part of the *command file*, which instructs the computer what analysis to perform on your data. In the box that follows, the "**LIST VARIABLES**", the "**=**", and the "**.**" are all part of the instructions given to SPSS/PC+, and they constitute a portion of the command file.

LIST VARIABLES = <u>LASTNAME</u> <u>FIRSTNAM</u> <u>QUIZ1</u>**.**

Material from the examples: Inside the boxes all material from our examples will be UPPERCASE, but normally shaded (not boldface) and <u>UNDERLINED</u>. This material is just for the sake of illustration and should be replaced by similar information in your own data file (unless you are working with the sample file). In the example above, the underlined words (<u>LASTNAME</u>, <u>FIRSTNAM</u>, and <u>QUIZ1</u>) are three of the variables in our example. The fact that the spaces *between* the words are not underlined indicates that spaces between variable names are required for SPSS/PC+ to read variable names properly.

Spacing: The spacing we show in the command files will ALWAYS be correct. There are many instances where alternative spacing is acceptable, but unless you want to hunt through 1,340 pages of the SPSS/PC+ manuals to find alternatives, we suggest that you always use the spacing that we show.

Italics: *Italicized text* refers to line numbers, step numbers, and general comments. When you see *italicized text* inside a box, don't type what it says; this is for *you* to read, not for the computer.

---

5) Position cursor under "R" of the "RECODE" | F10 | | C | *1*

LINE 1 The first line of the 5th sequence step instructs us to position the cursor under the **R** of the word RECODE (which is already in the command file), then press **F10**, and then press **C**.

NOTE FOR EXPERIENCED USERS

If you're not experienced with using SPSS/PC+, then skip this section.

If you already know how to create files, make system files, and so forth, this section will tell you how to navigate through this book with minimal tedium.

Experienced users should use this book as a reference. This book assumes that you will be creating your data file as an ASCII file using the SPSS/PC+ review editor or creating a similar file on another word processor and importing it to the SPSS/PC+ editor. Chapter 3 will provide a good summary of the use of keys and commands for editing an ASCII file under the SPSS/PC+ review editor. Once the data file is created, Chapter 4 guides you through the process of reading in your data file (using the **DATA LIST** command), creating **VARIABLE LABELS** and **VALUE LABELS**, and saving everything as a system file. (Chapter 5 will prove a useful reference of the various commands used to transform data.) Although a certain amount of flexibility is lost in always using a system file as the starting point for the various statistical procedures, we think that novice users will appreciate the simpler, step-by-step approach, and experienced users (like yourself) will not be significantly hindered by it.

All of the remaining chapters assume that you are starting from an SPSS/PC+ system file. These chapters (6-30) will probably be the ones that will be most useful for you. When you have to run a particular analysis, each chapter will provide a summary not only of the basic steps needed to perform that analysis (serving as a valuable memory refresher) but also of exactly what that statistical procedure is best suited for (in case you need a reminder). All of the important elements of the printout you will get are also described (for although you may remember what F's and t's are, BETAs and POUTs often need a reminder or explanation).

Chapter 2

How to Create a New Data File

The process described in this chapter is generally the first step to take when you want to compute statistics on some set of data: Type the data into the computer. This is a fairly simple process, but you do have to be careful. The basic idea is to enter all of the variables measured for each subject (or observation of some sort) in one or more lines, using exactly the same spacing and format for each subject.

These instructions assume that you are starting SPSS from within DOS (the most common disk operating system for IBM and compatible computers). There are actually several other operating systems that could be used to control everything within your computer, such as Windows and OS/2. Unfortunately, there are many different ways of doing the first step. Our method assumes that you are using the simplest, most common method. The first thing that you should do, when you turn on your computer to use SPSS, is to change into the directory that you want to use for all SPSS procedures. This operation also varies among different computers. You may need help from someone who is computer literate to assist you with this step. Once you have done this, you are ready to perform step 1. The DOS prompt may be many different things, depending on how your computer is configured; but whatever it says, it will end with a " > " and a cursor to identify the place where you will begin typing.

Note for experienced computer users: There may be times that you want to read your data file from, or write your data file to, a particular disk drive or directory. If you wish, you may specify the disk drive or directory when you type in the file name. If you want to specify a particular disk drive, type the character name of the disk drive (usually A, B, C, or D) before you type the name of the data file, followed by a colon and backslash. Don't put any spaces between the colon, the backslash, and the file name. Drive letters A and B are usually floppy disk drives, and higher disk drives are usually hard disk drives. If you want a particular directory, type the name of the directory immediately *before* the file name (and after the colon-backslash, if you have specified a disk drive). Use this format for specifying any files throughout this book. For example, if you want to create the GRADES.DAT file in the SPSS directory on drive A, then enter the file name as:

dos > A:\SPSS\GRADES.DAT

STEP BY STEP

Once you have managed to get the computer to the DOS prompt, type:

1) dos > **SPSSPC /RE <u>GRADES</u>.DAT** ⏎	*1*

LINE 1 One space after typing **SPSS /RE**, type the file name that you want to use (<u>GRADES</u> is our example). The "**RE**" stands for *review editor*, the segment of the SPSS program where data entry takes place. This step will open an empty file (and an empty screen to begin typing), with the name you have designated shown in the lower right-hand corner of the screen. The next step (step 2) is to enter data onto the blank screen. The file name must conform to the following standards.

- It must be a maximum of eight (8) characters long.
- It may be any combination of letters and numbers, but it must begin with a letter.
- It must be followed by "**.DAT**".

At this point, your computer will show you a blank screen, where you are ready to start typing in your data:

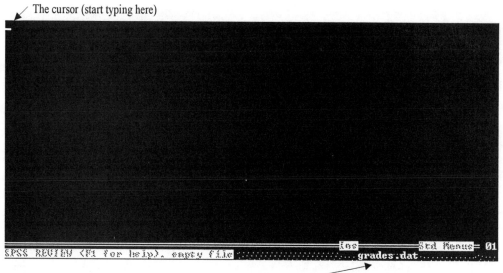

The cursor (start typing here)

The name of your data file

2) Enter your data, observing the following rules:

- The data for each subject or case you enter must be in the same format and have the same variable measures in the same columns.

- Numeric data must be lined up by decimals in columns. For example:

```
1 3 3 12 3 3.35
2 5 4  2 3 2.40
1 2 3 25 1 3.90
2 3 3  8 1 3.42
2 4 3 14 2 2.96
```

- Begin data from the extreme left column.
- Include space or spaces between columns to ease reading, entering, and interpretation. Be aware that spacing is for visual clarity only. It is not necessary to have spaces between variable values for SPSS to read your data. Use the space bar for spacing since the SPSS editor does not include a tab function.
- If you are missing some data for a particular subject there are two ways you may indicate this: (a) simply leave that column position blank or (b) place a period (.) where the number or label should go. The preferred method is to leave the positions blank because when periods are entered (instead of blanks), SPSS will print a separate warning message for each period in your data file during output. The file will be read correctly, but a long list of warnings wastes time and tries patience. What follows shows a data file with five values missing. This file is in a format that SPSS could read accurately. (The larger question of what one should do when attempting different analyses when data are missing is addressed in Chapter 5.)

```
1 3   2 3
2 5 4 2 3 2.40
1 2 3 2   3.90
2 3 3 2 1
  4 3 2 2 2.96
```

- Names and other alphabetic data (as opposed to numeric data) must be lined up by their first characters. For example:

```
JONES      LISA     1 3 3 2 3 3.35
ANDERSON   ERIC     2 5 4 2 3 2.40
KWON       SHELLY   1 2 3 2 1 3.90
LANGFORD   BLAIR    2 3 3 2 1 3.42
LANGFORD   TREVOR   2 4 3 2 2 2.96
```

- For most analyses, it is easier for the computer if you code character variables as numbers. For example, instead of entering gender as **F** and **M** for female and male, the data could be entered as **1** for females and **2** for males. (This is what was done in the first column of numbers in the example listed immediately above.)
- If you have too much data for each subject to fit all on a single line, simply use more than one line for each subject. When you run out of room on one line, press the **ENTER** key and continue typing on the next line. Please do not split an individual variable measure into two parts when you hit **RETURN!** It is important in this case that columns line up by lines—that is, first lines for all subjects have identical column positions, second lines for all subjects have identical column positions, and so forth. SPSS allows a maximum of 500 variables, so it is possible to have several lines of data per subject.
- You may use any of the editing keys and functions discussed in Chapter 3 while you are entering your data.

Once you have typed in all of the data in the example file, the screen should look something like this:

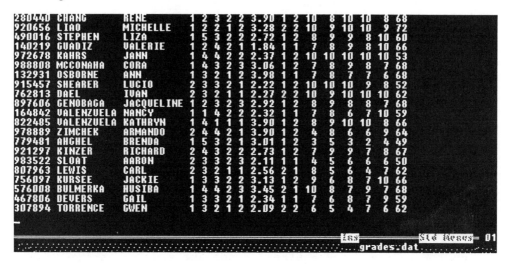

```
280440 CHANG      RENE       1 2 3 2 2 3.90 1 2 10  8 10 10  8 68
920656 LIAO       MICHELLE   1 2 2 1 2 3.28 2 2 10  9 10 10  9 72
490016 STEPHEN    LIZA       1 5 3 2 2 2.72 1 2  8  9  9  8 10 60
140219 GUADIZ     VALERIE    1 2 4 2 1 1.84 1 1  7  8  9  8 10 66
972678 KAHRS      JANN       1 4 4 2 2 2.37 1 2 10 10 10 10 10 53
988808 MCCONAHA   CORA       1 4 3 2 3 3.06 1 2  7  8  9  8  7 68
132931 OSBORNE    ANN        1 3 2 1 2 3.98 1 1  7  8  7  7  6 68
915457 SHEARER    LUCIO      2 3 3 2 1 2.22 1 2 10 10 10  9  8 52
762813 DAEL       IVAN       2 3 2 1 1 2.27 2 2 10  9 10 10 10 62
897606 GENOBAGA   JACQUELINE 1 2 3 2 3 2.92 1 2  8  9  8  8  7 68
164842 VALENZUELA NANCY      1 1 4 2 2 2.32 1 1  7  8  6  7 10 59
822485 VALENZUELA KATHRYN    1 4 1 1 1 3.90 1 2  8  9 10 10  8 66
978889 ZIMCHEK    ARMANDO    2 4 4 2 1 3.90 1 2  4  8  6  6  9 64
779481 AHGHEL     BRENDA     1 5 3 2 1 3.01 1 2  3  5  3  2  4 49
921297 KINZER     RICHARD    2 4 3 2 2 2.73 1 2  7  9  9  7  8 67
983522 SLOAT      AARON      2 3 3 2 3 2.11 1 1  4  5  6  6  6 50
807963 LEWIS      CARL       2 3 2 1 1 2.56 2 1  8  5  6  4  7 62
756097 KURSEE     JACKIE     1 3 3 2 2 3.13 1 2  9  6  8  7 10 66
576008 BULMERKA   HUSIBA     1 4 4 2 3 3.45 2 1 10  8  7  9  7 68
467806 DEVERS     GAIL       1 3 3 2 1 2.34 1 1  7  6  8  7  9 59
307894 TORRENCE   GWEN       1 3 2 1 2 2.09 2 2  6  5  4  7  6 62
```

`Ins                                                          Std News= 01`
`                                                        grades.dat`

---

3) *When finished, save your file by typing:* `F9` `W` `↵`

- You may type a new file name at the prompt (which will be located in the bottom left corner of the screen) if you desire. Otherwise SPSS automatically saves the file under the original name.
- It is a good idea to save your data file periodically throughout the course of data entry (by repeating step 3 every few minutes) to avoid losing your data in case the computer blows up or something less dramatic but equally devastating happens.

4) *To exit the program to the DOS prompt, type:* `F10` `E` **FINISH.** `↵`

Your file has now been created and saved under the name you gave it. You may now edit your file (Chapter 3) or format your data file for use by SPSS (Chapter 4).

EXAMPLE

The following is the text of the sample data file that is used for examples through most of this book. The entire text is included, but if you just want to practice SPSS procedures, then you may not want to type in all of the data. Only 10 or 20 cases are necessary for many of the examples.

The data file is the raw data for calculating the grades in a particular class. The example consists of a single file, used by a teacher who teaches three sections of a class with approximately 35 students in each section. From left to right, the variables that are used in the data file are:

Variable	Columns	Description
ID	1 - 6	Six-digit student ID number
LASTNAME	8 - 17	The last name of the student
FIRSTNAM	19 - 28	First name of the student
GENDER	30	Gender of the student: 1=female, 2=male
ETHNICIT	32	Ethnicity of the student: 1=American Indian, 2=Asian, 3=Afro-American, 4=White, 5=Hispanic
YEAR	34	Year in school; 1=First-year, 2=Sophomore, 3=Junior, 4=Senior
LOWUP	36	Lower or upper division student: 1=Lower division, 2=Upper division
SECTION	38	Section of the class (1 through 3)
PREVGPA	40 - 43	GPA at the beginning of the course; includes decimal point
EXTRCRED	45	Whether or not the student did the extra credit project: 1=No, 2=Yes
REVIEW	47	Whether or not the student attended the review sessions: 1=No, 2=Yes
QUIZ1 to QUIZ5	49 - 50 to 61 - 62	Scores out of 10 points on five quizzes throughout the term
FINAL	64 - 65	Final exam worth 75 points.

The sample data file, with column numbers as headings:

```
COLUMN NUMBER
          1    1    2    2    3    3    4    4    5    5    6    6
....5....0....5....0....5....0....5....0....5....0....5....0....5
973427 ROSS       MARIA      1 4 4 2 1 3.19 1 2  9  7 10  9  7 65
390203 SHIMA      MIHAELA    1 2 3 2 2 2.28 1 2  6  7  9  6  8 61
703740 SUNYA      DALE       2 5 3 2 3 3.58 1 2 10  9 10 10  7 62
354601 CARPIO     MARY       1 2 2 1 1 2.03 1 2 10 10 10 10  9 71
979028 NEUHARTH   JIM        2 4 3 2 3 1.80 1 2  3  6  3  4  5 49
768995 DUMITRESCU STACY      2 4 4 2 2 2.88 1 1  7 10  8  9 10 60
574170 HURRIA     WAYNE      2 1 2 1 2 3.84 1 1  4  5  6  6 48
380157 LUTZ       WILLIAM    2 4 3 2 2 2.25 2 2 10  9 10 10  8 61
167664 SWARM      MARK       2 4 3 2 3 2.35 1 2  8 10 10 10  9 71
245473 DAYES      ROBERT     2 4 3 2 1 2.74 1 1  8  9  6  7 10 48
436413 PANG       SUZANNE    1 2 3 2 1 2.66 1 2  8  6  7  8  7 60
515586 FIALLOS    LAUREL     1 4 2 1 2 3.90 1 1  7  8  8  6  6 63
106484 VILLARUIZ  ALFRED     2 2 2 1 2 1.18 1 2  6  5  7  6  3 53
725987 BATILLER   FRED       2 2 2 1 2 1.77 1 2  6  7  7  7  5 60
870810 REYNO      NICHOLAS   2 4 3 2 3 3.66 2 1 10  8 10 10 10 68
127285 GALVEZ     JACKIE     1 4 4 2 2 2.46 2 2 10  7  8  9  7 57
623857 CORTEZ     VIKKI      1 3 4 2 3 2.56 1 2  5  7  6  5  6 58
905109 JENKINS    ERIC       2 3 2 1 3 2.84 1 1  6  8  6  6 10 64
```

The sample data file (continued):

```
COLUMN NUMBER
              1    1    2    2    3    3    4    4    5    5    6    6
    ....5....0....5....0....5....0....5....0....5....0....5....0....5
392464 DOMINGO    MONIKA     1 4 3 2 3 3.02 2 1 10 10 10  9  9 55
447659 GLANVILLE  DANA       1 5 4 2 3 2.77 1 1  6  8  9  5  8 63
958384 RONCO      SHERRY     1 4 2 1 1 2.30 1 2 10  9 10 10  7 60
414775 RATANA     JASON      2 2 3 2 1 2.38 1 2  8  9 10 10  9 50
237983 LEE        JONATHAN   2 2 4 2 2 1.66 2 2  5  7  4  7  6 63
818528 CARRINGTON JYLL       1 4 3 2 1 1.95 1 2  9 10 10  8  8 53
938881 YEO        DENISE     1 1 3 2 3 3.53 1 2  7 10  9  8  9 72
944702 LEDESMA    MARTINE    1 4 3 2 2 3.90 1 2  6  7  7  5  9 67
154441 LIAN       JENNY      1 5 2 1 1 3.57 1 2 10  9 10 10 10 71
108642 VALAZQUEZ  SCOTT      2 4 3 2 2 2.19 2 1 10 10  7  6  9 54
985700 CHA        LILY       1 4 2 1 1 2.43 2 2 10  9 10 10  7 63
911355 LESKO      LETITIA    1 3 2 1 3 3.49 1 2 10  9 10 10  8 71
249586 STOLL      GLENDON    2 4 3 2 2 2.51 1 1  5  9  5  6 10 63
164605 LANGFORD   DAWN       1 3 3 2 2 3.49 2 1 10 10  9 10 10 75
419891 DE CANIO   PAULA      1 4 3 2 2 3.53 1 2  6  7  7  9  9 54
615115 VASENIUS   RUSS       2 3 3 2 3 1.77 1 2  6  7  6  8  6 59
192627 MISCHKE    ELAINE     1 4 1 1 2 2.90 1 1  3  8  4  6  8 55
595177 WILLIAMS   OLIMPIA    1 3 3 2 3 1.24 1 1  7  6  7 10  5 53
434571 SURI       MATTHEW    2 2 3 2 2 2.80 1 1  7  6  9  8  8 60
506467 SCARBROUGH CYNTHIA    1 4 3 2 2 1.33 1 2  8  5  6  4  7 58
546022 HAMIDI     KIMBERLY   1 5 3 2 1 2.96 1 1  7  7  6  9  8 61
498900 HUANG      JOE        2 5 3 2 3 2.47 1 1  0  5  0  2  5 40
781676 WATKINS    YVONNE     1 3 4 2 1 4.00 1 2  9  9 10 10  9 70
664653 KHAN       JOHN       2 4 3 2 3 1.24 1 2  3  8  5  2  7 59
908754 MARQUEZ    CHYRELLE   1 4 1 1 2 1.85 1 2  4  8  5  7  9 57
142630 RANGFIO    TANIECE    1 4 3 2 3 3.90 1 2 10 10 10  9  9 74
175325 KHOURY     DENNIS     2 4 3 2 1 2.45 1 1  8  8 10 10  6 69
378446 SAUNDERS   TAMARA     1 1 2 1 2 2.80 1 2  4  6  5  4  5 57
289652 BRADLEY    SHANNON    1 4 3 2 1 2.46 1 2  6  9  8  9  9 68
466407 PICKERING  HEIDI      1 3 3 2 3 2.38 1 1  4  7  6  4  7 56
898766 RAO        DAWN       1 2 3 2 1 3.90 1 2  8 10 10  8  9 73
302400 JONES      ROBERT     2 3 4 2 3 1.14 1 2  2  5  4  5  6 43
157147 BAKKEN     KREG       2 4 3 2 1 3.95 2 2 10 10 10 10  9 74
519444 RATHBUN    DAWN       1 4 4 2 2 3.90 1 1 10  9 10 10  8 74
420327 BADGER     SUSAN      1 4 3 2 3 2.61 1 2 10 10 10 10 10 53
260983 CUSTER     JAMES      2 4 4 2 1 2.54 1 1 10  9 10 10  7 60
554809 JONES      LISA       1 3 3 2 3 3.35 1 1  7  8  8  9  6 69
777683 ANDERSON   ERIC       2 5 4 2 3 2.40 1 1  3  6  3  2  6 50
553919 KWON       SHELLY     1 2 3 2 1 3.90 2 2 10 10 10 10  8 75
479547 LANGFORD   BLAIR      2 3 3 2 1 3.42 2 1 10 10 10  9 10 75
755724 LANGFORD   TREVOR     2 4 3 2 2 2.96 1 2  8  9  9  9  8 62
337908 UYEYAMA    VICTORINE  1 1 3 2 2 2.34 2 1 10  8 10 10  7 63
798931 ZUILL      RENEE      1 4 3 2 1 2.22 2 2 10  9 10 10  8 62
843472 PRADO      DON        2 5 3 2 3 3.54 1 2  9  9 10  8  9 68
762308 GOUW       BONNIE     1 4 2 1 3 3.90 1 2  8  7  9 10  8 57
700978 WEBSTER    DEANNA     1 3 2 1 3 3.90 1 2  8  9  9 10 10 67
721311 SONG       LOIS       2 2 3 2 3 1.61 1 1  6  9  9  7 10 64
417003 EVANGELIST NIKKI      1 2 3 2 2 1.91 1 2  9  8 10 10  6 66
153964 TOMOSAWA   DANIEL     2 2 3 2 3 2.84 2 1 10  9 10 10 10 63
765360 ROBINSON   ERIC       2 3 3 2 2 2.43 1 2  8  8  7  8 10 65
```

The sample data file (continued):

```
COLUMN NUMBER
          1    1    2    2    3    3    4    4    5    5    6    6
....5....0....5....0....5....0....5....0....5....0....5....0....5
463276 HANSEN     TIM        2 4 3 2 1 3.84 2 2 10 10 10  9 10 74
737728 BELTRAN    JIM        2 3 3 2 1 2.57 1 1  6  8  9  5  7 62
594463 CRUZADO    MARITESS   1 4 4 2 2 3.05 1 2  9  8 10  8  8 65
938666 SUAREZ-TAN KHANH      1 2 3 2 3 2.02 2 2 10  8 10 10  7 52
616095 SPRINGER   ANNELIES   1 4 3 2 1 3.64 1 2 10 10 10 10 10 72
219593 POTTER     MICKEY     1 5 3 2 3 2.54 1 2  5  8  6  4 10 61
473303 PARK       SANDRA     1 3 4 2 2 3.17 1 2  8  8  8 10  9 70
287617 CUMMINGS   DAVENA     1 5 3 2 3 2.21 1 2  9 10  9  9  9 52
681855 GRISWOLD   TAMMY      1 4 3 2 2 1.50 1 2  5  7  8  5  8 57
899529 HAWKINS    CATHERINE  1 3 4 2 2 2.31 1 1 10  8  9 10  7 49
576141 MISHALANY  LUCY       1 4 3 2 1 3.57 1 2  0  3  2  2  2 42
273611 WU         VIDYUTH    1 2 2 1 2 3.70 1 2  3  6  2  6  6 55
900485 COCHRAN    STACY      2 4 3 2 2 2.77 2 2 10  9 10 10  9 61
211239 AUSTIN     DERRICK    2 4 3 2 3 2.33 1 2  5  5  7  6  4 52
780028 ROBINSON   CLAYTON    2 4 3 2 1 3.90 1 2 10 10 10  9 10 73
896972 HUANG      MIRNA      1 2 3 2 1 2.56 1 1  7  6 10  8  7 57
280440 CHANG      RENE       1 2 3 2 2 3.90 1 2 10  8 10 10  8 68
920656 LIAO       MICHELLE   1 2 2 1 2 3.28 2 2 10  9 10 10  9 72
490016 STEPHEN    LIZA       1 5 3 2 2 2.72 1 2  8  9  9  8 10 60
140219 GUADIZ     VALERIE    1 2 4 2 1 1.84 1 1  7  8  9  8 10 66
972678 KAHRS      JANNA      1 4 4 2 2 2.37 1 2 10 10 10 10 10 53
988808 MCCONAHA   CORA       1 4 3 2 3 3.06 1 2  7  8  9  8  7 68
132931 OSBORNE    ANN        1 3 2 1 2 3.98 1 1  7  8  7  7  6 68
915457 SHEARER    LUCIO      2 3 3 2 1 2.22 1 2 10 10 10  9  8 52
762813 DEAL       IVAN       2 3 2 1 1 2.27 2 2 10  9 10 10 10 62
897606 GENOBAGA   JACQUELINE 1 2 3 2 3 2.92 1 2  8  9  8  8  7 68
164842 VALENZUELA NANCY      1 1 4 2 2 2.32 1 1  7  8  6  7 10 59
822485 VALENZUELA KATHRYN    1 4 1 1 1 3.90 1 2  8  9 10 10  8 66
978889 ZIMCHEK    ARMANDO    2 4 4 2 1 3.90 1 2  4  8  6  6  9 64
779481 AHGHEL     BRENDA     1 5 3 2 1 3.01 1 2  3  5  3  2  4 49
921297 KINZER     RICHARD    2 4 3 2 2 2.73 1 2  7  9  9  7  8 67
983522 SLOAT      AARON      2 3 3 2 3 2.11 1 1  4  5  6  6  6 50
807963 LEWIS      CARL       2 3 2 1 1 2.56 2 1  8  5  6  4  7 62
756097 KURSEE     JACKIE     1 3 3 2 2 3.13 1 2  9  6  8  7 10 66
576008 BULMERKA   HUSIBA     1 4 4 2 3 3.45 2 1 10  8  7  9  7 68
467806 DEVERS     GAIL       1 3 3 2 1 2.34 1 1  7  6  8  7  9 59
307894 TORRENCE   GWEN       1 3 2 1 2 2.09 2 2  6  5  4  7  6 62
```

Chapter 3

Editing a Data File

Once you have entered your data, you will probably have to go back and edit it at some point. This chapter tells you how to access an already existing data file and how to make changes. You will need to make changes when you have more data to enter or when you discover errors in the data you have already typed in.

It is important to realize that, after you have made any edits in your data file, you must save the data file again (step 3 of this chapter) and then format it (as discussed in Chapter 4), *even if the file has been previously saved and formatted.*

STEP BY STEP

To access and edit an already existing file, from the DOS prompt, type:

> 1)   *dos* > **SPSSPC /RE** <u>GRADES</u>.**DAT**   ↵

Remember that <u>GRADES</u> (as indicated by the underlining) is our example; you will want to put the name of *your* data file in its place when you type the command.

> 2)   *Edit your data, using the following keys and commands.*

Cursor movement within the data screen is similar to many other word processing programs, involving the following keys:

You will save yourself much time if you spend a few minutes now to try out each of the editing keys, particularly the **CTRL** key combined with other keys. Faster cursor movement will take place by pressing **CTRL** and holding it down while you type any of the keys shown below:

Other important keys used when editing data files include the **INS** (Insert) key and the **F4** key (in combination with other keys). The **INS** key will switch back and forth from the *overtype* mode to the *insert* mode. Insert is the most frequently used editing mode; however, the overtype mode can be useful when editing because you retain the already existing column positions while you type. In the insert mode, anything you type will be added wherever the cursor is currently located, and any preexisting text will be moved to the right to make room for the new text. The overtype mode will simply type over and replace existing text. To switch from one to the other, press the **INS** key. You can tell which mode you are in by looking at the bottom right of the screen:

Insert mode   Overtype mode

A note of warning: During the course of data input or editing, it is not uncommon to occasionally hit the **INS** key by accident. If you find that pressing **ENTER** does not move the cursor down to the next line or that the results of your editing suddenly seem strange and inexplicable, check whether you are in insert or overtype mode.

The **F4** key is used, in combination with other keys, to manipulate <u>lines</u> of data. The four functions include:

[F4][I] Provides room to **INSERT** a line **AFTER** the line where the cursor is located.

[F4][B] Provides room to **INSERT** a line **BEFORE** the current line.

[F4][D] **DELETES** the current line.

[F4][U] **UN-DELETES** (replaces) the line just deleted.

Manipulating *blocks* of text is accomplished by use of the **F7** and **F8** keys, again in combination with other keys. Use of these keys allows you to move or copy several lines of text, one or more columns of text, or a particular rectangle of text. Although moving or copying *lines* of text is straightforward, copying or moving *rectangles* (this includes columns) of text can be a little tricky. Most data files are symmetric, that is, they have identical variables for each subject (or case) with the variable values in identical columns. SPSS is eager for you to retain symmetry in your data file, and if you attempt to make changes that eliminate this symmetry, your machine will beep unhappily and prove to be most uncooperative. So, be careful when you have to move columns of data around; in particular, *never move columns for only some of the subjects (or cases) in the data file.* If you move some, move them all. For this reason, it is very difficult to move columns of data in files that have more than one line per subject.

The **F7** key **HIGHLIGHTS** portions of data to be manipulated. The **F8** key carries out the desired manipulations on the highlighted text.

To highlight a group of lines:
First place the cursor at the first **LINE** of data to be highlighted, then press `F7` `L` .
Then move the cursor to the last line of data to be selected and press `F7` .

To highlight a column or rectangle of text:
Place cursor at one corner of the column or **RECTANGLE** of text and press `F7` `R` .
Then, move to the opposite corner of the desired text and press `F7` .

To highlight the entire document:
To highlight the entire (**COMPLETE**) document, press `F7` `C` .

When text has been highlighted, the next step is to perform some operation with it (e.g., move it, copy it, delete it). When you have completed the desired manipulations, press **F7** once more to **CLEAR** the highlighted area.

When you have highlighted the text that you wish to manipulate, that text will remain highlighted until you clear it. While it is highlighted, you may move the cursor anywhere in the file and even do further editing before you choose what to do with the highlighted text. Once you have the cursor at the desired location, you may perform any of the following commands:

`F8` `C` will **COPY** highlighted material to the current cursor position.
`F8` `M` will **MOVE** highlighted material to the current cursor position.
`F8` `D` will **DELETE** highlighted material.

Remember to hit the **F7** after you have manipulated data, to clear highlighted text.

---

3) *When finished editing, save your file by typing:* F9 W ↵

You may type a new file name at the prompt (displayed in the bottom left of the screen after the W) if you desire.

---

4) *To exit the program, type:* F10 E **FINISH.** ↵

Chapter 4

Formatting the Data File

Once you have typed in the raw data, there is one more thing that you must do before you begin calculating statistics using these data: Format your data file so that the computer can read it. In particular, you must tell SPSS exactly where your data are located (which file, what column positions, etc.) and what form (e.g., integer, decimal, alphabetic) your data are in. This step must be done each time you make a change to your raw data file—SPSS doesn't know you've made the change until you format the file as described here. The purpose of this chapter is to show you, step by step, how to format the data file.

STEP BY STEP

To illustrate the process of formatting a data file to be read by SPSS, we will continue to make use of the fictitious data file **GRADES.DAT**. First, we enter SPSS, access the file, and identify its variables by column.

From the DOS prompt, type:

1) dos> **SPSSPC** ⏎

Your screen should now look something like this:

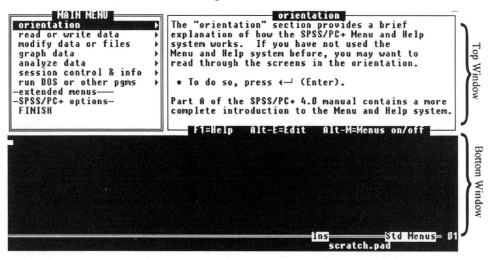

---

2) ALT ⊣M   *This clears the menu from the top window.*

At this point, your screen will look something like this:

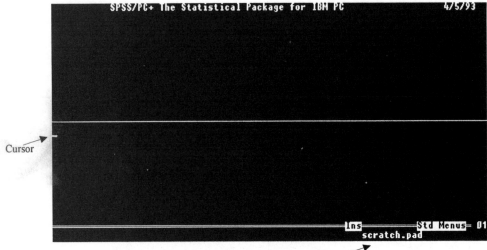

Cursor

Name of the file of the window that the cursor is in
(the bottom one right now)

---

3) F2 S   *Switches the cursor from the lower to the upper window.*

---

4) F3 E GRADES.DAT ◄┘   *This step accesses the GRADES.DAT data file.*

The data file will now appear in the upper window, so that you can refer to it while you are entering its format in the lower window.

---

5) F2 S   *Switches the cursor back to the lower window.*

You will now begin to type in the *command file* (instructions to the computer) in the lower window, called the *scratch pad*. This information tells the computer what type of formatting or analysis you wish to do.

From the upper left corner of the lower window, type:

---

6) **DATA LIST FILE = 'GRADES.DAT'**   1
   /ID 1-6 LASTNAME 8-17(A) FIRSTNAM 19-28(A) GENDER 30 ETHNICIT 32   2
   YEAR 34 LOWUP 36 SECTION 38 PREVGPA 40-43 EXTRCRED 45 REVIEW 47   3
   QUIZ1 49-50 QUIZ2 52-53 QUIZ3 55-56 QUIZ4 58-59 QUIZ5 61-62 FINAL 64-65.   4
   FORMATS PREVGPA (F4.2).   5
   LIST.   6

LINE 1 The **DATA LIST FILE** command allows SPSS to gain access to the data file that is named within single quotes following the equals sign.

LINES 2-4 These lines name each variable and locate the column positions for each variable. If the variable list is more than one line long (as it is here and usually will be), you need to press the return key after each line of text. There is no automatic scroll (or "wrap") function on the SPSS editor. In creating this section of the command file, be sure to adhere to the following specifications:

- Note the slash (/) that opens the list of variable names. This is required. The slash may also be placed at the *end* of the *previous* line (rather than the beginning of the current line), but *not* in both places.
- Variable names (e.g., **ID, LASTNAME, FIRSTNAM, GENDER, ETHNICIT,** and **YEAR**) in line 2 are made up of a maximum of eight characters.
- Variable names start with letters and contain only characters that are letters or numbers.
- The numbers after the variable names represent column positions of each variable. If you need to, you can switch to the top window to see what column positions the variables are in. To do that, repeat step 3 (above) and then move the cursor around while you note the column number of the cursor (it's in the bottom right corner of the screen). When you are done, repeat step 5 (above) to switch back to the lower window.

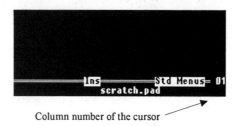

Column number of the cursor

- There is a single space only (never other punctuation) between the different variable names and column positions.
- **(A)** is placed after the column numbers of any data that are alphabetic (as opposed to numeric). For example, in line 2 above, the variables **LASTNAME** and **FIRSTNAM** contain letters (the names of students) instead of numbers.
- If your subjects have more than one line each in the data file, place a slash (/) before the start of the name of the first variable in the second line of your data in the command file, to indicate to SPSS that a new line or *record* of data is to be read.
- A period (.) is typed at the end of the column position following the last variable. This instructs the computer to end the **DATA LIST** command.

LINE 5 The purpose of the **FORMATS** command is to identify which variables have decimals, how many column positions each variable occupies, and how many place values are to the right of the decimal point. The **PREVGPA** variable is four (4) characters long (including the decimal point) and has two (2) digits to the right of the decimal point. If you have more than one variable that uses decimal format, then list each variable followed by its format, one after another. There should be only single spaces between variable names and the formats within parentheses. An example of a formats line with 2 variables that contain decimals follows:

FORMATS PREVGPA (F4.2) PERCENT (F4.1).

LINE 6 is optional but highly recommended. It tells the computer to list the data file once it has been processed, so that you can check to see that you didn't make any typos when you were entering either (a) the data into the original data file or (b) the column numbers in this command file.

To run the program you have just created, press the following keys:

7) `HOME` `F10` `C`   *Positions cursor under the "D" of DATA LIST FILE and runs the program.*

When SPSS is running a program, it will show you what it is doing one screen at a time. The word **MORE** will appear in the upper right corner of the screen. Press the **SPACEBAR** each time you see the word **MORE** when you wish to move to the next screen of output.

If you have made a mistake (few people get through a data file and/or a command file without errors), when you attempt to run the program the computer will beep unhappily, and usually an error message will flash on the screen. What the error message actually *says* will often be unintelligible, but it is indicating that an error exists in the data or command file. The most common errors found in the data file are (a) misalignment of your data or (b) incorrect numbers or number formats within the file. Common errors in the command file include: (a) incorrect variable name (usually too long), (b) a misplaced period or slash, (c) misspelling of command names (for instance **LISZT** instead of **LIST** is not a valid SPSS command), or (d) incorrect spacing. If an error message is displayed, these are the most obvious sorts of things to look for first.

When SPSS finishes displaying your output (whether or not errors were made), it automatically returns to the original command file (lines 1-6 of step 6), and the program menu once again appears in the upper window, like this:

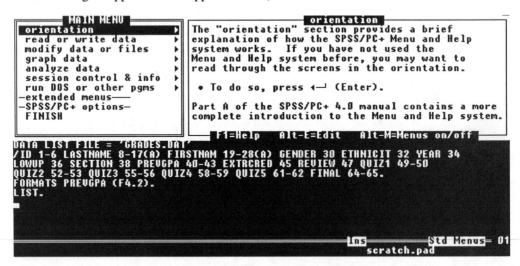

As a rule, whenever you see the program menu in the upper window, you will want to clear it:

8) `ALT`-`M`   *clears the menu from the top window.*

At this point there are two possible directions to go: (1) If no mistakes are indicated then proceed directly to step 9 (do not pass GO, do not collect $200). (2) If mistakes (errors) have been indicated, go back and perform sequence steps 3 and 4 again. When your cursor is in the top window (step 3) and the data file is once again displayed (step 4), check for errors and make necessary corrections in your data file, making use of the editing keys described in the previous chapter. Be sure to save the data file (Chapter 3, step 3) after you have edited the data file.

When errors have been corrected, once more perform sequence step 5 (this returns the cursor to the lower window where your command file awaits). Check the command file for errors and make changes, making use of the editing keys (as you did in the data file, above). Then repeat sequence step 7 to run the program once more. After you have observed the output on the screen (again, pressing the **SPACEBAR** whenever the word **MORE** appears), if no errors are indicated, then repeat step 8 and move on to step 9 (below). If there are <u>still</u> errors, you will need to repeat the instructions of the previous paragraph until all errors have been corrected.

Move the cursor to the position one space after the period (.) of the "LIST." command and press the ENTER key. The cursor should now be positioned one line beneath the L of LIST. Now type:

```
9) VARIABLE LABELS YEAR 'YEAR IN SCHOOL'          7
   /LOWUP 'LOWER OR UPPER DIVISION'               8
   /EXTRCRED 'DID EXTRA CREDIT PROJECT?'          9
   /REVIEW 'ATTENDED REVIEW SESSIONS?'.          10
```

LINES 7-10 The **VARIABLE LABELS** command is optional. Its purpose is to clarify the meaning of variables when their meaning is not clear from the 8-character variable name. It is recommended that you be generous in the use of variable labels because what may be clear now may not be clear to you six months from now when you are looking at the output. In most outputs, SPSS will print out the full description of the variable that you have entered here. For instance, if the **REVIEW** variable was included in a particular analysis; when referring to the variable in the output, SPSS would print "**REVIEW--ATTENDED REVIEW SESSIONS?**" (if there was enough room to print the whole label) rather than the single variable name (**REVIEW**) alone. When spacing is crowded in the output section, the variable label will frequently be truncated to something shorter than the full description. When using the **VARIABLE LABELS** command, keep the following in mind:

- The first variable name follows exactly one space after the **VARIABLE LABELS** command, followed by another space, single quote, the description of your variable, then single quote.
- Each variable that follows opens with a slash (/) (or you can close the previous line with a slash instead—*don't* put slashes both places), this is followed by the variable name, space, single quote, description of the variable, and single quote.
- You may use up to 40 characters for a description of the variable.
- Any letters, numbers, or other characters are acceptable to use except the single quote (or apostrophe) mark.
- Close the final variable label with a period (.).

Next, move the cursor to the space following the period of the final line (" . . . SESSIONS?'. ").
Press the ENTER key. The cursor should now be positioned one line under the slash of the
"/REVIEW 'ATTENDED . . ." line. Now type:

10) **VALUE LABELS** GENDER 1 'FEMALE' 2 'MALE'	11
/ETHNICIT 1 'AMERICAN INDIAN' 2 'ASIAN' 3 'AFRO-AMERICAN'	
4 'CAUCASIAN '5 'HISPANIC'	12
/YEAR 1 'FIRST-YEAR' 2 'SOPHOMORE' 3 'JUNIOR' 4 'SENIOR'	13
/LOWUP 1 'LOWER DIVISION' 2 'UPPER DIVISION'	14
/EXTRCRED 1 'NO' 2 'YES'	15
/REVIEW 1 'NO' 2 'YES'.	16

LINES 11-16 The VALUE LABELS command is designed to identify the meaning of each level of
categorical variables. As is indicated in the file above, for the GENDER variable, 1 = female and
2 = male; for the ETHNICIT variable, 1 = American Indian, 2 = Asian, and so forth. While the
VARIABLE LABELS (above) are optional, the VALUE LABELS certainly are necessary. It is critical
to identify the meaning of the levels of any categorical variable. For the VALUE LABELS
command, keep the following in mind:

- Single space between each word or number.
- Open each new variable with a slash (/).
- Close the *last* variable with a period (.).
- Put the desired label within single-quote marks (apostrophes). You may include any character within the single-quotes that you wish, except for apostrophes.
- A maximum of 20 characters is allowed for each level of each variable.

The final line of the current command file deals with saving the formatted and
labeled DATA FILE as a SYSTEM FILE. In a system file, SPSS stores all information
concerning location of each data point entered in the data file, plus all the variable/value
label information. Once you have formatted the data file (as you have seen demonstrated
in this chapter), you need never do it again for that data set. From now on you will
access the system file by a GET FILE command each time you wish to conduct analysis on
your data. Just one word of caution: If you go back and change the *original* data file,
you will need to redo the formatting procedure described in this chapter to conform to
your new data changes.

We follow a convention that simplifies any confusion concerning which file you
may be referring to. There will be three files of primary interest: the raw data file, the
command file, and the system file. They are designated as follows:

GRADES.DAT	This designates the raw DATA FILE you typed in originally.
GRADES.CTL	This designates the COMMAND FILE you typed in the lower window.
GRADES.SYS	This designates the formatted and labeled SYSTEM FILE that SPSS will read each time you do statistics on this data set.

We now move to the final line of the command file, the line that instructs SPSS to
save the formatted file as a system file.

From the end of the last line, press the enter key. The cursor should now be located one line under the slash (/) of the "/REVIEW 1 'NO' 2 'YES'." line. From that position, type:

11) **SAVE OUTFILE** = 'GRADES.SYS'.	*17*

LINE 17 The **SAVE OUTFILE** command instructs SPSS to save your formatted and labeled data file as a system file. Use the same name as your data file (we use **GRADES** here), but the name should be followed by a **.SYS** to remind *you* that this is a system file (SPSS doesn't care what you call it). As you will notice in Chapter 5, the **SAVE OUTFILE** command is used any time you wish to save variations on your data set that have been accomplished through SPSS procedures.

To run the latter portion of your program, which creates the variable and value labels and saves your data as a system file, position the cursor at the beginning of the "VARIABLE LABELS . . ." line and then:

12)	F10 C	*This runs the last section of the program and saves the outfile.*

13)	ALT ┤M	*This again clears the menu from the top window.*

After you have spaced through the output on the screen (after each **MORE** appears) and cleared the menu from the top screen (**ALT-M**), there are once more, two options:

1. If you have made mistakes, and error messages flash on the screen, you will need to correct errors in the command file (there will no longer be any problems with the *data* file, they were corrected earlier). The cursor will already be in the lower window, where the command file has reappeared on the screen, and you will once again make use of the edit keys to correct any mistakes. Once errors are corrected, then execute steps 12 and 13 again.

2. If the program has run successfully, then you will want to save the **COMMAND FILE**. There are essentially three reasons for saving the command file: (a) It serves as a record of what procedures you have already run with this data set; (b) if you wish to make changes in the *original* data file, you will need to make corresponding changes in the formatting segment of the command file (the 17 lines described in this chapter); and (c) if you add subjects (or observations) to your data set, you will need to rerun this command file to correspondingly update the system file. It is much easier to make minor modifications in the previous **COMMAND FILE** than to retype the whole thing. There are other reasons for saving the command file that will be discussed in future chapters.

Save your command file by typing:

14)	F9 W GRADES.CTL ↵	

As mentioned earlier, the **.CTL** identifies this file as the command file associated with the **GRADES** data and system files. If for any reason you wish to change the name of the file, simply type in the new name at the prompt (between the **W** and the **ENTER** in step 14). If in the future you wish to use the command file again do this: After you have entered SPSS (sequence step 1), clear the menu from the top window (step 2), press the **F3** key, press the **E** key, type **GRADES.CTL**, and then hit the **ENTER** key. The command file will then appear in the lower window, and you may then use or modify the file.

15) `F10` `E` **FINISH.** `←` *to exit SPSS and return to the DOS prompt.*

If you wish to print a copy of the output, from the DOS prompt type:

16) **PRINT SPSS.LIS** `←` `←` *Note: Sometimes the second ENTER is not necessary.*

This final command will print your entire file, including all commands and output. You *do* need to address certain basic concerns when printing the output, such as making sure the printer is turned on and is connected to your computer. You are now ready to run statistics! To do this, turn to the chapter (Chapters 6-30 deal with different types of analyses) that describes the type of statistics you wish to perform and follow the step-by-step procedures. There is one additional data manipulation chapter (Chapter 5), which explains how to compute new variables, replace missing values, change coding, select certain portions of text for analysis, or reorder the data. If you have no need to perform these operations, you are ready to conduct data analysis.

A RECAP OF THE COMMAND FILE

Here's what your command file should look like when you are finished:

```
DATA LIST FILE = 'GRADES.DAT'
/ID 1-6 LASTNAME 8-17(A) FIRSTNAM 19-28(A) GENDER 30 ETHNICIT 32 YEAR
34 LOWUP 36 SECTION 38 PREVGPA 40-43 EXTRCRED 45 REVIEW 47 QUIZ1 49-50
QUIZ2 52-53 QUIZ3 55-56 QUIZ4 58-59 QUIZ5 61-62 FINAL 64-65.
FORMATS PREVGPA (F4.2).
LIST.
VARIABLE LABELS YEAR 'YEAR IN SCHOOL'
/LOWUP 'LOWER OR UPPER DIVISION'
/EXTRCRED 'DID EXTRA CREDIT PROJECT?'
/REVIEW 'ATTENDED REVIEW SESSIONS?'.
VALUE LABELS GENDER 1 'FEMALE' 2 'MALE'
/ETHNICIT 1 'AMERICAN INDIAN' 2 'ASIAN' 3 'AFRO-AMERICAN'
4 'CAUCASIAN' 5 'HISPANIC'
/YEAR 1 'FIRST-YEAR' 2 'SOPHOMORE' 3 'JUNIOR' 4 'SENIOR'
/LOWUP 1 'LOWER DIVISION' 2 'UPPER DIVISION'
/EXTRCRED 1 'NO' 2 'YES'
/REVIEW 1 'NO' 2 'YES'.
SAVE OUTFILE = 'GRADES.SYS'.
```

Chapter 5

The LIST, COMPUTE, IF, RECODE, SELECT IF, PROCESS IF, and SORT Commands:

Managing Data

This chapter is possibly the most difficult of the book. If you have a single data file and want to run a single operation, fine; just use the data as you originally entered and formatted it. Chapters 2 and 4 tell you how to create and format your data file, and Chapters 6-30 give understandable step-by-step instructions about how to analyze data. However, it is common to want to analyze variables that are not *in* the original data file but are derived *from* the original variables (such as total points, percentage of possible points, or others). It is also sometimes desirable to display the data differently (e.g., alphabetically by student last names, by total points from high to low, or class records listed by sections), to code variables differently (e.g., 90-100 coded A, 80-89 coded B, and so forth), or to calculate data on only a certain portion of the data set (e.g., scores for females, GPAs for Caucasians, final percentages for sophomores, final grades for Section 2, etc.).

All these operations may be necessary if you wish to do more than a single analysis on a single set of data. Some operations are complex, and it is possible that you may encounter difficulties that are not covered in this book. The different functions covered in this chapter are considered one at a time, and we do our best to present them as clearly and succinctly as space allows. In the Appendix, we also include an explanation of typical error messages and common problems. We also refer you to SPSS documentation whenever a more detailed understanding of a procedure might be helpful.

Despite the potential difficulty involved, a thorough understanding of these procedures will give you fluency in the use of all SPSS operations. Once you have learned to manage data effectively, many statistical processes can be accomplished with almost ridiculous ease. We will present here six different types of data management:

1. Using the LIST command judiciously to assist in proofing and editing your data.

2. Using the **RECODE** command for replacing missing values.
3. Computing and creating new or different variables from the already existing data set by using the **COMPUTE** and **IF** commands.
4. Using the **RECODE** command to change the coding associated with certain variables.
5. Employing the **SELECT IF** and **PROCESS IF** commands to allow statistical operations on only a portion of your data.
6. Utilizing the **SORT** command to reorder your data.

Beginning with this chapter we introduce the convention that allows all chapters that follow to be self-contained. The five steps necessary to get as far as the **GET FILE** command (steps 1-5) will begin each Step by Step section, and the four steps necessary to save the command file, run the program, exit the program, and print the results (steps 7-10) will always end each section. The critical command file(s) for each chapter will be one or more versions of step 6. If there is more than one step-6 version, the steps will be designated 6, 6a, 6b, 6c, and so forth.

This chapter will be formatted somewhat differently from the analysis chapters (6-30) because we are presenting six different types of computations or manipulations of data. We will begin the Step by Step section with the five steps mentioned above and then present each of the six operations with its own title, introduction, and discussion. After the sixth of these presentations, we will conclude with the final four steps. Unlike the analysis chapters, there will be no Output section in this chapter.

STEP BY STEP
Manipulation of Data

> 1) *Name and create a data file (Chapter 2), or edit (if necessary) an already existing file (Chapter 3).*

> 2) *Name variables, locate column positions, format, create VARIABLE/VALUE LABELS, and then save the formatted DATA FILE as a SYSTEM FILE (Chapter 4).*

From the DOS prompt, type:

> 3) *dos>* **SPSSPC** ↵   *This step gets you into the SPSS system.*

To clear the menu from the top window prior to analyzing data:

> 4) ALT – M   *Positions cursor to begin to create the command file.*

From the extreme upper left corner of the scratch pad (lower window), type:

```
5) GET FILE = 'GRADES.SYS'.                                    1
```

LINE 1 Accesses the formatted **SYSTEM FILE** to begin to analyze data. All statistical procedures in this book will begin with the **GET FILE** step.

The LIST Command: Listing All or a Portion of the Data

One of the best ways you can ensure that SPSS has followed your instructions and created, formatted, or arranged your data correctly is to make generous use of the **LIST** command. If you use only the **LIST** command without further alterations, SPSS will print out the entire data file. If the data set is large, this can be a distressing waste of time (and paper if you print it). However, SPSS allows the use of several modifications (called *subcommands*) of the **LIST** command that can keep you from wasting paper. A subcommand is used to provide additional instructions to an SPSS command. There are subcommands available for almost all SPSS procedures. Within the **LIST** command, the **VARIABLES** subcommand and the **CASES** subcommand allow you to list only a subset of your variables and/or a subset of your subjects (or cases). This provides opportunity to make sure that the desired manipulations have occurred and are correct without listing the entire file. Finally, although here we show the use of the **LIST** command following the **GET FILE** command, **LIST** may be used at any point of the command file to check results of previous steps. Just make sure the previous line of the command file ends with a period (indicating that the preceding procedure is completed).

To access the GRADES.SYS system file and list data, type in the following command file

```
6) GET FILE = 'GRADES.SYS'.                                    1
   LIST VARIABLES = QUIZ1 QUIZ2 QUIZ3 QUIZ4 QUIZ5 FINAL/       2
   CASES = FROM 1 TO 20.                                       3
```

LINE 1 This line "calls up" the **GRADES.SYS** system file. It is the same as step 5, line 1, above.

LINE 2 If only the "**LIST.**" is included here (instead of the two lines shown above), SPSS will list the entire data file. When the **VARIABLES** subcommand follows, you may designate which variables you wish to list, and SPSS will display only that portion of the data file. Type in variable names one at a time with a single space between each. If the variables are in order in the system file, the word **TO** may be used to designate them (e.g., **LIST VARIABLES = QUIZ1 TO FINAL/**). End this line with a slash (/) only if the **CASES** subcommand follows. Otherwise end the line with a period.

LINE 3 If your data file is long, you may choose to select just a portion of it. The line shown above will list the first 20 cases (or subjects). Another option allows you to list every other case or every fifth case or every seventh case by including the connector **BY**. For instance, if you wished to list every fifth case of the entire file you would replace line 3 with "**CASES = FROM 1 TO 105 BY 5.**". This would list case numbers 1, 6, 11 etc. "**CASES = FROM 5 TO 105 BY 5.**" would list case numbers 5, 10, 15 etc. Make sure to end this line with a period.

The RECODE Command: Replacing Missing Values

During the course of data entry you will discover soon enough that several subjects refused to answer the ethnicity question, three subjects did not take the first quiz, and other gaps in your data file appear. These are called *missing values*. Missing values are not only an irritant but can influence your analyses in other and undesirable ways. Missing values often make your data file more difficult to work with. There are a number of SPSS procedures that force any case (or subject) that has any missing values to be dropped from consideration prior to analysis. If, for instance, you are computing correlations, and 13 of your 35 subjects have one or more missing values in the data file, SPSS will compute correlations for only the 22 subjects that have *no* missing values. This results in a distressing loss of legitimate information that should be available. There are several ways that you might deal with this.

● If you have missing values in categorical data (e.g., subjects didn't answer the ethnicity or level-of-income questions), you can create an additional level for that variable and replace the missing values with a different number. For instance, if you have five levels of ethnicity coded for five different ethnic groups, you could create a sixth level (coded 6) labeled "unknown". This would not interfere with any analyses you wished to conduct with the ethnicity variable, and there would no longer be missing values to contend with.

● For *continuous* data a frequent procedure is to replace missing values with the mean score of all other subjects for that variable. Although replacing *many* missing values by this technique can sometimes bias the results, a small number of replacements has little influence on the outcome of your analyses. An often-used rule of thumb suggests that it is acceptable to replace up to 15% of data by the mean of the distribution, with little damage to the resulting outcomes. If a particular subject (or case) or a certain variable has more than 15% missing data, it is recommended that you drop that subject or variable from the analysis entirely.

● A more sophisticated way to replace missing values in continuous data is to create a regression equation with the variable of interest as the dependent (or criterion) variable and replace missing values with the *predicted* values. This requires a fair amount of work (SPSS has no automatic procedures to accomplish this) and a substantial knowledge of multiple regression analysis (Chapter 20); but it is considered one of the better methods for dealing with missing data. If you make use of predicted values, you would not be able to use the procedure that follows (in the box on p. 31). You would need to compute the new values separately, insert them into the original data file, and then run the formatting command file (Chapter 4) once more.

Concerning research ethics: If you replace missing data in research that you plan to publish, it is required that you state in the article how you handled any missing values that may influence your outcome. The reviewers and the readers then know what procedures you have used and can interpret accordingly.

If you spend time in the SPSS manuals, you will often see the phrases *user-missing values* and *system-missing values*. Just to clarify, user-missing values are simply omissions in your data set. A system-missing value is most frequently a value that cannot be computed by some transformational device that you employed, but it may also be an instance of a value in the data file that does not adhere to the specifications in the command file (for instance a decimal number when an integer is coded).

The procedure that replaces missing values is quite simple and makes use of the **RECODE** command. While **RECODE** is described in more detail later in this chapter, we felt it important to provide a separate section to deal with the missing-values issue. While the **GRADES.SYS** file does not contain missing values, we will still use it to demonstrate the procedure. The command file that follows will include a sixth level of **ETHNICIT** (6 = unknown) and will replace any missing values for **QUIZ1** with the mean value (see Chapter 7) for that quiz rounded to the nearest integer ($M = 8$). Please note that it is more common to replace a missed quiz by the *subject's* average quiz score, but in this case the teacher felt the average score for the quiz would be more appropriate.

```
6)  GET FILE = 'GRADES.SYS'.                          1
    RECODE ETHNICIT (MISSING = 6).                   2
    RECODE QUIZ1 (MISSING = 8).                      3
    LIST VARIABLES = ETHNICIT QUIZ1/                 4
    CASES = FROM 1 TO 20.                            5
    SAVE OUTFILE = 'GRADES.SYS'.                     6
```

LINE 1 Same as line 1 of step 5 above.

LINE 2 This line replaces all missing values in the **ETHNICIT** variable with a 6. Be sure to follow each **RECODE** line with a period. If you ran a **FREQUENCIES** breakdown on **ETHNICIT** after you have completed the recoding procedure, there should be no missing values. When you add a level to a categorical variable (such as level 6 to **ETHNICIT**), it is often desirable to follow it with a **VALUE LABELS** command. The new command would update your value label for **ETHNICIT** by including a sixth level. The line would look like this:

VALUE LABELS ETHNICIT 1 'INDIAN' 2 'ASIAN' 3 'AFRO-AMERICAN' 4 'CAUCASIAN' 5 'HISPANIC' 6 'UNKNOWN'.

If you have more than one value label, follow the format shown in Chapter 4.

LINE 3 This is the format for replacing all missing values in the **QUIZ1** variable with an 8. In most instances you want to replace missing values with a number in the same *format* as the values in the original variable. The rule that applies is as follows: If you enter an integer for a variable that is in decimal format, the integer will be entered accurately in a decimal format. If you enter a decimal for a variable that is coded for an integer, SPSS will truncate the decimal and retain just the integer portion.

LINES 4-5 As suggested in the previous section, it is often desirable to list all or a portion of your data file to be sure that SPSS has performed the requested manipulations. These lines may simply be omitted if you trust that SPSS has accomplished the requested operations.

LINE 6 The **SAVE OUTFILE** line will appear several times in this chapter. This is *not* an automatic step. If you wish to make the requested changes permanent, then the **SAVE OUTFILE** step is necessary. If you wish these changes only for the procedures that follow, then you would not include the **SAVE OUTFILE** command.

The COMPUTE Command: Creating Variables

In the current data set, it would be quite normal for the teacher to instruct the computer to create new variables that sum the quizzes and final exam and to determine the percent of total points for each student. The command file that follows will compute two new variables called **TOTAL** and **PERCENT**.

To compute new variables TOTAL and PERCENT, create the following command file:

```
6) GET FILE = 'GRADES.SYS'.                                              1
   COMPUTE TOTAL  =  QUIZ1 + QUIZ2 + QUIZ3 + QUIZ4 + QUIZ5 + FINAL.      2
   COMPUTE PERCENT  =  RND(100*TOTAL/125).                               3
```

LINE 1 Same as line 1 of step 5 above.

LINE 2 This line creates a new variable named **TOTAL** that sums the 5 quizzes and the final for each subject in the file. If a variable named **TOTAL** already existed, the values for that variable would be replaced with the new-variable values, in this case the *sum of the 5 quizzes and the final*. Note that the spacing within the mathematical operation is optional. Just as acceptable would be: **QUIZ1+QUIZ2+QUIZ3+QUIZ4+QUIZ5+FINAL.** Always end each **COMPUTE** command line with a period.

LINE 3 This line computes the total percentage rounded to the nearest integer. The **RND** rounds the *argument* (the portion within parentheses) to the nearest integer, the **100*** multiplies (*****) the total number of points by 100 to yield a percent rather than a decimal, and dividing by the number of points possible (**/125**) yields the final percent. Again, remember to end with a period.

A wide variety of computational resources are available to create new variables. What follows are some of the most frequently used operations, with an example of a sample command demonstrating how the command would be written and what the result would be.

+ Addition: COMPUTE TOTAL = PAPER + FINAL. Creates or modifies a variable named **TOTAL** that adds the preexisting **PAPER** score and the preexisting **FINAL** score for each subject (or case).

– Subtraction: COMPUTE DIFF = HISCORE – LOWSCORE. Creates a variable named **DIFF** that subtracts the **LOWSCORE** from the **HISCORE** for each subject.

* Multiplication: COMPUTE PERCENT = 100*DECIMAL. Creates a variable named **PERCENT** that multiplies a variable named **DECIMAL** by 100 for each subject.

/ Division: COMPUTE DECIMAL = PERCENT/100. Creates a variable named **DECIMAL** that divides a variable named **PERCENT** by 100 for each subject.

** Exponential: COMPUTE CUBE = SCORE**3. Creates a new variable named **CUBE** that raises a variable named **SCORE** to the 3rd power for each subject.

ABS (absolute value): COMPUTE ZPOSITIV = ABS(ZSCORE). Creates a variable named **ZPOSITIV** that calculates the absolute value of a variable named **ZSCORE** for each subject.

RND (round to the nearest integer): COMPUTE SIMPLE = RND(GPA). Computes a variable named **SIMPLE** by rounding off each subject's **GPA** to the nearest integer.

TRUNC (truncates decimal portion of a number): COMPUTE EASY = TRUNC(GPA). Computes a variable named **EASY** that truncates each subject's **GPA** (*truncate* means "cut off").

MOD10 (remainder after dividing by 10): **COMPUTE REMAIN = MOD10(NUMBER).** Creates a variable named **REMAIN** that selects the last digit of the variable **NUMBER** (or last digit plus decimal portion) for each subject.

SQRT (square root): **COMPUTE SCORERT = SQRT(SCORE).** Creates a variable named **SCORERT** by taking the square root of each **SCORE** for each subject.

EXP (exponential—*e* raised to a power): **COMPUTE CONFUSE = EXP(GPA).** Computes a variable named **CONFUSE** that calculates the value of *e* raised to each subject's **GPA**'s power. *e* equals approximately 2.721 (it is irrational). For a particular subject with a 3.49 **GPA**, **EXP**(3.49) = $(2.721 \ldots)^{3.49} = 32.900506 \ldots$).

LOG10 (base 10 logarithm): **COMPUTE RHYTHM = LOG10(TOTAL).** Creates a new variable named **RHYTHM** that calculates the base 10 logarithm for the variable **TOTAL** for each subject.

LN (natural logarithm): **COMPUTE NATURAL = LN(TOTAL).** Creates a new variable named **NATURAL** that calculates the natural logarithm for the variable **TOTAL** for each subject.

It is, of course, possible to use several of these functions in a single command. The example in step 6 demonstrates a computation that includes rounding, multiplying by 100, and dividing by 125. In creating a more complex computation, be sure to adhere strictly to the basic algebraic rules of orders of operations. Generous use of parentheses is encouraged. If you wish to do an operation on a complex expression, be sure to include it within parentheses.

To save the two new variables in the system file (GRADES.SYS), use the SAVE OUTFILE command. To check that the variables have been correctly computed, use the LIST command to display the data file with the new variables.

```
6a)  GET FILE = 'GRADES.SYS'.                                        1a
     COMPUTE TOTAL = QUIZ1 + QUIZ2 + QUIZ3 + QUIZ4 + QUIZ5 + FINAL.  2a
     COMPUTE PERCENT = RND(100*TOTAL/125).                           3a
     SAVE OUTFILE = 'GRADES.SYS'.                                    4a
     LIST VARIABLES = QUIZ1 TO FINAL TOTAL PERCENT/                  5a
     CASES = FROM 1 TO 20.                                           6a
```

LINES 1a-3a Same as above.

LINE 4a The **SAVE OUTFILE** command will probably be one of your most frequently used commands. This allows you to save any manipulations in the system file that you wish to use in the future. Note the inclusion of the **.SYS** at the end of the file name to indicate this is a system file (not a data or command file). Be careful in the use of the **SAVE OUTFILE** command. There are times when you do manipulations for a single process and are *not* interested in saving those changes in a system file. Any time the **SAVE OUTFILE** command is used it will automatically replace the existing file by the new file just generated, unless you change the name to a different file. (For example, if we had renamed and saved the file as **GRADES2.SYS** instead of **GRADES.SYS**, both files would be retained: **GRADES2.SYS** with the modifications, **GRADES.SYS** without.)

LINE 5a The **LIST** command allows you to check that modifications were successfully accomplished. If there are problems, you may make changes and run the file again (see Chapter 4 for specifics on how to do this). The **LIST** command will display only the **QUIZ** scores, the **FINAL**, and the two new variables **TOTAL** and **PERCENT**. This is a reasonable selection of variables because it allows you to check a few scores for accuracy.

LINE 6a This line instructs SPSS to list only the first 20 cases rather than the whole file.

The IF Command: Creating or Modifying Variables

A second way to create new variables is with the **IF** command. The **IF** command is most frequently used to create *new* variables (rather than modifications on preexisting variables). In this section we will show how to compute two new variables, **GRADE** and **PASSFAIL**, based on the **PERCENT** variable created in the previous section. The **IF** function may also be used to recode already existing variables. For example you might have a variable named **MARITAL** that is coded 1 = never married, 2 = divorced, 3 = widowed, 4 = separated, 5 = married. You could use the **IF** command to change the **MARITAL** variable so that 1 = single (a combination of 1, 2, and 3) and 2 = married (a combination of 4 and 5).   This type of recoding, however, is more frequently done using the **RECODE** command (next section).

To create new variables, you need to indicate how they will be related to each other, in terms of whether they are equal, greater than, less than, greater than or equal, less than or equal, or not equal. SPSS allows you to use either a 2-letter code or certain symbols or combinations of symbols to accomplish this:

EQ or $=$	equals
GT or $>$	greater than
LT or $<$	less than
GE or $\geq$	greater than or equal
LE or $\leq$	less than or equal
NE or $<>$	not equal

To compute new variables GRADE and PASSFAIL, create the following command file:

```
6)  GET FILE = 'GRADES.SYS'.                              1
    IF (PERCENT GE 90) GRADE = 'A'.                       2
    IF (PERCENT LT 90) GRADE = 'B'.                       3
    IF (PERCENT LT 80) GRADE = 'C'.                       4
    IF (PERCENT LT 70) GRADE = 'D'.                       5
    IF (PERCENT LT 50) GRADE = 'F'.                       6
    IF (PERCENT LT 50) PASSFAIL = 'F'.                    7
    IF (PERCENT GE 50) PASSFAIL = 'P'.                    8
    SAVE OUTFILE = 'GRADES.SYS'.                          9
    LIST VARIABLES = PERCENT GRADE PASSFAIL/             10
    CASES = FROM 1 TO 20.                                11
```

LINE 1 Same as above.

LINES 2-6 Notice that these lines create a variable named **GRADE** based on the value of the **PERCENT**.
Follow the format shown here: First, within parentheses, the relationship between the first variable

and its values, followed by a space, then the name of the new variable followed by space, an equals sign, and the desired value for the new variable. Notice also that if the new coding is alphabetic, you need to include the symbol or symbols in single quotes. If the values were numeric, the single quotes would **not** be necessary. Also notice the structure and logic of the command file. First SPSS will designate grades for all persons with a percent greater than or equal to 90 as A's. Then it designates all persons lower than 90% as B's. Then it designates all persons lower than 80% as C's (leaving those between 80 and 89.999 as B's) and so forth for D's and F's.

LINES 7-8 These lines are straightforward. Subjects with a **PERCENT** lower than 50 will receive an F grade, while those with a **PERCENT** greater than or equal to 50 will receive a grade of P.

LINE 9 This allows you to save any manipulations in the data file that you wish to use in the future. A convention that helps you keep track of your file names and coding is to include the letters **SYS** after the period to indicate that this is an already formatted file designed for use in data analysis. Anytime the **SAVE OUTFILE** command is used, it will automatically replace the file with the new file just generated.

LINE 10 The **LIST** command allows you to check that modifications were successfully accomplished. This command lists only the three related variables.

LINE 11 This line requests that only the first 20 cases be listed.

The RECODE Command: Changing the Coding of Variables

There are times when you may wish to change the coding of your variables. There are usually two reasons why it is desirable to do so. The first is when you wish to reverse coding to be consistent with other data files, or when one coding pattern makes more sense than another. For instance if you had a file in which the **GENDER** variable was coded male = 1 and female = 2, you may have other files where it is coded female = 1, male = 2. It would be desirable to recode one of the files so that they are consistent. Or perhaps you have an **INCOME** variable that has >$100,000 coded 1 and <$10,000 coded 7. If you felt that it would make more sense to have the lower income coded with the lower numbers, the **RECODE** command could accomplish that easily for you.

The second reason for recoding is to group variables that are ungrouped in the original data. The example from the last section serves well to illustrate: You might have a variable named **MARITAL** that is coded 1 = never married, 2 = divorced, 3 = widowed, 4 = separated, 5 = married. You could use the **RECODE** command to change the marital variable so that 1 = single (a combination of 1, 2, and 3) and 2 = married (a combination of 4 and 5).

To recode GENDER so that the coding for male and female are reversed, type:

```
6) GET FILE = 'GRADES.SYS'.                              1
   RECODE GENDER (1 = 2) (2 = 1).                        2
   SAVE OUTFILE = 'GRADES.SYS'.                          3
   LIST VARIABLES = FIRSTNAM GENDER/                     4
   CASES = FROM 1 TO 10.                                 5
```

LINE 1 Same as above.

LINE 2 This line reverses the coding on the **GENDER** variable such that persons coded 1 will now be coded 2 and persons coded 2 will now be coded 1. If you wished to recode the **MARITAL** variable described above, the recode line would look like this:

RECODE MARITAL (1 THRU 3=1) (4,5=2).

LINE 3 The use of the **SAVE OUTFILE** command is optional. If you wish to reverse the coding for <u>only</u> the coming sequence of analyses, then you omit this step. However, if you wish to make a permanent change of the coding, then the **SAVE OUTFILE** command is necessary. If you wish to reverse the coding again in the future, you simply write another **RECODE** step.

LINE 4 The **LIST** command will satisfy you that SPSS has correctly recoded your variable.

LINE 5 This line instructs SPSS to list only the first 10 subjects.

The SELECT IF and PROCESS IF Commands: Selecting a Portion of the Data for Analysis

The purpose of the **SELECT IF** and the **PROCESS IF** commands is to allow the user to conduct analyses on only a portion of data. This will be a frequently used function. Often we want to know what the mean rating for females is, or the average total score for Section 3, or the mean total score for sophomores. **SELECT IF** and **PROCESS IF** both enable you to accomplish this type of selection. Both of them choose, from the complete data set, a subset of data for analysis. They differ in that a **SELECT IF** command will select a portion of data for *all* the analyses that follow. Once those data are selected, it is not possible to revert to the complete set of data except by returning to step 5 (the **GET FILE** step) and beginning again. The **PROCESS IF** command selects the data only for the statistical operation that immediately follows the command. If you wish to select the same data for the next type of analysis, you will need to write another **PROCESS IF** statement. The **PROCESS IF** command does allow you the flexibility to select different portions of your data for analysis during the same session. The choice of one or the other is a matter of which better fits your needs.

To select males for any type of analysis, type:

```
6) GET FILE = 'GRADES.SYS'.                                              1
   SELECT IF (GENDER = 2).                                               2
   This will be followed by operations you wish to conduct with this subset of data.   3
```

LINE 1 Same as above.

LINE 2 This line selects all the males in the data file for any type of investigation. Any analysis you conduct for the remainder of this session will be analysis for only the male subjects in the data set. If you wish to use the **SELECT IF** procedure for a range of values for a some variable (such as **TOTAL** points for sophomores = 2, juniors = 3 and seniors = 4), make use of the six symbols introduced on page 34 (EQ, GT, LT, GE, LE, or NE). For instance, the selection suggested in the previous sentence would be rendered: **SELECT IF (YEAR GE 2).**

The following file shows the use of the PROCESS IF command:

```
6a) GET FILE = 'GRADES.SYS'.                                      1a
     PROCESS IF (GENDER = 1).                                     2a
     Selection of these data will influence only the command that immediately follows. 3a
```

LINE 1a Same as above.

LINE 2a This line selects all the females in the data file for any type of investigation. The next statistical process you conduct will include females only. If you do not include another **PROCESS IF** command, all analyses that follow will revert back to the entire file. If you wish to use the **PROCESS IF** procedure for a range of values for some variable, make use of the six symbols introduced on page 34 (EQ, GT, LT, GE, LE, or NE). See description in line 2 (previous page) for an example of this.

The SORT Command: Rearranging Your Data

There are many reasons one may wish to rearrange data. With the **GRADES.SYS** file, the professor may wish to list final grades by **ID** number. If so, it would be useful to be able to list scores with **ID** numbers arranged from low to high. She may also be interested in the distribution of total scores of students in order to make grade breakdowns. Then it might be appropriate to list the file from high to low based on total points or total percentage. A class list is usually arranged alphabetically, but it is often necessary to list students alphabetically within each section. All these functions (and more) can be accomplished by the **SORT** command.

To sort cases by ID:

```
6) GET FILE = 'GRADES.SYS'.                                       1
   SORT CASES BY ID.                                              2
   LIST.                                                          3
```

LINE 1 Same as above.

LINE 2 This line will sort all cases by the variable **ID** from smallest to largest.

LINE 3 Listing the file is the most common thing most people want to do after sorting by variables within a data file. In this case you would usually want to list the *whole* file, not just a subset. Other procedures sometimes need a sorted file (such as **AGGREGATE** and **REPORT**), but they are not described in this book.

To sort cases by LASTNAME:

```
6a) GET FILE = 'GRADES.SYS'.                                      1a
    SORT CASES BY LASTNAME.                                       2a
    LIST VARIABLES = LASTNAME FIRSTNAM SECTION PERCENT GRADE.     3a
```

LINE 1a Same as above.

LINE 2a This line will sort all cases alphabetically by the variable **LASTNAME**.

LINE 3a As compared to line 3 (above), we have included selected variables that might be of interest to the teacher for entering final grades. As suggested earlier in this chapter, the LIST command is wonderfully adaptable to the demands of a particular situation.

To sort cases by PERCENT, from high score to low score:

```
6b)  GET FILE = 'GRADES.SYS'.                    1b
     SORT CASES BY PERCENT(D).                    2b
     LIST.                                        3b
```

LINE 1b Same as above.

LINE 2b This line will sort all cases of the variable **PERCENT** from high score to low score. With numeric data, SPSS will always list from low score to high score (as with **ID**) unless you place the **(D)** directly after the variable name, to indicate *descending* order.

LINE 3b Same as line 3 above.

NOTE: It is possible to create multiple orders with the SORT command. For example, if you wanted to sort by last name and then by first name, you could type "**SORT CASES BY LASTNAME FIRSTNAM.**". If you tell SPSS to sort only by **LASTNAME**, however, SPSS would leave any individuals that had the same last name in the order that they were before the sort command. Also, when the computer alphabetizes things, numbers are lower than letters, and the space character is lower than any numbers or letters.

To finish any of the procedures listed in this chapter, conduct the final four steps shown below.

7) F9 W ↵   *to save your command file for future access.*

If file is not already named, enter the file name (e.g., **GRADES.CTL**) at the prompt between the **W** and the **ENTER**.

To run the program, first position cursor at the beginning of the GET FILE line, then:

8) F10 C   *to run your program from the cursor.*

After viewing the results:

9) F10 E FINISH ↵   *to exit to the DOS prompt.*

To print command files and results:

10) dos> PRINT SPSS.LIS ↵ ↵   *(Sometimes the second RETURN is not necessary.)*

Chapter 6

The FREQUENCIES Command:

Frequencies, Bar Charts, Histograms, and Percentiles

FREQUENCIES

FREQUENCIES is one of the simplest yet one of the most useful of all SPSS procedures. The FREQUENCIES command simply sums the number of instances within a particular category: There were 56 males and 37 females. There were 16 Caucasians, 7 Afro-Americans, 14 Hispanics, 19 Asians, and 5 others. There were 13 A's, 29 B's, 37 C's, 7 D's, and 3 F's. Under the FREQUENCIES command, SPSS will list the following information: Value labels, the value code of each variable (the number associated with each level, e.g., female = 1, male = 2), the frequency, the percent of total for each value, and the cumulative percent at each level. Specifics are in the Output section.

BAR CHARTS

The BARCHART subcommand is used to create a visual display of frequency information. BARCHART should be used only for categorical (rather than continuous) data. A bar chart is appropriate for displaying the gender, ethnicity, or grades (categorical variables) breakdowns. It is not appropriate for showing the breakdown of final scores, IQs, or GPAs (continuous variables).

HISTOGRAMS

For continuous data, the HISTOGRAM subcommand will create the appropriate visual display. A histogram is used to indicate frequencies of a *range* of values. A histogram is used when the number of instances of a variable is too large to want to list all of them. A good example is the breakdown of the final point totals in a class of students. Since it would be too cumbersome to list *all* scores on a graph, it is more practical to list the frequencies within a *range* of values (e.g., 60 to 69 points, 70 to 79 points, and so forth).

PERCENTILES

The **PERCENTILES** subcommand will compute any desired percentiles for continuous data. Percentiles are used to indicate what percent of a distribution lies above and below a particular value. For instance if a score of 111 was at the 75th percentile, this would mean that 25% of values are higher than 111 and 75% of values are lower than 111. Percentiles are used extensively in educational and psychological measurement.

THE LOGICAL PROGRESSION FOR COMPUTING FREQUENCIES

1. Create a file of data, or edit (if necessary) an already existing file.
2. Format file by use of **DATA LIST FILE, FORMATS,** and **VALUE/VARIABLE LABELS,** then save as a system file.
3. Access the formatted file by the **GET FILE** command.
4. Use the **FREQUENCY** command to access frequencies.
5. Use the **BARCHART** subcommand to create bar charts.
6. Use the **HISTOGRAM** subcommand to create histograms.
7. Use the **PERCENTILES** subcommand to compute percentiles.
8. View the results and exit the program.
9. Print data, commands, and output.

The file we use to illustrate **FREQUENCIES** is the example described in the first chapter. The system file is called **GRADES.SYS** and has an $N = 105$. This analysis computes frequencies, bar charts, histograms, and percentiles for the variables **GENDER, ETHNICIT, GRADE,** and **TOTAL.**

STEP BY STEP
Frequencies, Bar Charts, Histograms, and Percentiles

---

1) Name and create a data file (Chapter 2), or edit (if necessary) an already existing file (Chapter 3).

> *2)* *Name variables, locate column positions, format, create VARIABLE/VALUE LABELS, and then save the formatted DATA FILE as a SYSTEM FILE (Chapter 4).*

From the DOS prompt, type:

> *3)* *dos >* **SPSSPC** ↵   *This step gets you into the SPSS system.*

To clear the menu from the top window prior to analyzing data:

> *4)* ALT ─M   *Positions cursor to begin to create the command file.*

From the extreme upper left corner of the scratch pad (lower window), type:

> *5)* **GET FILE = 'GRADES.SYS'.**   *1*

LINE 1 Accesses the formatted **SYSTEM FILE** to begin to analyze data. All statistical procedures in this book will begin with the **GET FILE** step.

To create a table of frequencies for the variables GENDER, ETHNICIT, and GRADE, type:

> *6)* **GET FILE = 'GRADES.SYS'.**   *1*
> **FREQUENCIES VARIABLES = GENDER ETHNICIT GRADE.**   *2*

LINE 1 Same as step 5, line 1 above.
LINE 2 This line will generate the frequencies of each level within that category. Output will include the name of each variable, the name of each level of the variables (if you have created value labels; otherwise it lists only the number of each level), the frequency, percent, valid percent (percent after missing values have been removed), and the cumulative percent (without missing values). A word of caution: For any continuous variable, a list of frequencies is cumbersome and wastes paper and computer time. For continuous data, use a histogram for visual display and the **DESCRIPTIVES** command (Chapter 7) to describe characteristics of the variable.

To generate a graphical representation of frequencies, use the BARCHART subcommand.

> *6a)* **GET FILE = 'GRADES.SYS'.**   *1a*
> **FREQUENCIES VARIABLES = GENDER ETHNICIT GRADE/**   *2a*
> **BARCHART.**   *3a*

LINE 1a Same as above.
LINE 2a Identical to the line 2 above except that it is followed by a slash instead of a period because a subcommand follows.
LINE 3a This command will create a barchart to represent your frequency data graphically. The command file above will generate the frequency information about **GENDER**, **ETHNICIT**, and **GRADE**, immediately followed by a horizontal bar chart to illustrate the frequencies.

If you wish to create a graphical representation of a <u>continuous</u> variable, you will use the HISTOGRAM subcommand. The following command file will create a histogram of total points (TOTAL) between 45 and 125 points in increments of 10 points.

```
6b) GET FILE = 'GRADES.SYS'.                              1b
     FREQUENCIES VARIABLES = TOTAL/                       2b
     FORMAT NOTABLE/                                      3b
     HISTOGRAM MIN(45) MAX(125) INCREMENT(10).            4b
```

LINE 1b Same as above.

LINE 2b Accesses the **FREQUENCIES** command and identifies the variable of interest as **TOTAL**. If you wish to do histograms for more than one variable, list variables of interest with a space between each variable and the last variable followed by a slash. Be aware, however, that this should be done only if you wish to have the same **MIN, MAX,** and **INCREMENT** for each graph. If you wish different values it is necessary to begin with a new 3-line **FREQUENCIES** statement. Note that this line ends with a slash because a subcommand follows it.

LINE 3b The **FORMAT NOTABLE** ("no table") step is necessary if you do not wish to have the frequencies *listed* for the continuous variable. To list such frequencies is a waste of time and paper since there will often be as many lines as there are subjects. This line ends with a slash.

LINE 4b The **HISTOGRAM** subcommand will generate a histogram of the desired variable. The **MIN, MAX,** and **INCREMENT** identify the range of values you wish to have the histogram cover (it does *not* need to cover all values) and the size of each increment. In this case we are creating a histogram of total points between 45 and 125 with intervals of 10 points (e.g., 45 to 54.999, 55 to 64.999, and so forth). If you do not include the **MIN, MAX,** and **INCREMENT**, SPSS will create a histogram with "reasonable" intervals and covering all values.

To compute PERCENTILES for a continuous variable create the following command file.

```
6c) GET FILE = 'GRADES.SYS'.                              1c
     FREQUENCIES VARIABLES = TOTAL/                       2c
     FORMAT NOTABLE/                                      3c
     PERCENTILES = 2 16 25 50 75 84 98.                   4c
```

LINES 1c-3c Same as above.

LINE 4c The **PERCENTILES** subcommand will compute any percentile you wish. The numbers listed above indicate percentile values for the mean ± 2 standard deviations (2, 16, 84, 98) and for the quartiles (25, 50, 75). If you wish to create a histogram and percentiles on the same variable, include both subcommands (any order) after the **FORMAT NOTABLE/** line.

The full range of descriptive statistics is also available with the FREQUENCIES command. Descriptive statistics will not be described until next chapter but are identified here if you would prefer to compute descriptive statistics using the FREQUENCIES command.

```
6d) GET FILE = 'GRADES.SYS'.                              1d
     FREQUENCIES VARIABLES = TOTAL/                       2d
     FORMAT NOTABLE/                                      3d
     PERCENTILES = 2 16 25 50 75 84 98/                   4d
     STATISTICS = MEAN STDDEV.                            5d
```

LINES 1d-4d Same as above except that line 4d concludes with a slash instead of a period because a subcommand follows.

LINE 5d This is the format for requesting statistics. In line 5d we have requested the mean and standard deviation for the variable **TOTAL**. List each descriptive statistic desired with a single space between each following the equals sign. End this command with a period. The available statistics follow. They will be described in some detail in the next chapter (Chapter 7).

MEAN	Mean
SEMEAN	Standard error of the mean
MEDIAN	Median
MODE	Mode
STDDEV	Standard deviation
VARIANCE	Variance
SKEWNESS	Skewness
SESKEW	Standard error of the skewness statistic
KURTOSIS	Kurtosis
SEKURT	Standard error of the kurtosis
RANGE	Range
MINIMUM	Minimum
MAXIMUM	Maximum
SUM	Sum
DEFAULT	Mean, standard deviation, minimum, and maximum
ALL	All available statistics

---

7) $\boxed{\text{F9}}$ $\boxed{\text{W}}$ $\boxed{\hookleftarrow}$ *to save your command file for future access.*

If file is not already named, enter the file name (e.g., **GRADES.CTL**) at the prompt between the **W** and the **ENTER**.

To run the program, first position cursor at the beginning of the GET FILE line, then:

---

8) $\boxed{\text{F10}}$ $\boxed{\text{C}}$ *to run your program from the cursor.*

After viewing the results:

---

9) $\boxed{\text{F10}}$ $\boxed{\text{E}}$ **FINISH** $\boxed{\hookleftarrow}$ *to exit to the DOS prompt.*

To print command files and results:

---

10) *dos* > **PRINT SPSS.LIS** $\boxed{\hookleftarrow}$ $\boxed{\hookleftarrow}$ *(Sometimes the second RETURN is not necessary.)*

OUTPUT
Frequencies, Bar Charts, Histograms, and Percentiles

FREQUENCIES and BAR CHARTS

The following OUTPUT *is produced by this* COMMAND FILE. INTERPRETATION *follows.*

```
GET FILE = 'GRADES.SYS'.
FREQUENCIES VARIABLES = GENDER ETHNICIT/
BARCHART.
```

```
--------------------------------------------------------------------------------
Page #                              SPSS/PC+                               Date

GENDER                                              Valid      Cum
Value Label         Value   Frequency   Percent    Percent    Percent
FEMALE                1         64         61.0      61.0       61.0
MALE                  2         41         39.0      39.0      100.0
                                105        100.0     100.0

     FEMALE ********************************************** 64
       MALE ************************** 41
            +---------+---------+---------+---------+---------+
            0        15        30        45        60        75

--------------------------------------------------------------------------------
ETHNICIT                                            Valid      Cum
Value Label         Value   Frequency   Percent    Percent    Percent
AMERICAN INDIAN       1          5          4.8       4.8        4.8
ASIAN                 2         20         19.0      19.0       23.8
AFRO-AMERICAN         3         24         22.9      22.9       46.7
CAUCASIAN             4         45         42.9      42.9       89.5
HISPANIC              5         11         10.5      10.5      100.0
                                105        100.0     100.0

AMR INDIAN ***** 5
     ASIAN ******************** 20
AFRO AMERI ************************ 24
 CAUCASIAN ********************************************* 45
  HISPANIC *********** 11
            +---------+---------+---------+---------+---------+
            0        10        20        30        40        50

Valid cases    105        Missing cases    0
--------------------------------------------------------------------------------
```

VALUE LABEL: Names for levels of a variable.

VALUE: The number associated with each level of the variable.

FREQUENCY: Number of data points for a variable or level.

PERCENT: The percent for each component part, including missing values. If there were missing values, they would be listed under the last value label as **MISSING** along with the frequency and percent of missing values. The total would still sum to 100.0%.

VALID PERCENT: Percent of each value excluding missing values.

CUM PERCENT: Cumulative percentage of the **VALID PERCENT**.

HISTOGRAMS

The following OUTPUT *is produced by this* COMMAND FILE. *INTERPRETATION follows.*

```
GET FILE = 'GRADES.SYS'.
FREQUENCIES VARIABLES = TOTAL/
FORMAT NOTABLE/
HISTOGRAM MIN(45) MAX(125) INCREMENT(10).
```

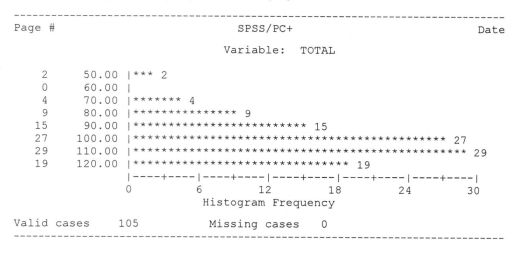

```
--------------------------------------------------------------------------------
Page #                           SPSS/PC+                              Date
                           Variable:  TOTAL

     2      50.00  |*** 2
     0      60.00  |
     4      70.00  |******* 4
     9      80.00  |************** 9
    15      90.00  |************************ 15
    27     100.00  |*********************************************** 27
    29     110.00  |************************************************* 29
    19     120.00  |**************************** 19
                   |----+----|----+----|----+----|----+----|----+----|
                   0         6        12        18        24        30
                             Histogram Frequency

Valid cases      105         Missing cases    0
--------------------------------------------------------------------------------
```

For the variable **TOTAL**, there were 2 values between 45 and 54.99 points, zero (0) values between 55 and 64.99 points, 4 values between 65 and 74.99 points and so forth.

PERCENTILES

The following OUTPUT *is produced by this* COMMAND FILE. *INTERPRETATION follows.*

```
GET FILE = 'GRADES.SYS'.
FREQUENCIES VARIABLES = TOTAL/
FORMAT NOTABLE/
PERCENTILES = 2 16 25 50 75 84 98.
```

```
--------------------------------------------------------------------------------
Page #                           SPSS/PC+                              Date
Variable:   TOTAL
```

Percentile	Value	Percentile	Value	Percentile	Value
2.00	53.560	16.00	87.960	25.00	92.000
50.00	103.000	75.00	111.000	84.00	117.040
98.00	123.880				

```
Valid cases  105      Missing cases    0
--------------------------------------------------------------------------------
```

For the **TOTAL** points variable, 2% of values fall below 53.56 points and 98% of values are higher. 16% of values fall below 87.96 and 84% of values are higher, and so forth.

Chapter 7

The DESCRIPTIVES Command:

Measures of Central Tendency, Variability, Deviation from Normality, Size, and Stability

DESCRIPTIVES is another frequently used SPSS procedure. Descriptive statistics are designed to give you information about the distribution of your variables. Within this broad category are included measures of central tendency (**MEAN, MODE, MEDIAN**), measures of variability around the mean (**STANDARD DEVIATION** and **VARIANCE**), measures of deviation from normality (**SKEWNESS** and **KURTOSIS**), information concerning the spread of the distribution (**MAXIMUM, MINIMUM**, and **RANGE**), and information about the stability of certain measures (**STANDARD ERROR OF THE MEAN, STANDARD ERROR OF THE KURTOSIS, STANDARD ERROR OF THE SKEWNESS**). Using the **DESCRIPTIVES** command, it is possible to access all of these statistics or any subset of them. In this introductory section of the chapter, we begin with a brief description of the normal distribution (since most descriptive statistics are based on a normal distribution of values) and then give a brief definition of each of the statistics mentioned above.

THE NORMAL DISTRIBUTION

Many naturally occurring phenomena produce distributions of data that approximate a normal distribution. Some examples include the height of adult humans in the world, the weight of collie dogs, the scoring averages of players in the NBA, and the IQs of residents of the United States. In all of these distributions, there are many mid-range values (e.g., 60-70 inches, 22-28 pounds, 9-14 points, 90-110 IQ points) and few extreme values (e.g., 30 inches, 80 pounds, 60 points, 12 IQ points). There are other distributions that approximate normality but deviate in predictable ways. For instance, times of runners in a 10-kilometer race will have few values less than 30 minutes (none less than 27), but many values greater than 40 minutes. The majority of values will lie above the mean (average) value. This is called a *negatively skewed distribution*. Then there is the distribution of ages of persons living in the United States. While there are individuals who are 1 year old and others who are 100 years old, there are far more 1-

year-olds, and in general the population has more values below the mean than above the mean. This is called a *positively skewed distribution*. It is possible for distributions to deviate from normality in other ways, some of which are described in this chapter.

A normal distribution is symmetric about the mean or average value. In a normal distribution, 68% of values will lie between plus-or-minus (±) 1 standard deviation (described below) of the mean, 95% of values will lie between ± 2 standard deviations of the mean, and 99.7% of values will lie between ± 3 standard deviations of the mean. A normal distribution is illustrated in the figure below.

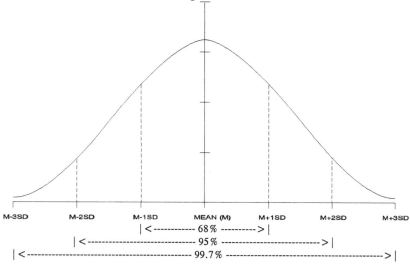

A final example will complete this section. The average (or mean) height of an American adult male is 69 inches (5 ft 9 in.) with a standard deviation of 4 inches. Thus, 68% of American men are between 5 ft 5 in. and 6 ft 1 in. (69 ± 4), 95% of American men are between 5 ft 1 in. and 6 ft 5 in. (69 ± 8), and 99.7% of American men are between 4 ft 9 in. and 6 ft 9 in. (69 ± 12) in height (don't let the NBA fool you).

MEASURES OF CENTRAL TENDENCY

The **MEAN** is the average value of the distribution, or, the sum of all values divided by the number of values. The mean of the distribution [3 5 7 5 6 8 9] is

$$(3 + 5 + 7 + 5 + 6 + 8 + 9)/7 = \underline{6.14}.$$

The **MEDIAN** is the middle value of the distribution. The median of the distribution [3 5 7 5 6 8 9], (reorder from small to large, 3 5 5 **6** 7 8 9), is $\underline{6}$, the middle value.

The **MODE** is the most frequently occurring value. The mode of the distribution [3 5 7 5 6 8 9] is $\underline{5}$, because the 5 occurs most frequently (twice, all other values occur only once).

MEASURES OF VARIABILITY AROUND THE MEAN

The VARIANCE is the sum of squared deviations from the mean divided by $N - 1$. The variance for the distribution [3 5 7 5 6 8 9] is

$$((3-6.14)^2 + (5-6.14)^2 + (7-6.14)^2 + (5-6.14)^2 + (6-6.14)^2 + (8-6.14)^2 + (9-6.14)^2)/6 = \underline{\textbf{4.1429}}.$$

Variance is used mainly for computational purposes. Standard deviation is the more commonly used measure of variability.

The STANDARD DEVIATION is the positive square root of the variance. For the distribution [3 5 7 5 6 8 9], the standard deviation is the square root of 4.1429, or <u>2.0354</u>.

MEASURES OF DEVIATION FROM NORMALITY

KURTOSIS is a measure of the "peakedness" or the "flatness" of a distribution. A kurtosis value near zero (0) indicates a shape close to normal. A negative value for the kurtosis indicates a distribution more peaked than normal. A positive kurtosis indicates a shape flatter than normal. An extreme positive kurtosis (e.g., > 5.0) indicates a distribution where more of the values are in the tails of the distribution than around the mean. A kurtosis value between ±1.0 is considered excellent for most psychometric purposes, but a value between ±2.0 is in many cases also acceptable, depending on the particular application.

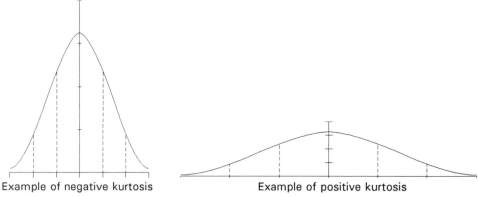

Example of negative kurtosis   Example of positive kurtosis

SKEWNESS measures to what extent a distribution of values deviates from symmetry around the mean. A value of zero (0) represents a symmetric or evenly balanced distribution. A positive skewness indicates a greater number of *smaller* values (sounds backward, but this is correct). A negative skewness indicates a greater number of *larger* values. As with kurtosis, a skewness value between ±1.0 is considered excellent for most psychometric purposes, but a value between ±2.0 is in many cases also acceptable, depending on your particular application.

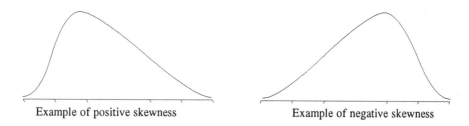

Example of positive skewness   Example of negative skewness

MEASURES FOR SIZE OF THE DISTRIBUTION

For the distribution [3 5 7 5 6 8 9], the MAXIMUM value is 9, the MINIMUM value is 3, and the RANGE is 9 − 3 = 6. The SUM of the scores is 3 + 5 + 7 + 5 + 6 + 8 + 9 = 43.

MEASURES OF STABILITY: STANDARD ERROR

SPSS computes the STANDARD ERRORS for the mean, the kurtosis, and the skewness. As indicated above, standard error is designed to be a measure of stability or of sampling error. The logic behind standard error is this: If you take a random sample from a population, you can compute the mean, a single number. If you take another sample of the same size from the same population you can again compute the mean—a number likely to be slightly different from the first number. If you collect many such samples, the standard error of the mean is the standard deviation of this sampling distribution of means. A similar logic is behind the computation of standard error for kurtosis or skewness. A small value (what is "small" depends on the nature of your distribution) indicates *greater* stability or *smaller* sampling error.

THE LOGICAL PROGRESSION FOR DESCRIPTIVE STATISTICS

1. Create file of data, or edit (if necessary) an already existing file.
2. Format file by use of DATA LIST FILE, FORMATS, and VALUE/VARIABLE LABELS, then save as a system file.
3. Access file and formats by the GET FILE command.
4. Use the DESCRIPTIVES command to access descriptive statistics.
5. Use the STATISTICS subcommand to request certain subsets of the available statistics.
6. View the results and exit the program.
7. Print data, commands, and output.

The file we use to illustrate DESCRIPTIVES is our example described in the first chapter. The system file is called GRADES.SYS and has an N = 105. This analysis computes descriptive statistics for the variables PREVGPA and TOTAL.

STEP BY STEP
Descriptive Statistics

---

1) Name and create a data file (Chapter 2), or edit (if necessary) an already existing file (Chapter 3).

---

2) Name variables, locate column positions, format, create VARIABLE/VALUE LABELS, and then save the formatted DATA FILE as a SYSTEM FILE (Chapter 4).

From the DOS prompt, type:

*3) dos> **SPSSPC** ⏎   This step gets you into the SPSS system.*

To clear the menu from the top window prior to analyzing data:

4) ALT –M   Positions cursor to begin to create the command file.

From the extreme upper left corner of the scratch pad (lower window), type:

*5) **GET FILE** = '<u>GRADES</u>.**SYS**'.   1*

LINE **1** Accesses the formatted **SYSTEM FILE** to begin to analyze data. All statistical procedures in this book will begin with the **GET FILE** step.

To create a table of frequencies only, type:

*6) **GET FILE** = '<u>GRADES</u>.**SYS**'.   1*
*   **DESCRIPTIVES VARIABLES** = <u>PREVGPA</u> <u>TOTAL</u>.   2*

LINE 1 Same as line 1 in step 5 above.
LINE 2 This line accesses by default four basic descriptive statistics (mean, standard deviation, maximum, minimum) and the sample size (*N*) for variables **PREVGPA** and **TOTAL**. You may include any number of variables. Just list them with a space between each and end with a period (or slash, if a subcommand follows). If you wish descriptives for *all* variables in the file, replace the list of variables with the single word **ALL** followed by a period. If you wish to have descriptives for a large number of variables and they are in order in your data file you may use the word **TO**. If, for instance we wished to have descriptives for the 5 quizzes, the final grade, the total, and the percent, these variables are in order in our **GRADES.SYS** file. To write descriptives for these, replace the **PREVGPA TOTAL** with **QUIZ1 TO PERCENT**. Be sure to end the command with a period.

If you wish to access more or different descriptive statistics, it is necessary to use the STATISTICS subcommand.

```
6a)  GET FILE = 'GRADES.SYS'.                              1a
     DESCRIPTIVES VARIABLES = PREVGPA TOTAL/             2a
     STATISTICS = 9 10 11 12.                             3a
```

LINE 1a Same as above.

LINE 2a Identical to the line 2 above except that it is followed by a slash instead of a period because a subcommand follows.

LINE 3a Following the equals sign (=) after **STATISTICS**, fill in one or more numbers to indicate which statistics you wish to have printed. In our example, we have requested SPSS to print the sample size, range, minimum, maximum, and sum, for **PREVGPA** and **TOTAL**. If you wish *all* descriptive statistics that SPSS offers, type the word **ALL** in place of **9 10 11 12**. Be sure to end this line with a period. If you wish different descriptive statistics than those requested here, insert the appropriate numbers in place of the **9 10 11 12**. The numbers for subsets of descriptive statistics follow:

1	=	Mean, N
2	=	Standard error of the mean, N
5	=	Standard deviation, N
6	=	Variance, N
7	=	Kurtosis, standard error of the kurtosis, N
8	=	Skewness, standard error of the skewness, N
9	=	Range, N
10	=	Minimum, N
11	=	Maximum, N
12	=	Sum, N
ALL	=	All of the above

You may have noticed the absence of median and mode in the previous list. To access these measures, it necessary to use the FREQUENCIES command. The command file that will access the mode and median for the first four quizzes follows:

```
6b)  GET FILE = 'GRADES.SYS'.                              1b
     FREQUENCIES VARIABLES = QUIZ1 QUIZ2 QUIZ3 QUIZ4/     2b
     FORMAT NOTABLE/                                      3b
     STATISTICS = MODE MEDIAN.                             4b
```

LINE 1b Same as above.

LINE 2b Accesses the **FREQUENCIES** command and identifies the variables of interest as **QUIZ1 QUIZ2 QUIZ3 QUIZ4**. This line ends with a slash to indicate that a subcommand follows.

LINE 3b The **FORMAT NOTABLE** ("no table") step is necessary if you do not wish to have the frequencies listed for the continuous variable. This line also ends with a slash.

LINE 4b Will list the mode and median for each variable of interest.

7) F9 W ↵   *to save your command file for future access.*

If file is not already named, enter the file name (e.g., **GRADES.CTL**) at the prompt between the **W** and the **ENTER**.

To run the program, first position cursor at the beginning of the GET FILE line, then:

> *8)* F10 C   *to run your program from the cursor.*

After viewing the results:

> *9)* F10 E **FINISH** ↵   *to exit to the DOS prompt.*

To print command files and results:

> *10) dos >* **PRINT SPSS.LIS** ↵ ↵   *(Sometimes the second RETURN is not necessary.)*

OUTPUT
Descriptive Statistics

The following OUTPUT is produced by this COMMAND FILE:

```
GET FILE = 'GRADES.SYS'.
DESCRIPTIVES VARIABLES = PREVGPA TOTAL/
STATISTICS = ALL.
```

Page #		SPSS/PC+		Date

Number of Valid Observations (Listwise) = 105

Variable   PREVGPA

Mean	2.779	S.E. Mean	.075
Std Dev	.764	Variance	.583
Kurtosis	-.811	S.E. Kurt	.467
Skewness	-.052	S.E. Skew	.236
Range	2.860	Minimum	1.140
Maximum	4.000	Sum	291.780

Variable   TOTAL

Mean	100.571	S.E. Mean	1.493
Std Dev	15.229	Variance	234.074
Kurtosis	.943	S.E. Kurt	.467
Skewness	-.837	S.E. Skew	.236
Range	73.000	Minimum	51.000
Maximum	124.000	Sum	10560.000

Valid Observations   105   Missing Observations   0

Note: All terms are defined and explained in the first four pages of this chapter.

Chapter 8

The CROSSTABS Command:

Crosstabulation and Chi-Square (χ^2) Tests of Independence

The purpose of crosstabulation is to show in tabular format the relationship between two or more categorical variables. Categorical variables include those in which distinct categories exist such as gender (female, male), ethnicity (Asian, Caucasian, Hispanic), place of residence (urban, suburban, rural), responses (yes, no), grade (A, B, C, D, F), and many more. Crosstabulation can be used with continuous data only if such data are divided into separate categories, such as age (0-19 years, 20-39 years, 40-59 years, 60-79 years, 80-99 years), total points (0-99, 100-149, 150-199, 200-250), and so on. While it is acceptable to perform crosstabulation with continuous data that has been categorized, it is rare to perform chi-square analyses with continuous data because a great deal of useful information about the distribution is lost by the process of categorization. For instance, in the total points distribution (above), two persons who scored 99 and 100 points, respectively, would be in the first and second categories and would be considered identical to two persons who scored 0 and 149 points, respectively. Nonetheless, crosstabulation with continuous data is often used for purposes of data description and display. The SPSS command CROSSTABS and the subcommands CELLS and STATISTICS are used to access all necessary information about comparisons of frequency data.

CROSSTABULATION

While the FREQUENCIES command can tell us there are 5 American Indians, 20 Asians, 24 Afro-Americans, 45 Caucasians, and 11 Hispanics (and that there are 64 females and 41 males) in our GRADES.SYS file, it cannot tell us how many female Asians or male Caucasians there are. This is the function of the CROSSTABS command. It would be appropriate to "cross" two variables (ETHNICIT by GENDER) to answer the questions posed above. This would produce a table of 10 different cells with associated frequencies inserted in each cell by crossing two (2) levels of GENDER with five (5) levels of ETHNICIT. It is possible to cross three or more variables, although only with a very large data set would a researcher be likely to cross more than three variables because there would be many low-count and empty cells if the number of subjects was not sufficient. For the present sample, an **ETHNICIT** by **GENDER** by **GRADES** crosstabulation would probably not be recommended. This procedure would create a 5 (**ETHNICIT**) × 2 (**GENDER**) × 5 (**GRADES**) display of frequencies—a total of 50 cells to be filled with only 105 subjects. A large number of low-count or empty cells would be guaranteed. If such a crosstabulation were created with a larger *N*, SPSS would produce five different 5 × 2 tables to display these data.

CHI-SQUARE (χ^2) TESTS OF INDEPENDENCE

In addition to frequencies (or the *observed values*) within each cell, SPSS can also compute the expected value for each cell. *Expected value* is based on the assumption that the two variables are independent of each other. A simple example demonstrates the derivation of expected value. Suppose there is a group of 100 persons in a room and that 30 are male and 70 are female. If there are 10 Asians in the group, it would be anticipated (expected)--if the two variables are independent of each other--that among the 10 Asians there would be 3 males and 7 females (the same proportion as is observed in the entire group). However, with the same group of 100, if 10 of them were football players we would *not* expect 3 male football players and 7 female football players. In American society, most football players are male, and the two categories (gender and football players) are *not* independent of each other. If there were no additional information given, it would be expected that all 10 of the players would be male. The purpose of a chi-square test of independence is to determine whether the observed value for any cell deviates significantly from the expected value for that cell.

The chi-square statistic is computed by summing the squared deviations (observed value minus expected value) divided by the expected value for each cell:

$$\chi^2 = \Sigma[(f_o - f_e)^2/f_e]$$

As you can see, if there is a large discrepancy between the observed values and the expected values, the χ^2 statistic would be large, suggesting a significant difference between observed and expected values. Along with this statistic, a probability value is computed. With $p < .05$, it is commonly accepted that the observed values differ significantly from the expected values and that the two variables are *not* independent of each other. More complete descriptions and definitions will be included in the Output section of this chapter.

An additional concern addresses the fact that a chi-square statistic is often thought of as a test of association (the opposite of independence) between variables. This assumption can create difficulty because a chi-square value is largely dependent on the number of dimensions and sample size, and thus comparisons of one chi-square value with another are often meaningless. To control for this difficulty, Pearson suggested the phi (ϕ) statistic, which divides the chi-square value by N and then takes the positive square root of the result. The purpose was to standardize a measure of association to values between 0 and 1 (with 0 indicating completely independent variables and a value close to 1 indicating a strong association between variables). However, if one of the dimensions of the crosstabulation is larger than 2, ϕ may attain a value larger than 1.0. To control for this, Cramer's V was introduced (the positive square root of $\chi^2/[N(k-1)]$, where k is the smaller of the number of rows and columns). This measure *does* vary between 0 and 1.0 and is a commonly used measure of association between variables in a chi-square analysis.

LOGICAL PROGRESSION FOR COMPUTING CHI-SQUARE (χ^2) ANALYSES

1. Create file of data, or edit (if necessary) an already existing file.
2. Format file by use of **DATA LIST FILE, FORMATS,** and **VALUE/VARIABLE LABELS,** then save as a system file.
3. Access file and formats by the **GET FILE** command.
4. Use the **CROSSTABS** command to access the crosstabulation procedure.
5. Use the **CELLS** subcommand to indicate which values you wish to have included within each cell (actual values, expected values, percentages, residuals).
6. Use the **STATISTICS** subcommand to access chi-square, phi, or Cramer's V statistics.
7. View the results and exit the program.
8. Print data, commands, and output.

The file we use to illustrate **CROSSTABS** is our example described in the first chapter. The system file is called **GRADES.SYS** and has an $N = 105$. This analysis creates crosstabulations and calculates chi-square statistics for **GENDER** by **ETHNICIT**.

STEP BY STEP
Crosstabulation and Chi-Square (χ^2) Analyses

1) *Name and create a data file (Chapter 2), or edit (if necessary) an already existing file (Chapter 3).*

2) *Name variables, locate column positions, format, create VARIABLE/VALUE LABELS, and then save the formatted DATA FILE as a SYSTEM FILE (Chapter 4).*

From the DOS prompt, type:

---
3) *dos >* **SPSSPC** $\boxed{\leftarrow}$ *This step gets you into the SPSS system.*

To clear the menu from the top window prior to analyzing data:

---
4) $\boxed{\text{ALT}}\boxed{\text{M}}$ *Positions cursor to begin to create the command file.*

From the extreme upper left corner of the scratch pad (lower window), type:

---
5) **GET FILE = 'GRADES.SYS'.**   *1*

LINE **1** Accesses the formatted **SYSTEM FILE** to begin to analyze data. All statistical procedures in this book will begin with the **GET FILE** step.

To access the frequencies for each cell of a GENDER by ETHNICIT crosstabulation, type the following:

---
6)   **GET FILE = 'GRADES.SYS'.**   *1*
    CROSSTABS TABLES = GENDER BY ETHNICIT.   *2*

LINE **1** The same as step 5 line 1 above.
LINE **2** The first variable listed (**GENDER**) is the *row variable* and the words *female* and *male* will appear to the left of the table followed by the number associated with each level (1 and 2 respectively). The second variable (**ETHNICIT**) is the *column variable,* and the words *American Indian, Asian, Afro-American, Caucasian,* and *Hispanic* will appear across the top of the table with the number associated with each level beneath it (1, 2, 3, 4, and 5 respectively). Within each of the 10 cells the number (frequency) of Asian males, Caucasian females, and so on will appear. See Output section for specifics.

If you wish to access frequencies for each cell of a crosstabulation of three variables, the following command file will accomplish this for GENDER, ETHNICIT, and YEAR:

6a) **GET FILE = 'GRADES.SYS'.**   *1a*
    CROSSTABS TABLES = GENDER BY ETHNICIT BY YEAR.   *2a*

LINE **1a** Same as above.
LINE **2a** Identical to the line 2 above except that the third variable, **YEAR,** is included. With this command file, SPSS will output four (4) different tables to represent each of the four levels of year (First-year, Sophomore, Junior, Senior), and each table will be identical to the one described in step 6 above; that is, a 2 (**GENDER**) × 5 (**ETHNICIT**) table, with **GENDER** the row variable and **ETHNICIT** the column variable. A 3-way cross tabulation is not usually done unless the number of subjects is quite large because there are likely to be many empty or low-count cells.

It is rare for a researcher to want to compute only cell frequencies (as steps 6 and 6a do above). In addition to frequencies (COUNT), SPSS can also access expected values (EXPECTED), column percents (COLUMN), row percents (ROW), total percents (TOTAL), and residuals (RESIDUAL: observed value − expected value) for each cell. The following command file shows how to access all of these statistics for a GENDER by ETHNICIT crosstabulation.

```
6b)  GET FILE = 'GRADES.SYS'.                                    1b
     CROSSTABS TABLES = GENDER BY ETHNICIT/                      2b
     CELLS = COUNT ROW COLUMN TOTAL EXPECTED RESIDUAL.          3b
```

LINE **1b** Same as above.

LINE **2b** Same as line 2 (not 2a: the **CLASS** variable has been dropped) above. This line is followed by a slash instead of a period because a subcommand follows.

LINE **3b** This line includes *all* possible options for inclusions within each cell. Typically, researchers will wish to include as minimum the **COUNT** and **EXPECTED** values, and they will include other values depending on circumstances. When you create your own command file, simply omit the options you do not wish and adhere to the format shown above. A definition of each option follows:

> **COUNT**: The observed value or frequency within each cell
> **ROW**: The percent of values in each cell for that row
> **COLUMN**: The percent of values in each cell for that column
> **TOTAL**: The percent of values in each cell for the whole table
> **EXPECTED**: The expected value for each cell (see p. 54)
> **RESIDUAL**: Observed value minus expected value

To conduct a chi-square test of independence it is necessary to use the STATISTICS subcommand:

```
6c)  GET FILE = 'GRADES.SYS'.                                    1c
     CROSSTABS TABLES = GENDER BY ETHNICIT/                      2c
     CELLS = COUNT EXPECTED/                                    3c
     STATISTICS = CHISQ PHI.                                     4c
```

LINE **1c** Same as above.

LINE **2c** Same as above.

LINE **3c** Several of the options included in step 6b have been dropped. What remains are statistics that are more frequently desired in a crosstabulation and chi-square analysis. This line now ends with a slash (instead of a period) because a subcommand follows.

LINE **4c** This line will instruct SPSS to compute chi-square statistics. It also requests phi and Cramer's V measures of association between variables (**GENDER** and **ETHNICIT**).

It is possible to use subsets of the categories of the variables. By default, SPSS will include all levels unless you specify otherwise. The following command file will compute a χ^2 for GENDER (both levels) by the first four levels of ETHNICIT (excluding the fifth level).

```
6d)  GET FILE = 'GRADES.SYS'.                                    1d
     CROSSTABS VARIABLES = GENDER(1,2) ETHNICIT(1,4)/           2d
     TABLES = GENDER BY ETHNICIT/                               3d
     CELLS = COUNT EXPECTED/                                    4d
     STATISTICS = CHISQ PHI.                                     5d
```

LINE **1d** Same as above.

LINE 2d In order to create crosstabulations with something other than *all* levels of all variables included, it is necessary to use the **VARIABLES** subcommand. When this procedure is used, it is required that you indicate in parentheses the levels of the variable you wish to use in the analysis. This is true even for a variable in which you use *all* levels (such as in the **GENDER** variable above). With the inclusion of the **VARIABLES** subcommand, SPSS will compute a crosstabulation of both levels of **GENDER** with the first four levels of **ETHNICIT**. For other variations, the format shown above should be followed. Within the parentheses, include the first category of interest, followed by a comma, followed by the last category of interest. If we had wished to exclude the first level of **ETHNICIT**, then **(1,4)** would be replaced by **(2,5)**.

LINE 3d The tables subcommand now produces a crosstabulation of the two levels of **GENDER** with the first four levels of **ETHNICIT**.

LINES 4d-5d Same as above.

Often you may already have information concerning the frequencies (observed values) within each cell but do not have the raw data. The following command file will allow you to do a chi-square analysis by entering cell frequencies only. What follows will produce identical results as the command file in step 6c (above) .

```
6e)  DATA LIST FREE/                                         1e
     GENDER ETHNICIT COUNT.                                  2e
     BEGIN DATA.                                             3e
     1 1 4
     1 2 13
     1 3 14
     1 4 26
     1 5 7
     2 1 1
     2 2 7
     2 3 10
     2 4 19
     2 5 4                                                   4e
     END DATA.                                               5e
     VALUE LABELS GENDER 1 'FEMALE' 2 'MALE'/                6e
     ETHNICIT 1 'AMERICAN INDIAN' 2 'ASIAN' 3 'AFRO-AMERICAN'
     4 'CAUCASIAN' 5 'HISPANIC'.                             7e
     WEIGHT BY COUNT.                                        8e
     CROSSTABS TABLES = GENDER BY ETHNICIT/                  9e
     CELLS = COUNT EXPECTED/                                 10e
     STATISTICS = CHISQ PHI.                                 11e
```

LINE 1e This line instructs the computer that the data to follow will be listed in *free format*. In free format, the exact column spacing of the variables is not important, as long as they are in order and the variables have a space between them.

LINE 2e Identifies the variables of interest. Since we are not reading data from a system file, the variable names must be included here.

LINE 3e This is the statement included when data are typed into the command file (rather than accessing a data file or a system file). End with a period.

LINE 4e This is the format used when you're not reading data from a previously selected file. The numbers in the first column represent the levels of your first variable (e.g., for **GENDER**, female =

1 and male = **2**). The numbers in the second column represent levels of the second variable. Note that the frequencies (third column) will always be integers, so they need not be lined up by decimal (this is called *free format*).

LINE **5e** Indicates the end of data; end with a period.

LINE **6e** This line identifies the different levels of the **GENDER** variable. End with a slash if another variable follows, otherwise end with a period.

LINE **7e** This line identifies the meaning for the five different levels of **ETHNICIT**. Note that when a line is too long you may just hit the return at a natural break and continue typing.

LINE **8e** This instructs SPSS to weight each of the 10 cells of the chi-square analysis by the number (observed value) indicated to the right in the data lines (line 4).

LINE **9e-11e** Same as lines 2c through 4c in sequence step 6c (above).

7) F9 W ↵   *to save your command file for future access.*

If file is not already named, enter the file name (e.g., **GRADES.CTL**) at the prompt between the **W** and the **ENTER**.

To run the program, first position cursor at the beginning of the GET FILE line, then:

8) F10 C   *to run your program from the cursor.*

After viewing the results:

9) F10 E FINISH ↵   *to exit to the DOS prompt.*

To print command files and results:

10) *dos >* **PRINT SPSS.LIS** ↵ ↵   *(Sometimes the second RETURN is not necessary.)*

OUTPUT
Crosstabulation and Chi-Square (χ^2) Analyses

The following OUTPUT *is produced by this* COMMAND FILE. INTERPRETATION *follows.*

```
GET FILE = 'GRADES.SYS'.
CROSSTABS TABLES = GENDER BY ETHNICIT/
CELLS = COUNT EXPECTED/
STATISTICS = CHISQ PHI.
```

Page #   SPSS/PC+   Date

GENDER BY ETHNICIT   ETHNICIT
        Count |
     Exp Val | AMERICAN ASIAN   AFRO-AME CAUCASIAN HISPANIC
             | INDIAN   RICAN | Row
             | 1 | 2 | 3 | 4 | 5 | Total
GENDER ------|----------|---------|---------|----------|--------|-
        1 | 4 | 13 | 14 | 26 | 7 | 64
FEMALE	3.0	12.2	14.6	27.4	6.7	61.0%
2	1	7	10	19	4	41
MALE	2.0	7.8	9.4	17.6	4.3	39.0%
      Column   5   20   24   45   11   105
       Total   4.8%   19.0%   22.9%   42.9%   10.5%   100.0%

     Chi-Square   Value   DF   Significance
Pearson   1.19288   4   .87927
Likelihood Ratio   1.26805   4   .86677
Mantel-Haenszel test for   .45288   1   .50097
  linear association
Minimum Expected Frequency   1.952
Cells with Expected Frequency < 5   3 OF 10   (30.0%)

     Statistic   Value   Approximate Significance
        Phi   .10659   .87927
      Cramer's V   .10659   .87927
```

-------------------------------------------------------------------------

**COUNT:** The top number in each of the 10 cells (4, 13, 14, . . .), indicating the number of subjects in each category (note coding in upper left corner of the table).

**EXP VAL:** The second number in each of the 10 cells (3.0, 12.2, 14.6, . . .), which indicates the number that would appear there if the two variables were perfectly independent of each other.

**ROW TOTAL:** The total number of subjects (with the percent listed) for each row (e.g., there are 64 females in the sample, 61% of the entire sample).

**COLUMN TOTAL:** The total number of subjects (with percent listed) for each column (e.g., there were 20 Asians in the sample, 19% of the total).

**CHI SQUARE: PEARSON** and **LIKELIHOOD RATIO** are two different methods for computing chi-square statistics. With a large *N*, these two values will be close to equal. The formula for the Pearson chi-square is:

$$\chi^2 = \Sigma[(f_o - f_e)^2/f_e]$$
```

VALUE: For **PEARSON** and **MAXIMUM LIKELIHOOD** methods, as this value gets larger the likelihood that the two variables are *not* independent (e.g., *are* dependent) also increases. The values close to 1 indicated here suggest that gender and ethnicity are independent of each other (which they are).

DF: Degrees of freedom is the number of levels in the first variable minus 1 (2 – 1 = 1) times the number of levels in the second variable minus 1 (5 – 1 = 4); 1 × 4 = 4.

SIGNIFICANCE: The likelihood that these results could happen by chance. The large *p* value here indicates that observed values do *not* differ significantly from expected values.

MANTEL-HAENSZEL TEST FOR LINEAR ASSOCIATION: This procedure tests whether the two variables correlate with each other. This measure is often meaningless because there is no logical or numeric relation to the order of the variables. For instance, there is no logical reason for the ordering of ethnicity from American Indian to Hispanic. Therefore, the correlation between gender and ethnicity is meaningless. If, however, the second variable were income, from high to low, the correlation would have meaning.

MINIMUM EXPECTED FREQUENCY: The minimum expected frequency is for the first cell of the second row (male American Indian). The expected value there is rounded off to the nearest tenth (2.0). The value accurate to three decimals is 1.952.

CELLS WITH EXPECTED FREQUENCY < 5: Three of the 10 cells have an expected frequency less than 5. If you have many low-count cells, the overall chi-square value is less likely to be valid.

PHI: A measure of the strength of association between two categorical variables. A value of .10659 represents a very weak association between gender and ethnicity. The equation is:

$$\phi = \sqrt{\chi^2 / N}$$

CRAMER'S V: A measure of the strength of association between two categorical variables. It differs from phi in that Cramer's V varies strictly between 0 and 1, while in certain cases phi may be greater than 1. The equation follows. (Note: *k* is the smaller of the number of rows and columns):

$$V = \sqrt{\chi^2 / [N(k-1)]}$$

APPROXIMATE SIGNIFICANCE: This is the same as the significance for the Pearson chi-square. The high value (.87927) indicates very weak association.

Chapter 9

The MEANS Command:

Describing Subpopulation Differences

While the CROSSTABS procedure allows you to identify the frequency of certain types of categorical data (Chapter 8), the MEANS command allows you to explore certain characteristics of continuous variables within certain categories. By way of comparison, a crosstabulation of ETHNICIT by GENDER would indicate that there were 13 Caucasian females, 22 Caucasian males, 8 Hispanic females, 6 Hispanic males, and so forth; the MEANS command allows you to view certain characteristics of continuous variables (such as total points, GPAs, percents) by groups. Thus if you computed TOTAL (number of points) for ETHNICIT by GENDER, you would find that there were 13 Caucasian females who scored an average (mean) of 113.12 points, 22 Caucasian males who scored a mean of 115.34 points, 8 Hispanic females who scored a mean of 116.79, 6 Hispanic males who scored a mean of 113.45, and so forth. This information is, of course, presented in tabular format for ease in reading and interpretation. The utility of the MEANS command for data such as our sample file is several-fold. For a class with more than one section, we might like to see mean scores for each section; or to compare the scores of males with females, or the performance of upper-division with lower-division students.

The MEANS command is one of SPSS's simplest procedures. For the selected groups it will list the mean for each group, the standard deviation, and the number of subjects for each category. There is an optional STATISTICS subcommand with which you may conduct an analysis of variance based on the means and standard deviations you have just produced. We will include that option in this chapter but will save a detailed explanation of analysis of variance for the ONEWAY and ANOVA chapters (Chapters 13-15).

THE LOGICAL PROGRESSION FOR DESCRIBING SUBPOPULATION DIFFERENCES

1. Create file of data, or edit (if necessary) an already existing file.
2. Format file by use of DATA LIST FILE, FORMATS, and VARIABLE/VALUE LABELS, then save as a system file.

3. Access file and formats by the **GET FILE** command.
4. Use the **MEANS** command to access variables of interest.
5. Use the **STATISTICS** subcommand to request analysis of variance statistics.
6. View the results and exit the program.
7. Print data, commands, and output.

STEP BY STEP
Describing Subpopulation Differences

> *1) Name and create a data file (Chapter 2), or edit (if necessary) an already existing file (Chapter 3).*

> *2) Name variables, locate column positions, format, create VARIABLE/VALUE LABELS, and then save the formatted DATA FILE as a SYSTEM FILE (Chapter 4).*

From the DOS prompt, type:

> *3) dos > SPSSPC* [↵]   *This step gets you into the SPSS system.*

To clear the menu from the top window prior to analyzing data:

> *4)* [ALT]–[M]   *Positions cursor to begin to create the command file.*

From the extreme upper left corner of the scratch pad (lower window), type:

> *5)* GET FILE = 'GRADES.SYS'.   *1*

LINE 1 Accesses the formatted **SYSTEM FILE** to begin to analyze data. All statistical procedures in this book will begin with the **GET FILE** step.

If you wish to determine the mean number of total points (TOTAL) in each section, type:

> *6)* GET FILE = 'GRADES.SYS'.   *1*
> MEANS TABLES = TOTAL BY SECTION.   *2*

LINE 1 Same as line 1 in step 5 above.

LINE 2 The **MEANS** command accesses sample size, means, and standard deviations for the variables of interest. The **TABLES** creates the format for the output. It is critical that the dependent variable (TOTAL) be the first variable named and that it be a *continuous* variable. It is all right if the other variables (these will always be discrete) are numeric or alphabetic (although if it is alphabetic, only the first eight characters will be displayed). This file will compute the means and standard deviations for each of the three sections.

If you wish to determine the total point scores for both *SECTION* and *for LOWUP (whether the student is lower division or upper division), create the following command file:*

6a) **GET FILE = 'GRADES.SYS'.**	*1a*
MEANS TABLES = TOTAL BY SECTION BY LOWUP.	*2a*

LINE **1a** Same as above.

LINE **2a** Identical to line 2 above except that this line divides subjects into six separate categories, with three levels of **SECTION** and two levels of **LOWUP**. The output will list sample size (*N*), means, and standard deviations for each category.

You may list more than one dependent variable. SPSS will then produce as many tables as there are dependent variables. In the command file that follows, we compute means and standard deviations for PREVGPA, TOTAL, and PERCENT (3 dependent variables) for the 6 categories (3 levels of SECTION by 2 levels of GENDER) included in the analysis.

6b) **GET FILE = 'GRADES.SYS'.**	*1b*
MEANS TABLES = PREVGPA TOTAL PERCENT BY SECTION BY LOWUP.	*2b*

LINE **1b** Same as above.

LINE **2b** This command file will create three tables, one for each of the dependent variables, **PREVGPA**, **TOTAL**, and **PERCENT**. Each chart will look identical to the chart produced by line 2a (above).

It is possible to compute a one-way analysis of variance using the MEANS command. The following will produce the means tables of TOTAL score for SECTION by GENDER and a one-way analysis of variance for TOTAL by SECTION.

6c) **GET FILE = 'GRADES.SYS'.**	*1c*
MEANS TABLES = TOTAL BY SECTION BY GENDER/	*2c*
STATISTICS = 1.	*3c*

LINE **1c** Same as above.

LINE **2c** This line will calculate means, standard deviations, and *N* for **TOTAL** for males and females for each section.

LINE **3c** This line will calculate the ANOVA statistics, producing a **TOTAL** by **SECTION** one-way analysis of variance. A more comprehensive description of analysis of variance will occur in Chapters 13, 14, and 15.

7) F9 W ↵   *to save your command file for future access.*

If file is not already named, enter the file name (e.g., **GRADES.CTL**) at the prompt between the **W** and the **ENTER**.

To run the program, first position cursor at the beginning of the GET FILE line, then:

8) `F10` `C`   to run your program from the cursor.

After viewing the results:

9) `F10` `E` **FINISH** `↵`   to exit to the DOS prompt.

To print command files and results:

10) *dos* > **PRINT SPSS.LIS** `↵` `↵`   (Sometimes the second RETURN is not necessary.)

OUTPUT
Describing Subpopulation Differences

The following OUTPUT is produced by this COMMAND FILE. INTERPRETATION follows.

```
GET FILE = 'GRADES.SYS'.
MEANS TABLES = TOTAL BY SECTION BY GENDER/
STATISTICS = 1.
```

Page #			SPSS/PC+		Date

Summaries of   TOTAL
By levels of   SECTION
                  GENDER

Variable	Value	Label	Mean	Std Dev	Cases
For Entire Population			100.5714	15.2995	105
SECTION	1		105.0909	16.1485	33
GENDER	1	FEMALE	103.9500	18.1354	20
GENDER	2	MALE	106.8462	13.0054	13
SECTION	2		99.4872	12.0129	39
GENDER	1	FEMALE	100.0000	12.3061	26
GENDER	2	MALE	98.4615	11.8224	13
SECTION	3		97.3333	17.1841	33
GENDER	1	FEMALE	102.8333	10.6785	18
GENDER	2	MALE	90.7333	21.2350	15

Total Cases = 105

```
-------------------------------------------------------------------------
Page #                         SPSS/PC+                            Date

Summaries of    TOTAL
By levels of    SECTION

    Value  Label               Mean       Std Dev      Sum of Sq      Cases
           1               105.0909       16.1485      8344.7273         33
           2                99.4872       12.0129      5483.7436         39
           3                97.3333       17.1841      9449.3333         33
                           100.5714       15.1067     23277.8042        105
-------------------------------------------------------------------------
Analysis of Variance

Criterion Variable:   TOTAL
                       Sum of                   Mean
Source                Squares       D.F.        Square         F        Sig.
Between Groups       1065.9101        2        532.9550      2.3353     .1019
Within Groups       23277.8042      102        228.2138

            Eta = .2093        Eta Squared = .0438
-------------------------------------------------------------------------
```

Note that the first half of the output is the simple means, standard deviations, and frequencies for the entire group and for each of the selected categories. While SPSS lists the marginal values for the first of the two categorical variables (SECTION), it does not list cumulative values for the second categorical variable (GENDER). If you desired the data for GENDER, you would need to switch the order of the two variables in the command file. Definitions of terms in the ANOVA output are listed below. With means of 105.1, 99.5, and 97.3, the test statistics yield a *p*-value of .1019, a value many researchers would interpret as marginally significant. This finding suggests that the sections have a marginally significant influence on the TOTAL scores. Pairwise comparisons are not possible with this very simple ANOVA procedure, but visual inspection reveals that the greatest difference is between the first ($M = 105.4$) and third ($M = 97.3$) sections.

WITHIN-GROUP SUM OF SQUARES: The sum of the squared deviations between the mean for each group and the observed values of each subject within that group.

BETWEEN-GROUP SUM OF SQUARES: The sum of squared deviations between the grand mean and each group mean, weighted (multiplied) by the number of subjects in each group.

BETWEEN-GROUPS DEGREES OF FREEDOM: Number of groups minus one: ($3 - 1 = 2$).

WITHIN-GROUPS DEGREES OF FREEDOM: Number of subjects minus number of groups ($105 - 3 = 102$).

MEAN SQUARE: Sum of squares divided by degrees of freedom.

F RATIO: Between-groups mean square divided by within-groups mean square.

SIGNIFICANCE: The probability of the observed values happening by chance. The *p*-value indicated here ($p = .10$) indicates that a marginally significant difference ($.05 < p < .10$) between means exists between at least one of the three pairings of the three sections.

ETA: A measure of correlation between two variables when one of the variables is discrete.

ETA SQUARED: The proportion of the variance in the dependent variable accounted for by the independent variable. For instance, an eta squared of .044 indicates that 4.4% of the variance in the TOTAL scores is due to membership in one of the three SECTIONs.

Chapter 10

The PLOT Command

Scatter Plots, Regression Plots, and Overlay Plots

It is often desirable to represent data graphically. Chapter 6 explained how to access bar charts and histograms. Both are excellent ways of visualizing frequency-related data to check for relative normality of a particular distribution. The reason for creating scatter plots differs from the purpose for bar charts and histograms. Scatter plots are usually generated to observe, visually, whether two or more *continuous* variables are correlated with each other. Whether or not each set of data is distributed normally is not of primary interest.

In this chapter we briefly describe three different types of scatter plots, give a step-by-step procedure for accessing and formatting these plots, and finally interpret the plots created in the output to clarify any ambiguities. It is possible to create a number of additional types of plots with SPSS (such as stem-and-leaf plots, dendograms, and others), but these plots are usually related to a particular statistical procedure and will be introduced in the chapter where that procedure is presented.

DESCRIPTIONS OF SCATTER PLOTS, REGRESSION PLOTS, AND OVERLAY PLOTS

The simplest and most frequently used plot is the SCATTER PLOT, a visual display of the relationship between two variables. For instance, if the two variables are College GPA and GRE scores, GPA would be on the vertical axis and GRE scores on the horizontal axis of a bicoordinate plane. For each subject there will be a GPA and a GRE score, and that student's single point will be graphed on this plane. There will be as many points as there are subjects. Because of size constraints and because some subjects will have identical values, SPSS codes each data point with a number to indicate how frequently that pair of values occurs. A 1 represents a single subject's pair of scores, a 2 means that two subjects have the same pair of scores, a 3 means that three subjects have the same pair, and so forth.

The **REGRESSION PLOT** is identical to the scatter plot except that it shows the regression line (often called the *line of best fit*) on the plot. After printing the plot, it contributes additional information, such as the correlation between the two variables, the significance of the correlation, and the intercept and slope of the regression line.

The **OVERLAY PLOT** allows you to represent more than two variables on the same plot. This procedure might be of interest, for instance, if you would like to plot both the marriage rate and the divorce rate over a number of years on the same graph. It is possible to plot any number of variables on the horizontal axis against a single variable on the vertical axis. Two things need to be noted, however: (1) With every variable you add, you lose detail simply because of the restraints of space, and (2) the overlay plot can show only locations of points; it is no longer able to show the frequency of a particular point. There are a number of additional formatting variations, some of which we will describe. For the others, we refer you to the *SPSS/PC+ 4.0 Base Manual*.

THE LOGICAL PROGRESSION FOR CREATING SCATTER PLOTS

1. Create file of data, or edit (if necessary) an already existing file.
2. Format file by use of **DATA LIST FILE, FORMATS,** and **VARIABLE/VALUE LABELS,** then save as a system file.
3. Access file and formats by the **GET FILE** command.
4. Use the **PLOT** command to create the desired plots of data.
5. Use the **FORMAT** or **SYMBOLS** commands to adapt the plot to your research needs.
6. View the results and exit the program.
7. Print data, commands, and output.

Once again we make use of the **GRADES.SYS** file to demonstrate scatter plots. This file has an $N = 105$ and a vertical-axis variable of **PREVGPA** (the student's GPA prior to entering the class). Horizontal-axis variables used here will include **FINAL** (score on the final exam), **TOTAL** (total points achieved in the class), and **PERCENT** (the final class percentage based on final points).

STEP BY STEP
Scatter Plots, Regression Plots, and Overlay Plots

1) Name and create a data file (Chapter 2), or edit (if necessary) an already existing file (Chapter 3).

> *2) Name variables, locate column positions, format, create VARIABLE/VALUE LABELS, and then save the formatted DATA FILE as a SYSTEM FILE (Chapter 4).*

From the DOS prompt, type:

> *3) dos>* **SPSSPC** ⏎   *This step gets you into the SPSS system.*

To clear the menu from the top window prior to analyzing data:

> *4)* ALT ─M   *Positions cursor to begin to create the command file.*

From the extreme upper left corner of the scratch pad (lower window), type:

> *5)* GET FILE = 'GRADES.SYS'.   *1*

LINE 1 Accesses the formatted SYSTEM FILE to begin to analyze data. All statistical procedures in this book will begin with the GET FILE step.

For a simple scatter plot of the two variables PREVGPA with FINAL, type:

> *6)* GET FILE = 'GRADES.SYS'.   *1*
> PLOT PLOT = PREVGPA WITH FINAL.   *2*

LINE 1 Same as line 1 in step 5 above.
LINE 2 The first **PLOT** accesses the plot-creating mechanism of SPSS. The second **PLOT** defines its parameters (which variables, in which order). The first variable listed (**PREVGPA**) will be on the vertical axis, the second (**FINAL**) on the horizontal axis. This command file will create a scatter plot but will provide no further information about the variables (such as correlations or significance).

To create two or more scatter plots with the same command, list multiple horizontal-axis variables with a single space between them, following the word WITH. The following file will produce two plots, PREVGPA with FINAL, and PREVGPA with TOTAL.

> *6a)* GET FILE = 'GRADES.SYS'.   *1a*
> PLOT PLOT = PREVGPA WITH FINAL TOTAL.   *2a*

LINE 1a Same as above.
LINE 2a Identical to the line 2 above except that the additional variable **TOTAL** is added. This command file will produce two separate scatter plots with no additional information about relationships between variables. The same format would hold if you wished to create more than two graphs; just enter additional variables.

The FORMAT subcommand creates a REGRESSION PLOT. The regression plot is identical to the scatter plot except that the output will include not only a scatter plot but also the regression line (or line of best fit) and list the correlation between variables, with the significance of the correlation. The following command file will create a regression plot of PREVGPA with TOTAL.

```
6b) GET FILE = 'GRADES.SYS'.                                       1b
     SET /LENGTH=57 /EJECT ON /BOXSTRING = '-|+'.                  2b
     PLOT FORMAT = REGRESSION/                                     3b
     PLOT = PREVGPA WITH TOTAL.                                    4b
```

LINE **1b** Same as above.

LINE **2b** The **SET** command assists in formatting the configuration of your output. This line is not necessary for the command file to run. Thus you may omit the line completely or eliminate any of the three subcommands that follow (making sure to eliminate the preceding slash along with the subcommand). The **/LENGTH=57** will increase the size of your graph to include the whole page. This allows for much greater detail. (The graphs in the Output section are the size produced if you do *not* include the **/LENGTH=57** line.) The **/EJECT ON** instructs SPSS to start a new page at each page break. This ensures that your graph will not be broken in the middle and continued on the next page. Unfortunately, it also wastes more paper when you print output. The **/BOXSTRING =** '**-|+**' addresses the reality that many printers print a variety of garbage as borders for your graph. This subcommand ensures that vertical lines will be printed as (|), horizontal lines will be (-), and the corners or other breaks will be (+). Always end the **SET** line with a period.

LINE **3b** The **FORMAT** subcommand identifies which type of plot you wish. This line identifies **REGRESSION** as the selected plot. A slash follows this line to indicate that a subcommand follows. The **REGRESSION LINE** is indicated on the graph by an *R* on each of the left and right vertical axes. The line that connects these *R*s is the regression line. Slope and intercept information is also provided in the output that follows.

LINE **4b** This line identifies **PREVGPA** as the vertical-axis variable and **TOTAL** as the horizontal-axis variable.

The OVERLAY PLOT is accessed in the same way as the regression plot—with the FORMAT subcommand. The OVERLAY PLOT differs from the scatter plot or the regression plot in that two or more variables are allowed on the horizontal axis to be plotted against a single vertical-axis variable. The following command file will produce an overlay plot of PREVGPA on the vertical axis, with FINAL (score out of 75 on the final) and PERCENT (percent of total points possible in the class) on the horizontal axis. Both horizontal-axis variables share the same scale (40 to 100).

```
6c) GET FILE = 'GRADES.SYS'.                                       1c
     SET /LENGTH=57 /EJECT ON /BOXSTRING = '-|+'.                  2c
     PLOT FORMAT = OVERLAY/                                        3c
     PLOT PREVGPA WITH FINAL PERCENT.                              4c
```

LINE **1c** Same as above.

LINE **2c** Same as line 2b above.

LINE **3c** The **FORMAT** subcommand accesses the **OVERLAY** plot in this file, as it did the regression plot in the previous file. Note again that a slash follows this line to indicate that a subcommand follows.

LINE **4c** This line identifies **PREVGPA** as the vertical-axis variable and **FINAL** and **PERCENT** as the variables that share the horizontal axis. Any variables listed before the word **WITH** go on the vertical axis, and any variables listed after the word WITH go on the horizontal axis. SPSS uses a scale of values that ranges from the lowest value in either variable to the highest value in either variable.

The overlay plot codes the first horizontal-axis variable (FINAL in the previous file) as 1, the second horizontal-axis variable (PERCENT) as 2, and (if there were additional variables on the same graph), 3, 4, and so on. Values on the graph may overlap. Subject #56 may have a previous GPA of 3.22 and a final score of 73. The same individual (with the same previous GPA of 3.22) may also have a final percent of 73. When there are overlapped values, SPSS, instead of putting a 1 or a 2, will put a $. Due to the limitations of space on a graph, the $ may also occur if there are pairs of value that are not identical but have nearly equal values. Another limitation of the overlay plot is that it is no longer possible to indicate the frequency of values at a certain point on the graph. It can simply indicate that one or more values lie at the point designated by a 1, 2, or $.

It is often desirable to use a coding system other than 1, 2, 3 and so on for the sake of clarity. For instance, if you were plotting frequency of marriage and frequency of divorce rates as a function of time, it would be desirable to designate marriages as M rather than 1, and to code divorces as D rather than 2. Furthermore, any symbol available on the keyboard may be used. This sometimes creates a more distinctive visual display because while, for instance, P and F look fairly similar at a glance, * and # look quite different. The **SYMBOLS** subcommand allows the user to choose how to code the variables in a plot.

The following command lines are identical to step 6c above except that the 1 used to code FINAL has been exchanged for F, and the 2 used to code PERCENT has been changed to %.

```
6d)  GET FILE = 'GRADES.SYS'.                                  1d
     SET /LENGTH=57 /EJECT ON /BOXSTRING = '-|+'.              2d
     PLOT SYMBOLS = 'F%'/                                      3d
     FORMAT = OVERLAY/                                         4d
     PLOT PREVGPA WITH FINAL PERCENT.                          5d
```

LINE **1d** Same as above.

LINE **2d** Same as line 2c above.

LINE **3d** The **SYMBOLS** subcommand allows you to replace the coding for the first variable with the first character in the single quotes, the coding for the second variable with the second character in the single quotes, and so forth if there are more than two horizontal-axis variables. Adhere exactly to the punctuation shown. Note the use of the % rather than P for percent because F and P are not as visually distinctive as F and %.

LINES **4d-5d** These lines create an overlay plot identical to that shown in step 6c (above) except that instead of 1's and 2's on the graph, there will be F's and %'s.

Note: There are a number of additional techniques listed in the *SPSS/PC+ 4.0 Base Manual* that extend beyond the scope of this book.

> 7) | F9 | W | ↵ | *to save your command file for future access.*

If file is not already named, enter the file name (e.g., **GRADES.CTL**) at the prompt between the **W** and the **ENTER**.

To run the program, first position cursor at the beginning of the GET FILE line, then:

> 8) | F10 | C | *to run your program from the cursor.*

After viewing the results:

> 9) | F10 | E | FINISH | ↵ | *to exit to the DOS prompt.*

To print command files and results:

> 10) *dos* > PRINT SPSS.LIS | ↵ | ↵ | *(Sometimes the second RETURN is not necessary.)*

OUTPUT
Scatter Plots, Regression Plots, and Overlay Plots

SCATTER AND REGRESSION PLOTS

The following OUTPUT is produced by this COMMAND FILE. INTERPRETATION follows.

```
GET FILE = 'GRADES.SYS'.
SET /BOXSTRING = '-|+'.
PLOT FORMAT = REGRESSION/
PLOT = PREVGPA WITH TOTAL.
```

Page #   SPSS/PC+   Date

                        PLOT OF PREVGPA WITH TOTAL

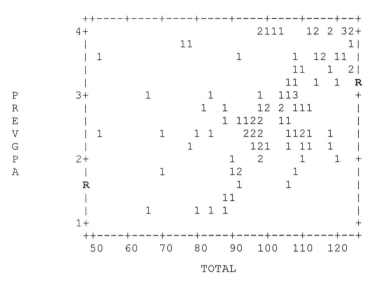

```
     ++----+----+----+----+----+----+----+----+--+
   4+                           2111    12 2 32+
    |                11                        1|
    |  1                        1        1  12 11 |
    |                                  11    1  2|
    |                                  11  1  1  R
P  3+          1          1         1  113           +
R   |                       1  1     12 2 111        |
E   |                         1 1122  11             |
V   |  1            1       1 1    222   1121  1     |
G   |                    1         121  1 11   1     |
P  2+                         1     2      1     1   +
A   |            1              12          1         |
    R                           1       1             |
    |                         11                      |
    |            1        1 1 1                       |
   1+                                                 +
     ++----+----+----+----+----+----+----+----+--+
      50   60   70   80   90  100  110  120
```

TOTAL

105 cases plotted, Regression statistics of PREVGPA on TOTAL:
Correlation .43228   R Squared .18687   S.E. of Est .69209 Sig .0000
Intercept(S.E.) .60844 (.45119)   Slope(S.E.) .02158 (.00444)

- The number of subjects, $N = 105$.
- The variable **PREVGPA** varies between values of 0.90 and 4.00.
- The variable **TOTAL** ranges from a low score of 50 to a high score of 125.
- The variable **PERCENT** ranges from a low of 42 to a high of 99 (next graph).
- If you add up all the numbers in the regression plot, they will sum to 105.
- The numbers 1 or 2 or 3 and so on indicate how many subjects have that particular pair of values.
- Note the tendency of the values to move from lower left to upper right. This indicates a positive correlation between the two variables.
- Note that the regression plots include the letter R in the left and right borders. A straight line connecting these two R's creates the "regression line" or the line of best fit. You have to draw the line on the graph since SPSS does not produce it.

Beneath the regression graph is some correlational information:

CORRELATION: Measures to what extent one variable varies systematically with another variable. The statistic presented here is the Pearson product-moment correlation, designated r or R.

R SQUARED: The square of the correlation represents the amount of variance explained by those two variables. For instance, the R^2 value associated with **PREVGPA** and **TOTAL** IS .187. This means that 18.7% of the variance on the final can be explained by the subject's previous GPA.

SIGNIFICANCE: The probability that such a pattern could happen by chance. The significance of $p < .0001$ indicates that the probability of this pattern occurring by chance is less than 1 in 10,000.

INTERCEPT: Indicates the point at which the regression line intersects the left vertical axis.

SLOPE: The slope of the regression line.

S.E.: Standard error is a measure of the stability or sampling error of the measures it is associated with. It is based on the size of the sample and the variance.

OVERLAY PLOTS

The following OUTPUT *is produced by this* COMMAND FILE. INTERPRETATION *follows.*

```
GET FILE = 'GRADES.SYS'.
SET /BOXSTRING = '-|+'.
PLOT SYMBOLS = 'F%'/
FORMAT = OVERLAY/
PLOT = PREVGPA WITH FINAL PERCENT.
```

```
--------------------------------------------------------------------------------
Page #                            SPSS/PC+                          Date

Group 1 - F (FINAL)
Group 2 - % (PERCENT)

                              OVERLAY PLOT
              +-----+----+----+----+----+----+-----+-+
          4+            F   FFFF F FF%% %%    %%%% %%+
           |        F   F  % %       F              %|
           |%F         F     F  FF%          %   %% %% |
    P      |               FFF  F          %%      %  %|
    R      |               F  FF           %     %   % |
    E    3+      F  %F   FF  F$       %    %%%             +
    V      |     F         FFFFF%F %     %%  %%% %          |
    G      |       F   FFFF   %  %%%%  %%                    |
    P      |F%    FFF  $FF  F%F$FF   %%%    %% %   %        |
    A      |      FF F   F$F         %%     %% %             |
         2+        FF    F F  F% %%      %        %       +
           |      F  %FF   F   %%         %               |
           |            FF      %     %               |
           |         F         %%                    |
           | F     %F   F  % % %                     |
         1+                                          +
          +-----+----+----+----+----+----+-----+-+
              48        64        80        96
          40        56        72        88

                           FINAL  PERCENT
--------------------------------------------------------------------------------
```

   Note that the vertical scale (**PREVGPA**) is identical to the previous graph. The horizontal scale varies from 40 (the low score on the **FINAL**) to 99 (the highest **PERCENT** observed in the class). On an overlay plot it is *very desirable* to have the same scale for the two or more variables measured on the horizontal axis. In our example, the scale for **FINAL** and **PERCENT** are different, but they are close enough to yield a meaningful graph. The different scale for **PREVGPA** (.90 to 4.00) is fine because it is on a different axis. As noted previously, some information is lost in an overlay plot. We cannot know the *frequency* of values where an F, %, or $ is placed. At those places, there may be one or several occurrences of that pair of values.

Chapter 11

The **CORRELATION** Command:

Correlations and the Correlation Matrix

Correlations may be computed by making use of the SPSS command CORRELATION. Correlations are designated by the lower case letter *r,* and range in value from –1 to +1. A correlation is often called a *bivariate correlation* to designate a simple correlation between two variables, as opposed to relationships among more than two variables as frequently observed in multiple regression analyses or structural equation modeling. A correlation is also frequently called the Pearson product-moment correlation or the Pearson *r*. Karl S. Pearson is credited with the formula from which these correlations are computed. There are other formulas from which correlations are derived that reflect characteristics of different types of data, but a discussion of these goes beyond the scope of this book. See the *SPSS/PC+ Statistics 4.0 Manual* for additional information.

WHAT IS A CORRELATION?

Perfect positive (r = 1) correlation: A correlation of +1 designates a perfect, positive correlation. *Perfect* indicates that one variable is precisely predictable from the other variable. *Positive* means that as one variable increases in value, the other variable also increases in value (or conversely, as one variable decreases, the other variable also decreases). Perfect correlations are essentially never found in the social sciences and exist only in mathematical formulas and direct physical or numerical relations. An example would be the relationship between the number of hours worked and the amount of pay received. As one number increases, so does the other. Given one of the values, it is possible to precisely determine the other value.

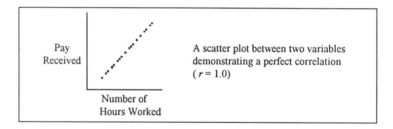

Pay Received — Number of Hours Worked

A scatter plot between two variables demonstrating a perfect correlation ($r = 1.0$)

Positive (0 < r < 1) correlation: A positive (but not perfect) correlation indicates that as the value of one variable increases, the value of the other variable also *tends* to increase. The closer the correlation value is to 1, the stronger is that tendency; and the closer the correlation value is to 0, the weaker is that tendency. An example of a strong positive correlation is the relation between height and weight in adult humans ($r = .83$). Tall people are usually heavier than short people. An example of a weak positive correlation is the relation between a measure of empathic tendency and amount of help given a needy person ($r = .12$). Persons with higher empathic tendency scores give more help than persons who score lower, but the relationship is weak.

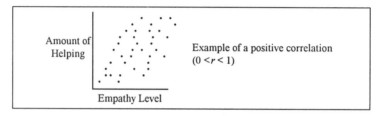

Amount of Helping — Empathy Level

Example of a positive correlation ($0 < r < 1$)

No (r = 0) correlation: A correlation of 0 indicates no relation between the two variables. For example, we would not expect IQ and height in inches to be correlated.

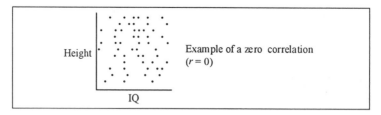

Height — IQ

Example of a zero correlation ($r = 0$)

Negative (–1 < r < 0) correlation: A negative (but not perfect) correlation indicates a relation in which as one variable *increases* the other variable has a tendency to *decrease*. The closer the correlation value is to –1, the stronger is that tendency. The closer the correlation value is to 0, the weaker is that tendency. An example of a strong negative correlation is the relation between anxiety and emotional stability ($r = -.73$). Persons who score higher in anxiety tend to score lower in emotional stability. Persons who score lower in anxiety tend to score higher in emotional stability. A weak negative correlation is demonstrated in the relation between a person's anger toward a friend suffering a problem and the quality of help given that friend ($r = -.13$). If a person's anger is *less* the quality of help given is *more*, but the relationship is weak.

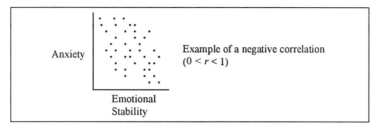

Perfect negative (r = –1) correlation: Once again, perfect correlations (positive or negative) exist only in mathematical formulas and direct physical or numerical relations. An example of a perfect negative correlation is based on the formula DISTANCE = RATE × TIME. When driving from point A to point B, if you drive *twice* as fast you will take *half* as long.

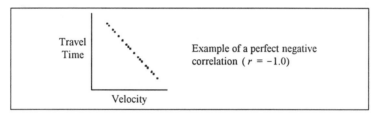

ADDITIONAL CONSIDERATIONS

It is important to understand that the CORRELATION command measures only *linear* relationships. There are many relations that are not linear. Take the example of nervousness before a major exam. Too much or too little nervousness generally hurts performance while a moderate amount of nervousness typically aids performance. The relation on a scatter plot would look like an inverted U, but computing a Pearson correlation would yield no relation or a weak relation. The chapters on simple regression and multiple regression analysis (Chapters 19 and 20) will consider curvilinear relationships in some detail. It is sometimes a good idea to create a scatter plot of your data (Chapter 10) before computing correlations, to see if the relationship between two variables is linear. If it is linear, the scatter plot will more or less resemble a straight line. While a scatter plot can aid in detecting a linear correlation, it is often true that significant correlations may exist even though they can not be detected by visual analysis alone.

As with most other statistical procedures, a significance or probability is computed to determine the likelihood that a particular correlation could occur by chance. The significance (or *p*-value) represents the *degree of rarity* of a certain result. A significance less than .05 ($p < .05$) means that there is less than a 5% chance of this relationship occurring by chance. SPSS has two different significance measures, one-tailed significance and two-tailed significance. To determine which to use, the rule of thumb generally followed is to use two-tailed significance when you compute a table of correlations in which you have little idea as to the *direction* of the correlations. If, however, you have prior expectations about the direction of correlations, then the statistic for one-tailed significance is generally used.

THE LOGICAL PROGRESSION FOR COMPUTING CORRELATIONS

1. Create file of data, or edit (if necessary) an already existing file.
2. Format file by use of **DATA LIST FILE**, **FORMATS**, and **VARIABLE/VALUE LABELS**; then save as a system file.
3. Access file and formats by the **GET FILE** command.
4. Use the **CORRELATION** command to calculate tables of correlations.
5. Use the **OPTIONS** subcommand to access one- or two-tailed probabilities.
6. Use the **STATISTICS** subcommand to access certain statistical data.
7. View the results and exit the program.
8. Print data, commands, and output.

The file we use to illustrate **CORRELATION** is our example introduced in the first chapter. The system file is called **GRADES.SYS** and has an $N = 105$. This analysis computes correlations between five variables in the file: Year in school (**YEAR**), previous GPA (**PREVGPA**), the first and fifth quizzes (**QUIZ1 QUIZ5**), and the final exam (**FINAL**).

STEP BY STEP
Correlations

> *1)* Name and create a data file (Chapter 2), or edit (if necessary) an already existing file (Chapter 3).

> *2)* Name variables, locate column positions, format, create VARIABLE/VALUE LABELS, and then save the formatted DATA FILE as a SYSTEM FILE (Chapter 4).

From the DOS prompt, type:

> *3)* dos > **SPSSPC** ⏎   This step gets you into the SPSS system.

To clear the menu from the top window prior to analyzing data:

> *4)* ALT ⊣ M   Positions cursor to begin to create the command file.

From the extreme upper left corner of the scratch pad (lower window), type:

5) **GET FILE** = 'GRADES.SYS'.	*1*

LINE **1** Accesses the formatted **SYSTEM FILE** to begin to analyze data. All statistical procedures in this book will begin with the **GET FILE** step.

To produce a correlation matrix of YEAR, PREVGPA, QUIZ1, QUIZ5, and FINAL, type the following lines:

6) **GET FILE** = 'GRADES.SYS'.	*1*
CORRELATION VARIABLES = YEAR PREVGPA QUIZ1 QUIZ5 FINAL.	*2*

LINE **1** Same as step 5, line 1 above.
LINE **2** First, follow spacing and punctuation exactly. If your variables take more than one line, hit the **ENTER** key and continue typing. There is no "automatic scroll" or "wrap" function in the SPSS editor. The connector **TO** is often used to produce correlation matrices. If the five variables listed above were in order in the data file (they aren't), the phrase **YEAR TO FINAL** would produce the same results. The **CORRELATION** command produces one-tailed significance values by default.

To produce an identical matrix that indicates two-tailed significances, type:

6a) **GET FILE** = 'GRADES.SYS'.	*1a*
CORRELATION VARIABLES = YEAR PREVGPA QUIZ1 QUIZ5 FINAL/	*2a*
OPTIONS = 3.	*3a*

LINE **1a** Same as above.
LINE **2a** Is identical to line 2 above, except the slash replaces the period because a subcommand follows.
LINE **3a** Only two options are available: **OPTION 3** yields two-tailed significance measures; **OPTION 5** prints out the correlation value, the *N*, and the probability values (accurate to 4 decimals) for each correlation. If you wish to have this information, in place of line 3a, type **OPTIONS** = **5.**

A STATISTICS option is available with the CORRELATION command. The following command lines will print means, standard deviations, cross-product deviations, and covariances in two tables prior to printing the correlation matrix:

6b) **GET FILE** = 'GRADES.SYS'.	*1b*
CORRELATION VARIABLES = YEAR PREVGPA QUIZ1 QUIZ5 FINAL/	*2b*
OPTIONS = 5/	*3b*
STATISTICS = ALL.	*4b*

LINE **1b** Same as above.
LINE **2b** Is identical to line 2a above.
LINE **3b** Duplicates line 3b above except the 3 is replaced by a 5 and the period is replaced by a slash.
LINE **4b** There are three options following the **STATISTICS** = subcommand: **1** prints out means and standard deviations. **2** prints out cross-product deviations and covariances. **ALL** prints out all four statistics. Replace the **ALL** with either a 1 or a 2 to designate the statistics desired.

Often you may wish to compute correlations between one or two variables and several others. To accomplish this, use the WITH connector:

6c) **GET FILE** = 'GRADES.SYS'.   1c
     CORRELATION VARIABLES = <u>GENDER</u> <u>TOTAL</u> **WITH** <u>YEAR</u> <u>PREVGPA</u> <u>QUIZ1</u>
     <u>QUIZ5</u> <u>FINAL</u>.   2c

LINE **1c** Same as above.

LINE **2c** Will produce a 2 × 5 matrix. The first column will produce correlations between **GENDER** and **YEAR** through **FINAL**; the second column will produce correlations between **TOTAL** and **YEAR** through **FINAL**. Any number of variables may be listed both before and following the **WITH**. **OPTIONS** and **STATISTICS** subcommands may follow (as in step 6b above) if desired.

---

7) | F9 | W | ← | *to save your command file for future access.*

If file is not already named, enter the file name (e.g., **GRADES.CTL**) at the prompt between the **W** and the **ENTER**.

To run the program, first position cursor at the beginning of the GET FILE line, then:

---

8) | F10 | C | *to run your program from the cursor.*

After viewing the results:

---

9) | F10 | E | FINISH | ← | *to exit to the DOS prompt.*

To print command files and results:

---

10) *dos* > PRINT SPSS.LIS | ← | | ← | *(Sometimes the second RETURN is not necessary.)*

OUTPUT
Correlations

The following OUTPUT is produced by this COMMAND FILE. INTERPRETATION follows.

```
GET FILE = 'GRADES.SYS'.
CORRELATION VARIABLES = YEAR PREVGPA QUIZ1 QUIZ5 FINAL.
```

```
-------------------------------------------------------------------------
Page #                            SPSS/PC+                          Date

Correlations:  YEAR     PREVGPA     QUIZ1     QUIZ5      FINAL
YEAR          1.0000    -.0828      .0718     .0725     -.0283
PREVGPA       -.0828    1.0000      .2459*    .2517*     .4981**
QUIZ1          .0718     .2459*    1.0000     .5039**    .5351**
QUIZ5          .0725     .2617*     .5039**  1.0000      .4715**
FINAL         -.0283     .4981**    .5351**   .4715**   1.0000

N of cases: 105    1-tailed Significance: * p<.01      ** p<.001
-------------------------------------------------------------------------
```

The diagonal of 1.0000s indicates that a variable is perfectly correlated with itself. Since the computation of correlations is identical regardless of which variable comes first, the half of the table above the diagonal of 1.0000s has identical values to the half of the table below that diagonal. Note the strong positive relationship between **FINAL** and **QUIZ5** ($r = .475$, $p < .001$). As described in the introduction of this chapter, these values indicate a strong positive relationship between the score on the fifth quiz and the score on the final. Those who scored higher on the fifth quiz tended to score higher on the final as well. As noted at the bottom of the output, the asterisks indicate one-tailed significance values.

The following OUTPUT is produced by this COMMAND FILE. INTERPRETATION follows.

```
GET FILE = 'GRADES.SYS'.
CORRELATION VARIABLES = YEAR PREVGPA QUIZ1 QUIZ5 FINAL/
OPTIONS = 5.
```

```
-------------------------------------------------------------------------
Page #                            SPSS/PC+                          Date

Correlations:     YEAR      PREVGPA     QUIZ1     QUIZ5      FINAL

   YEAR          1.0000     -.0828      .0718     .0725     -.0283
                 (105)      (105)       (105)     (105)      (105)
                 p=.        p=.200      p=.233    p=.231     p=.387

   PREVGPA       -.0828     1.0000      .2459     .2617      .4981
                 (105)      (105)       (105)     (105)      (105)
                 p=.200     p=.         p=.006    p= 003     p=.000

   QUIZ1          .0718      .2459      1.0000     .5039      .5351
                 (105)      (105)       (105)     (105)      (105)
                 p=.233     p=.006      p=.        p=.000     p=.000

   QUIZ5          .0725      .2617       .5039    1.0000      .4715
                 (105)      (105)       (105)     (105)      (105)
                 p=.231     p=.003      p=.000    p=.         p=.000

   FINAL         -.0283      .4981       .5351     .4715     1.0000
                 (105)      (105)       (105)     (105)      (105)
                 p=.387     p=.000      p=.000    p=.000     p=.000

(Coefficient / Cases / 1-tailed Significance)
" . " is printed if a coefficient cannot be computed.
-------------------------------------------------------------------------
```

The meaning of individual correlations is explained on the introductory pages of this chapter. The numbers in parentheses underneath each correlation are the number of data points (subjects) that were used in that particular correlation; these numbers may vary due to missing data. Actual *p*-values are given for every individual correlation. As noted at the bottom of the output, one-tailed significance values are reported.

Chapter 12

The T-TEST Command:

Independent-Samples, Paired-Samples, and One-Sample Tests

A *t*-test is a procedure used for comparing sample means to see if there is sufficient evidence to infer that the means of the corresponding population distributions also differ. More specifically, for an independent-samples *t*-test, a sample is taken from two populations. The two samples are measured on some variable of interest. A *t*-test will determine if the means of the two sample distributions differ significantly from each other. *t*-tests may be used to explore issues such as: Does treatment A yield a higher rate of recovery than treatment B? Does one advertising technique produce higher sales than another technique? Do males or females score higher on a measure of empathic tendency? Does one training method produce faster times on the track than another training method? The key word is *two*: *t*-tests always compare the means of *two* different distributions.

In its chapter on t-tests, the *SPSS/PC+ Statistics 4.0 Manual* spends several pages talking about null hypotheses, populations, random samples, normal distributions, and a variety of research concerns. All its comments are germane and of considerable importance for conducting meaningful research. However, discussion of these issues goes beyond the scope of this book. *t*-tests are the topic of this chapter: what they do, how to access them in SPSS, and how to interpret the results. We direct you to the manual if you wish to consider some of those additional concerns.

INDEPENDENT-SAMPLES t-TESTS

SPSS provides three different types of *t*-tests. The first type, the independent-samples *t*-tests, compares the means of two different samples. The two samples share some variable of interest in common, but there is no overlap between members of the two groups. Examples include: the difference between males and females on an exam score, the difference of performance on pull-ups by Americans and Europeans, the difference on achievement test scores for a class of Beverly Hills first-graders and a class of Watts first-graders, and the difference of life-satisfaction scores between those who are married and those who are unmarried. Note again that there is no overlap of membership between the two groups.

PAIRED-SAMPLES *t*-TESTS

The second type of *t*-test, the paired-samples *t*-tests, is usually based on groups of individuals who experience both conditions of the variables of interest. Examples include: students' scores on the first quiz versus the same students' scores on the second quiz; subjects' depression scores after treatment A as compared to the same subjects' scores after receiving treatment B; a set of students' scores on the SAT compared to the same students' scores on the GRE several years later; elementary school students' achievement test percentiles after one year at a low-SES school as compared to their achievement test percentiles after one year at a high-SES school. Note here that the same group experiences both levels of the variable.

ONE-SAMPLE *t*-TESTS

The third type of test is a one-sample *t*-test. It is designed to test whether the mean of a distribution differs significantly from some preset value. An example: Does a course offered to college seniors result in a GRE score greater than or equal to 1200? Did the performance of a particular class differ significantly from the professor's goal of an 82% average? During the previous season, the mean time for the cross country athletes' best seasonal performances was 18 minutes. The coach set a goal of 17 minutes for the current season. Did the athletes' times differ significantly from the 17-minute goal set by the coach? In this procedure, the sample mean is compared to a single fixed value.

TESTS OF SIGNIFICANCE

When using *t*-tests to determine if two distributions differ significantly from each other, the test that measures the probability associated with the difference between the groups may be either a one-tailed or a two-tailed test of significance. The two-tailed test examines whether the mean of one distribution differs significantly from the mean of the other distribution, regardless of the direction (positive or negative) of the difference. The one-tailed test measures only whether the second distribution differs in a particular direction from the first. For instance, at a weight-loss clinic, the concern is only about the amount of weight *loss*. Any amount of weight gain is considered failure. Likewise, an advertising campaign concerns itself only with sales *increases*.

Usually the context of the research will make clear which type of test is appropriate. The only computational difference between the two is that the *p*-value of one is twice as much as the *p*-value of the other. If SPSS output produces a two-tailed significance value (this is the default), simply divide that number by two to give you the probability for a one-tailed test.

THE LOGICAL PROGRESSION FOR COMPUTING *t*-TESTS

1. Create file of data, or edit (if necessary) an already existing file.
2. Format file by use of **DATA LIST FILE**, **FORMATS**, and **VARIABLE/VALUE LABELS**; then save the results as a system file.
3. Access file and formats by the **GET FILE** command.
4. Use the **T-TEST** command for computation with independent samples.
5. Use the **PAIRS** subcommand for analysis with paired samples, if desired.
6. Use the **COMPUTE** command to set up one-sample tests, if desired.
7. View the results and exit the program.
8. Print data, commands, and output.

For demonstration of these commands we once more make use of the **GRADES.SYS** file with $N = 105$. Variables of interest for this chapter include: **GENDER**, **TOTAL** (total points in the class), **YEAR** (first, second, third or fourth year in college), the quizzes **QUIZ1** to **QUIZ5**, and **PERCENT** (the final class percent).

STEP BY STEP
Computing t-tests

1) Name and create a data file (Chapter 2), or edit (if necessary) an already existing file (Chapter 3).

2) Name variables, locate column positions, format, create VARIABLE/VALUE LABELS, and then save the formatted DATA FILE as a SYSTEM FILE (Chapter 4).

From the DOS prompt, type:

3) dos > SPSSPC ↵   *This step gets you into the SPSS system.*

To clear the menu from the top window prior to analyzing data:

---

4) $\boxed{\text{ALT}}\!\!-\!\!\boxed{\text{M}}$ *Positions cursor to begin to create the command file.*

From the extreme upper left corner of the scratch pad (lower window), type:

---

5) **GET FILE = 'GRADES.SYS'.**   *1*

LINE 1 Accesses the formatted **SYSTEM FILE** to begin to analyze data. All statistical procedures in this book will begin with the **GET FILE** step.

INDEPENDENT-SAMPLES *t*-TESTS

To test whether there is a difference between males and females on TOTAL points earned, type:

---

6) **GET FILE = 'GRADES.SYS'.**   *1*
    T-TEST GROUPS = GENDER/   *2*
    VARIABLES = TOTAL.   *3*

LINE 1 The same as step 5, line 1 above.

LINE 2 **T-TEST** accesses the *t*-test function. **GROUPS = GENDER** specifies that we wish to contrast females with males. For *t*-tests, the **GROUPS** variable must have exactly two distinct categories. Follow this line with a slash.

LINE 3 This line identifies the variable (**TOTAL**) for which we wish to contrast scores between females and males.

Gender is coded only two ways, and the previous command compares females with males. If a group is coded in more *than two ways, you must specify how it is to be divided. The following lines will test whether upper-division students scored higher on the final exam than lower-division students.*

6a) **GET FILE = 'GRADES.SYS'.**   *1a*
    T-TEST GROUPS = YEAR(3)/   *2a*
    VARIABLES = FINAL.   *3a*

LINE 1a Same as above.

LINE 2a The **(3)** following **YEAR** designates that the two groups of interest are (a) those coded 3 and higher (3 and 4), and (b) those coded less than 3 (1 and 2).

LINE 3a The variable of interest is **FINAL,** the score on the final exam. This command file will compare the scores of first- and second-year students (as one group) with the scores of third- and fourth-year students (as the other group).

To contrast females and males on several *variables, there are two options: (a) In the VARIABLES line, list two or more variables with a space between each, or (b) use the TO connector to designate several variables in order in the system file. The following command requests t-tests for the differences between males and females for QUIZ1, QUIZ2, QUIZ3, QUIZ4, and QUIZ5.*

```
6b) GET FILE = 'GRADES.SYS'.                                           1b
    T-TEST GROUPS = GENDER/                                            2b
    VARIABLES = QUIZ1 TO QUIZ5.                                        3b
```

LINE **1b** Same as above.

LINE **2b** Calls for a *t*-test to contrast females and males.

LINE **3b** Designates variables **QUIZ1 TO QUIZ5**. The program will produce five different charts contrasting females' scores with males' scores on each of the five quizzes. If the quizzes were not in order in the data file (they are here), then you would need to list each variable with a space between each, followed by a period.

PAIRED-SAMPLES t-TESTS

If we wished to compare whether the scores on one quiz were significantly different from the scores on another quiz, paired-samples t-tests (more commonly referred to as "paired t-tests"), are used. Below, the scores for the first and second quizzes are compared.

```
6c) GET FILE = 'GRADES.SYS'.                                           1c
    T-TEST PAIRS = QUIZ1 QUIZ2.                                        2c
```

LINE **1c** Same as above.

LINE **2c** Requests a paired-samples *t*-test for the variables **QUIZ1** and **QUIZ2**. Note that the same set of subjects took both quizzes; thus, this procedure uses two different distributions of scores for the same 105 subjects.

If you wish to compute several t-tests with the same command, you may use the WITH connector. The following command line contrasts, on four different tables, the scores on QUIZ1 with the scores on each of the other four quizzes (QUIZ2 to QUIZ5).

```
6d) GET FILE = 'GRADES.SYS'.                                           1d
    T-TEST PAIRS = QUIZ1 WITH QUIZ2 TO QUIZ5.                          2d
```

LINE **1d** Same as above.

LINE **2d** Because **QUIZ2** through **QUIZ5** are in order in the data file, it is acceptable to use the **TO** connector to simplify the command line. If they were not in order, each one would need to be listed separately. Four different comparisons will be displayed: **QUIZ1** with **QUIZ2**, **QUIZ1** with **QUIZ3**, **QUIZ1** with **QUIZ4**, and **QUIZ1** with **QUIZ5**.

ONE-SAMPLE t-TESTS

It is often desirable to compare the mean of a distribution with some objective standard. With the GRADES.SYS file, the instructor may have taught the class a number of times and has determined what he feels is an acceptable mean value for a successful class. If the desired value for final PERCENT is 85, he may wish to compare the present class against that standard. Does this class differ significantly from what he considers to be an acceptable class performance? To accomplish this, we make use of the COMPUTE command.

6e) **GET FILE = 'GRADES.SYS'.**	*1e*
COMPUTE REF = <u>85</u>.	*2e*
T-TEST PAIRS = <u>PERCENT</u> <u>REF</u>.	*3e*

LINE **1e** Same as above.

LINE **2e** This generates a new variable called **REF,** in which all 105 subjects show a value of 85. Thus, this variable has a mean of 85 and a standard deviation of 0. If you already have a variable named **REF** in your data file, you will have to use a different name.

LINE **3e** This line conducts a *t*-test comparing the **PERCENT** distribution with the distribution of the new variable, **REF** (for *reference*). Results will indicate whether the performance of the present class differs significantly from the designated standard.

7) $\boxed{\text{F9}}$ $\boxed{\text{W}}$ $\boxed{\leftarrow}$	*to save your command file for future access.*

If file is not already named, enter the file name (e.g., **GRADES.CTL**) at the prompt between the **W** and the **ENTER.**

To run the program, first position cursor at the beginning of the GET FILE line, then:

8) $\boxed{\text{F10}}$ $\boxed{\text{C}}$	*to run your program from the cursor.*

After viewing the results:

9) $\boxed{\text{F10}}$ $\boxed{\text{E}}$ **FINISH** $\boxed{\leftarrow}$	*to exit to the DOS prompt.*

To print command files and results:

10) dos > **PRINT SPSS.LIS** $\boxed{\leftarrow}$ $\boxed{\leftarrow}$	*(Sometimes the second RETURN is not necessary.)*

OUTPUT
Independent-Samples, Paired-Samples, and One-Sample *t*-Tests

INDEPENDENT-SAMPLES *t*-TEST:

The following OUTPUT is produced by this COMMAND FILE. INTERPRETATION follows.

```
GET FILE = 'GRADES.SYS'.
T-TESTS GROUPS = GENDER/
VARIABLES = TOTAL.
```

Page #   SPSS/PC+   Date

Group 1: GENDER EQ 1 (FEMALE)   Group 2: GENDER EQ 2 (MALE)

t-test for: TOTAL

	Number of Cases	Mean	Standard Deviation	Standard Error
Group 1	64	102.0313	13.896	1.737
Group 2	41	98.2927	17.196	2.686

F Value	2-Tail Prob.	Pooled Variance Estimate t Value	Pooled Variance Estimate Degrees of Freedom	Pooled Variance Estimate 2-Tail Prob.	Separate Variance Estimate t Value	Separate Variance Estimate Degrees of Freedom	Separate Variance Estimate 2-Tail Prob.
1.53	.128	1.22	103	.224	1.17	72.42	.246

This independent-samples *t*-test analysis indicates that the 64 females had a mean of 102.03 total points for the class, the 41 males had a mean of 98.29 total points for the class, and the means do not differ significantly at the $\alpha = .05$ level (note: $p = .246$). (Definitions of terms are on pages 90 and 91.)

PAIRED-SAMPLES t-TEST:

The following OUTPUT is produced by this COMMAND FILE. INTERPRETATION follows.

```
GET FILE = 'GRADES.SYS'.
T-TEST PAIRS = QUIZ1 QUIZ2.
```

Page #   SPSS/PC+   Date

Paired samples t-test: QUIZ1
                       QUIZ2

Variable	Number of Cases	Mean	Standard Deviation	Standard Error
QUIZ1	105	7.4667	2.481	.242
QUIZ2	105	7.9810	1.623	.158

(Difference) Mean	Standard Deviation	Standard Error	Corr	2-Tail Prob	t Value	Degrees of Freedom	2-Tail Prob
-.5143	1.835	.179	.673	.000	-2.87	104	.005

This paired-samples *t*-test analysis indicates that for the 105 subjects, the mean score on the second quiz ($M = 7.98$) was significantly greater at the $\alpha = .01$ level (note: $p = .005$) than the mean score on the first quiz ($M = 7.47$). (Definitions of terms are on pages 90 and 91.)

ONE-SAMPLE t-TEST:

The following OUTPUT *is produced by this* COMMAND FILE. INTERPRETATION *follows.*

```
GET FILE = 'GRADES.SYS'.
COMPUTE REF = 85.
T-TEST PAIRS = PERCENT REF.
```

Page #			SPSS/PC+		Date

Paired samples t-test: PERCENT
REF

Variable	Number of Cases	Mean	Standard Deviation	Standard Error
PERCENT	105	80.3810	12.177	1.188
REF	105	85.0000	.000	.000

(Difference) Mean	Standard Deviation	Standard Error	Corr	2-Tail Prob	t Value	Degrees of Freedom	2-Tail Prob
-4.6190	12.177	1.188	.	.	-3.89	104	.000

This one-sample *t*-test analysis indicates that the mean percent for this class of 105 students (*M* = 80.38) was significantly lower at the α = .001 level (note: *p* < .001) than the instructor's goal of 85%.

DEFINITIONS OF TERMS

STANDARD ERROR: The standard deviation divided by the square root of *N*. This is a measure of stability or sampling error of the sample means.

F-VALUE: This value is used to determine if the standard deviations of the two distributions differ significantly from each other. The *F*-value is determined by the larger variance (17.635^2) divided by the smaller variance (13.896^2), or 1.61. Note that the variance is the square of the standard deviation.

2-TAIL PROB (associated with the *F*-value): If standard deviations are not significantly different, then the *pooled-variance estimate* may be used instead of the *separate-variance estimate*. The *p*-value here, .089, indicates that the two standard deviations do not differ significantly; so the statistically stronger pooled-variance estimate may be used.

t-VALUES: Based on either the pooled-variance estimate equation or the separate-variance estimate equation. Conceptually, both formulas compare the within-group deviations from the mean with the between-group deviations from the mean. The slightly larger (absolute values) pooled-variance estimate may be used here because of similar standard deviations (see the *F*-value, above).

DEGREES OF FREEDOM: For the pooled-variance estimate, number of subjects minus number of groups (105 − 2 = 103). The fractional degrees of freedom (71.02) for the separate-variance estimate is a formula-derived value. For the paired-samples and one-sample tests, the value is number of subjects minus 1 (105 − 1 = 104).

2-TAIL PROBABILITY (associated with the *t*-values): The probability that the difference in means could happen by chance.

(DIFFERENCE) MEAN: The difference between the two means.

STANDARD DEVIATION (last lines in the second and third analyses): This is the standard deviation of the difference, and it is used to calculate the *t*-value for the paired *t*-test. (Recall that the standard error is the standard deviation divided by the square root of *N*, and the *t*-value is the mean difference divided by the standard error.)

CORRELATION: Measures to what extent one variable varies systematically with another variable. The statistic presented here is the Pearson product-moment correlation, designated *r*. Note that it is not possible to compute a correlation if one of the variables has a variance of 0 (note the one-sample test).

2-TAIL PROBABILITY (of the correlation): The probability that such a pattern could happen by chance. In the paired-samples test, the $r = .67$ and $p < .001$ indicate a substantial and significant correlation between **QUIZ1** and **QUIZ2**.

Chapter 13

The ONEWAY Command:

One-Way Analysis of Variance

One-way analysis of variance is obtained through the SPSS ONEWAY command. While a one-way analysis of variance could also be accomplished using the ANOVA command (Chapters 14 and 15), the ONEWAY command has certain options not available in ANOVA, including post tests, such as Tukey and Scheffé, and planned comparisons of different groups or composites of groups.

INTRODUCTION TO ONE-WAY ANALYSIS OF VARIANCE

Analysis of variance is a procedure used for comparing sample means to see if there is sufficient evidence to infer that the means of the corresponding population distributions also differ. One-way analysis of variance is most easily explained by contrasting it with *t*-tests (Chapter 12). While *t*-tests compare only two distributions, analysis of variance is able to compare many. If, for instance, a sample of students takes a 10-point quiz and we wish to see whether females or males scored higher on this quiz, a *t*-test would be appropriate. There is a distribution of females' scores and a distribution of males' scores, and a t-test will tell if the means of these two distributions differ significantly from each other. If, however, we wished to see if any of five different ethnic groups' scores differed significantly from each other on the same quiz, it would require one-way analysis of variance to accomplish this. If we were to run such a test, ONEWAY could tell us if there are significant differences within any of the comparisons of the five groups in our sample. Further tests (such as the Scheffé test, which will be described in this chapter) are necessary to determine between *which* groups significant differences occur.

The previous paragraph briefly describes analysis of variance. What does the "one-way" part mean? Using the **ONEWAY** command, you may have only *one* dependent variable and only *one* independent variable. The independent variable illustrated above (ethnicity) is one variable, but it has several levels. In our example it has five: Indian, Asian, Afro-American, Caucasian, and Hispanic. **ANOVA** (next chapter) may also have a maximum of *one* dependent variable, but it may have two or more independent variables. In **MANOVA**, multivariate analysis of variance (Chapters 17 and 18), there may be multiple dependent variables *and* multiple independent variables.

The following explanation gives a conceptual feel for what one-way analysis of variance is attempting to accomplish. The mean (average) quiz scores for each of the ethnic groups are compared with each other: Indians with Asians, Indians with Afro-Americans, Indians with Caucasians, Indians with Hispanics, Asians with Afro-Americans, Asians with Caucasians, Asians with Hispanics, Afro-Americans with Caucasians, Afro-Americans with Hispanics, and Caucasians with Hispanics. **ONEWAY** will generate a significance value indicating whether there are significant differences within the comparisons being made. This significance value does not indicate where the difference is or the differences are, but a Scheffé test can identify which groups differ significantly from each other. Be aware that there are other tests besides Scheffé that are able to identify pairwise differences. The Scheffé procedure is selected here because it allows the researcher to choose a specific level of significance when comparing distributions.

THE LOGICAL PROGRESSION FOR COMPUTING ONE-WAY ANALYSIS OF VARIANCE

1. Create file of data, or edit (if necessary) an already existing file.
2. Format file by use of **DATA LIST FILE**, **FORMATS**, and **VARIABLE/VALUE LABELS**; then save as a system file.
3. Access file and formats by the **GET FILE** command.
4. Use the **ONEWAY** command to conduct Analysis of Variance.
5. Use the **RANGES** subcommand to access the Scheffé test (or other tests), if desired.
6. Use the **STATISTICS** subcommand to obtain additional statistical output.
7. Use the **CONTRASTS** subcommand if you wish to make specific comparisons.
8. View the results and exit the program.
9. Print data, commands, and output.

The file we use to illustrate **ONEWAY** is our familiar example. The system file is called **GRADES.SYS** and has an $N = 105$. This analysis contrasts grades on **QUIZ1** (the dependent variable) with five levels of ethnicity, **ETHNICIT** (the independent variable)— Indian, Asian, Afro-American, Caucasian, and Hispanic.

STEP BY STEP
One-Way Analysis of Variance

---

1) *Name and create a data file (Chapter 2), or edit (if necessary) an already existing file (Chapter 3).*

---

2) *Name variables, locate column positions, format, create VARIABLE/VALUE LABELS, and then save the formatted DATA FILE as a SYSTEM FILE (Chapter 4).*

From the DOS prompt, type:

---

3) *dos >* **SPSSPC** ⏎   *This step gets you into the SPSS system.*

To clear the menu from the top window prior to analyzing data:

---

4) ALT ─ M   *Positions cursor to begin to create the command file.*

From the extreme upper left corner of the scratch pad (lower window), type:

---

5) GET FILE = 'GRADES.SYS'.   1

LINE **1** Accesses the formatted **SYSTEM FILE** to begin to analyze data. All statistical procedures in this book will begin with the **GET FILE** step.

To conduct a one-way analysis of variance to see if any of five ethnic groups differ on their QUIZ1 scores, type:

---

6) GET FILE = 'GRADES.SYS'.   1
ONEWAY VARIABLES = QUIZ1 BY ETHNICIT(1,5)/   2
OPTIONS = 6.   3

LINE **1** Same as step 5, line 1 above.
LINE **2** Note the spacing pattern in line 2. Always place the dependent variable (**QUIZ1**) first. Following the word **BY** is the independent variable (**ETHNICIT**). Include the range of its values (in this case from 1 to 5) within parentheses following the independent variable. This line ends with a slash because a subcommand follows.
LINE **3** The **OPTIONS = 6** requests that value labels be listed in the output. Always include this step for clarity.

Since ONEWAY does not tell us <u>which</u> measures differ from each other, an additional test is required. While SPSS can access seven different tests, the Scheffé test is used here. SCHEFFE will identify which ethnic groups significantly differ from each other on their QUIZ1 scores.

```
6a) GET FILE = 'GRADES.SYS'.                                    1a
    ONEWAY VARIABLES = QUIZ1 BY ETHNICIT(1,5)/                  2a
    OPTIONS = 6/                                                3a
    RANGES = SCHEFFE.                                           4a
```

LINE **1a** Same as above.

LINES **2a-3a** Identical to lines 2-3 above, except the **OPTIONS = 6** is followed by a slash (not a period) because a subcommand follows.

LINE **4a** The **RANGES** subcommand accesses different tests. The test chosen here is **SCHEFFE**. By default, **SCHEFFE** will determine differences between means based upon a significance of .05. However, you may specify any level of significance you desire. For example, if you desire a significance of .01, replace line 4a with **RANGES = SCHEFFE(.01)**. There are many different tests that may be used. They are listed in the table below and are followed by **(P)** if you are allowed to specify a *p*-value (in parentheses following the **RANGES** subcommand). The default for all tests is $\alpha = .05$. You may specify several **RANGES** subcommands within a single **ONEWAY** command by repeating line 4a with different tests for each line.

Test	Explanation
SCHEFFE(P)	Scheffé's test (any α level is acceptable)
DUNCAN(P)	Multiple range test (you may specify $\alpha = .01, .05,$ or $.10$)
SNK	Student-Newman-Keuls
TUKEY	Tukey's honestly significant difference (HSD)
BTUKEY	Tukey's alternative procedure
LSD(P)	Least-significant difference (any α level is acceptable)
MODLSD(P)	Modified LSD (any α level is acceptable)

If in addition you wish to access certain statistical information about the data, use the STATISTICS subcommand. We use here STATISTICS 1 and 3, explained below.

```
6b) GET FILE = 'GRADES.SYS'.                                    1b
    ONEWAY VARIABLES = QUIZ1 BY ETHNICIT(1,5)/                  2b
    OPTIONS = 6/                                                3b
    RANGES = SCHEFFE/                                           4b
    STATISTICS = 1 3.                                           5b
```

LINE **1b** Same as above.

LINES **2b-4b** Are identical to lines above except that **SCHEFFE** is followed by a slash instead of a period.

LINE **5b** **STATISTICS** option **1** accesses and prints *N*, means, standard deviations, standard errors, 95% confidence intervals for the means, minimums, and maximums. **STATISTICS** option **3** conducts tests to determine homogeneity of the variances. This is of value in determining whether to use separate-variance statistics or pooled-variance statistics when conducting planned comparisons (sequence step 6c).

The final optional procedure explained in this chapter is planned comparisons by use of the CONTRASTS subcommand. If you have no background in planned comparisons, we suggest that you omit this section or get the help of someone more knowledgeable. If you have had background, it should be quite straightforward. Below we show two different contrasts.

```
6c) GET FILE = 'GRADES.SYS'.                                    1c
     ONEWAY VARIABLES = QUIZ1 BY ETHNICIT(1,5)/                 2c
     OPTIONS = 6/                                               3c
     RANGES = SCHEFFE/                                          4c
     STATISTICS = 1 3/                                          5c
     CONTRASTS = 0 1 -1 0 0/                                    6c
     CONTRASTS = 1 1 1 1 -4.                                    7c
```

LINE 1c Same as above.

LINES 2c-5c Identical to above except that **STATISTICS = 1 3** is followed by a slash instead of a period.

LINE 6c Requests SPSS to compare the means of group 2 and group 3. Levels of **ETHNICIT** not included in the comparison are coded 0. The entire line must sum to zero. This contrasts the scores on **QUIZ1** for Afro-Americans with the scores on **QUIZ1** for Asians.

LINE 7c This line requests SPSS to compare the combined mean of the first four groups with the mean of the fifth group. Note that the line once again sums to zero. For each **CONTRAST** subcommand only one comparison is possible. That is why it was necessary to write **CONTRAST** twice to request two comparisons. Observe the exact spacing and punctuation shown above. This line contrasts the scores on **QUIZ1** for Hispanic students with the scores on **QUIZ1** for students of all other ethnicities (as a single group).

7) [F9] [W] [↵]   *to save your command file for future access.*

If file is not already named, enter the file name (e.g., **GRADES.CTL**) at the prompt between the **W** and the **ENTER**.

To run the program, first position cursor at the beginning of the GET FILE line, then:

8) [F10] [C]   *to run your program from the cursor.*

After viewing the results:

9) [F10] [E] FINISH [↵]   *to exit to the DOS prompt.*

To print command files and results:

10) *dos>* **PRINT SPSS.LIS** [↵] [↵]   *(Sometimes the second RETURN is not necessary.)*

OUTPUT
One-Way Analysis of Variance

The following OUTPUT is produced by this COMMAND FILE. INTERPRETATION follows.

```
GET FILE = 'GRADES.SYS'.
ONEWAY VARIABLES = QUIZ1 BY ETHNICIT(1,5)/
OPTIONS = 6/
RANGES = SCHEFFE/
STATISTICS = 1 3/
CONTRASTS = 1 0 0 0 -1/
CONTRASTS = 1 1 1 1 -4.
```

Note: Some of the values shown in the output below have been fictionalized to demonstrate certain characteristics of the output that we were not able to achieve by a direct analysis of the **GRADES.SYS** file. A useful exercise might be to run the same procedure with the **GRADES.SYS** file on your data disk to see where the discrepancies lie.

```
--------------------------------------------------------------------------
            - - - - - - - O N E W A Y - - - - - - - - -
        Variable   QUIZ1
   By   Variable   ETHNIC            Analysis of Variance
                                 Sum of        Mean        F       F
           Source      D.F.     Squares       Squares     Ratio    Prob
Between Groups          4        47.4631     11.8658     10.3028   .0000
Within Groups         100       115.1702      1.1517
Total                 104       162.6333
--------------------------------------------------------------------------
Scheffe Procedure for the .050 level
Variable   QUIZ1
                          A A A C H
                          M S F A I
                          E I R U S
                          R A O C P
                            N - A N
                          I   A S I
Mean          Group       N   M I C

6.4000        AMER IND
7.4634        ASIAN         *
7.5444        AFRO-AMER
7.5867        CAUCASIAN
8.8667        HISPANIC     * * * *

(*) Denotes pairs of groups significantly different at the .050 level
--------------------------------------------------------------------------
                         Standard  Std.    95% Confidence
  Group     Count   Mean Deviation Error  Interval for Mean  Minimum  Maximum
  CAUCASIAN   45  7.5867   1.0883  .1700   7.1199 to 7.8069  3.0000   10.0000
  HISPANIC    11  8.8667   1.0224  .2640   8.3005 to 9.4328  4.0000   10.8000
  ASIAN       20  7.4634   1.0512  .2478   7.0217 to 8.0672  2.0000   10.0000
  AFRO-AMER   24  7.5444   1.2484  .3223   6.8954 to 8.2780  2.0000   10.0000
  AMER IND     5  6.4000    .9151  .2288   5.9124 to 6.8876  2.0000   10.0000

  Total      105  7.5333   1.2505  .1220   7.2913 to 7.7753  1.0000   10.0000
```

```
-----------------------------------------------------------------------
Tests for Homogeneity of Variance     [STATISTICS = 3]

Cochrans C = Maximum Variances/Sum of Variances  =  .272,    p = .534
Bartlett-Box F  =                                   .364,    p = .834
Maximum Variance / Minimum Variance                1.861
-----------------------------------------------------------------------

Contrast Coefficient Matrix
   Variable  QUIZ1
By Variable  ETHNIC
                   AMER IND   ASIAN    AFRO-AMER   CAUCASIAN HISPANIC
       Contrast 1    1.0       0.0       0.0          .0      -1.0
       Contrast 2    1.0       1.0       1.0         1.0      -4.0

                                      Pooled Variance Estimate
                   Value   S. Error   T-Value     D.F.      T Prob.
Contrast 1        1.3222    .3752      3.524      100.0       .001
Contrast 2        5.8612   1.1821      4.958      100.0       .000

                                      Separate Variance Estimate
Contrast 1        1.3222    .3620      3.652       30.2       .001
Contrast 2        5.8612   1.0494      5.585       25.2       .000
-----------------------------------------------------------------------
```

INTERPRETATION AND DEFINITIONS

Analysis of Variance

WITHIN-GROUPS SUM OF SQUARES: The sum of squared deviations between the mean for each group and the observed values of each subject within that group.

BETWEEN-GROUPS SUM OF SQUARES: The sum of squared deviations between the grand mean and each group mean weighted (multiplied) by the number of subjects in each group.

BETWEEN-GROUPS DEGREES OF FREEDOM: Number of groups minus one.

WITHIN-GROUPS DEGREES OF FREEDOM: Number of subjects minus number of groups.

MEAN SQUARE: Sum of squares divided by degrees of freedom.

F RATIO: Between-groups mean square divided by within-groups mean square.

SIGNIFICANCE: The probability of the observed value happening by chance. The result here indicates that there is/are significant difference(s) between means of the five groups as noted by a probability value less than .001.

Scheffé Procedure

MEAN: the mean (average) QUIZ1 score for each group.

The asterisks (*) indicate there are five pairs of groups whose means differ significantly (collectively at the $p < .05$ level) from each other: Asians and American Indians, Hispanics and American Indians, Hispanics and Asians, Hispanics and Afro-Americans, and Hispanics and Caucasians. The mean values printed to the left of each ethnic group indicate the direction of difference (e.g., Asians, with a mean score of 7.46, measured significantly higher than Indians, with a mean score of 6.40).

Statistics

COUNT: Number of subjects, N.

MEAN: Average score for each group.

STANDARD DEVIATION: The standard measure of variability around the mean.

STANDARD ERROR: Standard deviation divided by square root of N.

95% CONFIDENCE INTERVAL FOR MEAN: Given a large number of samples drawn from a population, 95% of the means for these samples will fall between the lower and upper confidence intervals. This value is based on the t-distribution and is approximately equal to the mean $\pm 2 \times$ the standard error.

MINIMUM: Lowest observed value for that group.

MAXIMUM: Largest observed value for that group.

Tests for Homogeneity of Variance

Both COCHRAN'S C and the BARTLETT-BOX F measure whether the variances of each group differ significantly from each other (heteroschedasticity). The high probability values indicate that the variances in these groups do not differ significantly.

Contrast Coefficient Matrix

The first two lines simply restate command lines 6 and 7. Two types of t-comparisons are made: The pooled-variance estimate and the separate-variance estimate. Since the homogeneity tests indicate there are no significant differences in variances, either estimate would be acceptable. If the homogeneity tests indicated significant differences of variances, then the separate-variance estimate should be used. The results indicate that in the first comparison, Hispanics ($M = 8.87$) scored significantly higher than American Indians ($M = 6.40$). For the second comparison, Hispanics scored significantly higher ($M = 8.87$) than all other groups combined ($M = 7.49$).

VALUE: Of little interest because it is a weighted number.

STANDARD ERROR: Standard deviation divided by square root of N.

T-VALUES: For either the pooled- or separate-variance estimate, t is determined by the VALUE divided by the standard error.

D.F. (DEGREES OF FREEDOM): Number of subjects minus number of groups for the pooled-variance estimate. It is a little-known formula that computes the fractional degrees of freedom value for the separate-variance estimate.

T PROBABILITY: The likelihood that these values would happen by chance. The results indicate that, for scores on QUIZ1, American Indians differ significantly from Hispanics ($p = .001$) and that Hispanics differ significantly from the rest of the groups combined ($p < .001$).

Chapter 14

The ANOVA Command:

Two-Way Analysis of Variance

This chapter describes a fairly simple two-way analysis of variance. A two-way analysis of variance is a procedure that designates a single dependent variable (always continuous) and utilizes exactly two independent variables (always categorical) in the analysis. This operation requires the use of the ANOVA command because the ONEWAY command (Chapter 13) is capable of conducting only one-way analyses.

A major difficulty of ANOVA is that it is so easy to get a statistical package, such as SPSS, to do a two-way, three-way, or higher-order analysis of variance. The computer does all the arithmetic, and you end up with reams of impressive-looking output of which you understand very little. The ease of conducting analysis of variance on a computer has a tendency to mask the fact that a successful study requires many hours of careful planning. Also, while a one-way ANOVA is straightforward and simple to interpret, a two-way ANOVA requires some training and frequently involves an examination of output and drawing of charts before interpretation is clear. To understand a three-way ANOVA usually requires an experienced researcher, and comprehending a four-way ANOVA extends beyond the abilities of most humans.

To address some of these difficulties, we have decided to separate the discussion of analysis of variance into three chapters. Chapter 13 described a one-way analysis of variance using the ONEWAY command. If you do not have a thorough grasp of analysis of variance, you should read through Chapter 13 before attempting Chapters 14 and 15. This chapter (Chapter 14) covers a fairly straightforward two-way analysis of variance that involves the ANOVA command. It shows the fundamentals of how to conduct the analysis, how to graph the cell means, and how to interpret the results. Chapter 15 presents a three-way ANOVA (along with the command file format, graphing, and interpretation of output), addresses the issue of covariance, and considers some more complex experimental concerns. Just as it was important for you to understand Chapter 13 before attempting Chapter 14, it is equally important to understand this chapter before attempting the next. For a full understanding of these three chapters it is highly desirable to have taken a course in analysis of variance. However, if you haven't taken a course, but understand the basic concepts and need to get results from a two-way ANOVA, this chapter should be sufficient to accomplish that.

TWO-WAY ANALYSIS OF VARIANCE

As described in the last chapter, analysis of variance attempts to find significant differences between groups (or populations) by comparing the means of those groups on some variable of interest. To assist in understanding two-way ANOVA, we'll briefly summarize a one-way analysis. In the one-way analysis of variance described in the previous chapter, we sought to discover if five ethnic groups differed from each other on their performances for QUIZ1. The *one-way* part of the term indicates that there is exactly one independent variable (ETHNICIT in the Chapter 13 example), and the ANOVA part (as opposed to MANOVA) indicates that there is exactly one dependent variable as well (QUIZ1). For conducting a one-way analysis of variance, the ONEWAY command is often preferable to the ANOVA command. While ANOVA is able to do two-way, three-way, or higher-order analyses, the ONEWAY command can produce contrasts, multiple comparisons of cell means, and homogeneity of variance statistics. ANOVA does not calculate any of these.

The sample we will use to demonstrate two-way analysis of variance will again be the GRADES.SYS file. The TOTAL variable (total points in the class) will serve as the dependent variable. The independent variables will be GENDER and SECTION. We will be attempting to discover if GENDER, or SECTION, or a GENDER by SECTION interaction has an effect on performance in the class. The typical research questions of interest are: (1) Is there a *main effect for gender*? That is, did females and males differ significantly in number of points earned, and which was higher than which? (2) Is there a *main effect for section*? Did students in the three sections differ significantly in how many points they scored in the class, and which section was higher than which? (3) Is there a *gender by section interaction*? Is the influence of the two variables idiosyncratic, such that in this case, gender has one effect in one section but a different effect in another section? For example: Perhaps females score significantly higher in Section 1 than do males, but males score significantly higher than females in Section 3. Interactions are often tricky to explain, and drawing a graph displaying the cell means (shown in the output section) often helps to clarify.

SPSS will print cell means for all combinations of variables, and compute *F*-values and associated significance values. These values will indicate if there are significant main effects and/or if there are significant interactions between variables. It is quite possible to have significant main effects but not to have a significant interaction. The reverse is also possible. The output section of this chapter clarifies some of these issues.

For additional material, two excellent books on analysis of variance are those written by Schulman (1992) and Lindman (1992). Please see the reference section for more detailed information.

THE LOGICAL PROGRESSION FOR CONDUCTING TWO-WAY ANALYSIS OF VARIANCE

1. Create file of data, or edit (if necessary) an already existing file.
2. Format file by use of **DATA LIST FILE, FORMATS,** and **VARIABLE/VALUE LABELS**; then save as a system file.
3. Access file and formats by the **GET FILE** command.
4. Use the **ANOVA** command to conduct analysis of variance.
5. Use the **STATISTICS** subcommand to access means and frequencies of each cell, if desired.
6. View the results and exit the program.
7. Print data, commands, and output.

STEP BY STEP
Two-Way Analysis of Variance

---

1) Name and create a data file (Chapter 2), or edit (if necessary) an already existing file (Chapter 3).

---

2) Name variables, locate column positions, format, create VARIABLE/VALUE LABELS, and then save the formatted DATA FILE as a SYSTEM FILE (Chapter 4).

From the DOS prompt, type:

---

3) dos> **SPSSPC** ⏎   *This step gets you into the SPSS system.*

To clear the menu from the top window prior to analyzing data:

---

4) ALT ⊣M   *Positions cursor to begin to create the command file.*

From the extreme upper left corner of the scratch pad (lower window), type:

---

5) **GET FILE = 'GRADES.SYS'.**   *1*

LINE 1 Accesses the formatted **SYSTEM FILE** to begin to analyze data. All statistical procedures in this book will begin with the **GET FILE** step.

The following lines compute an analysis of variance with a dependent variable of TOTAL (total points earned in the class) and independent variables of GENDER and SECTION. Be careful that the dependent variable is a continuous variable and the independent variables are discrete.

```
6)  GET FILE = 'GRADES.SYS'.                                          1
    ANOVA VARIABLES = TOTAL BY GENDER(1,2) SECTION(1,3).              2
```

LINE 1   Same as line 1 from step 5 above.

LINE 2   This is the **ANOVA** command line.   Note that the dependent variable comes first. The independent variables follow the **BY** connector.   This is *two*-way ANOVA because there are two independent variables.   The *range* of the independent variables must be coded in parentheses after the variable name. You may code for only a *subset* of the variable by listing a smaller range if you wish.   In this case, there are two levels of **GENDER** and three levels of **SECTION**.   However, if you wished to consider only the first two sections in the analysis, code the section variable as follows: **SECTION(1,2)**.

Note: To conduct a three-way, four-way or five-way ANOVA you will list three, four or five variables after the **BY**.   Be sure they follow the same coding format—(1,2), (1,3), and so forth—as used for **GENDER** and **SECTION** above.   Please do not attempt higher than a three-way analysis of variance unless you have clear conceptual reasons for doing so.

In most instances you will also want to have means and frequencies listed for each cell so you can easily graph your results.   Use the STATISTICS subcommand to accomplish this:

```
6a)  GET FILE = 'GRADES.SYS'.                                         1a
     ANOVA VARIABLES = TOTAL BY GENDER(1,2) SECTION(1,3)/             2a
     STATISTICS = 3.                                                  3a
```

LINE 1a   Same as above.

LINE 2a   Same as line 2 above except that it is followed by a slash instead of a period to show that a subcommand follows.

LINE 3a   This line accesses means and frequencies for each cell (the grand mean, the mean for both levels of **GENDER,** for the three levels of **SECTION**, and for the six **GENDER by SECTION** categories).   These are a necessity if you wish to graph data to gain a visual appreciation of the relationships.

```
7)  F9  W  ⏎        to save your command file for future access.
```

If file is not already named, enter the file name (e.g., **GRADES.CTL**) at the prompt between the W and the **ENTER**.

To run the program, first position cursor at the beginning of the GET FILE line, then:

```
8)  F10  C         to run your program from the cursor.
```

After viewing the results:

```
9)  F10  E  FINISH  ⏎        to exit to the DOS prompt.
```

To print command files and results:

```
10) dos > PRINT SPSS.LIS  ↵   ↵      (sometimes the second RETURN is not necessary)
```

OUTPUT
Two-Way Analysis of Variance

The following OUTPUT is produced by this COMMAND FILE. INTERPRETATION follows each section of output.

```
GET FILE = 'GRADES.SYS'.
ANOVA VARIABLES = TOTAL BY GENDER(1,2) SECTION(1,3)/
STATISTICS = 3.
```

```
------------------------------------------------------------------------------
                         * * *  CELL MEANS  * * *
        TOTAL
BY    GENDER
        SECTION
                                      GENDER     1 = FEMALE    2 = MALE
              |------------|                  |------------|------------|
TOTAL         |   100.57   |                  |   102.03   |   98.29   |
POPULATION    | (N = 105)  |                  | (N = 64)   | (N = 41)  |
              --------------                  ----------------------------


SECTION     SECTION 1    SECTION 2    SECTION 3
          |------------|------------|------------|
          |   105.09   |   99.49    |   97.33    |
          | (N = 33)   | (N = 39)   | (N = 33)   |
          ----------------------------------------


GENDER   SECTION|   SECTION 1     SECTION 2     SECTION 3
-----------------|------------|------------|------------|
1 = FEMALE       |   103.95   |   100.00   |   102.83   |
                 | (N = 20)   | (N = 26)   | (N = 18)   |
-----------------|------------|------------|------------|
2 = MALE         |   106.85   |   98.46    |   90.73    |
                 | (N = 13)   | (N = 13)   | (N = 15)   |
                 ----------------------------------------
------------------------------------------------------------------------------
```

The top number in each box (above) is the mean **TOTAL** score for each category. The lower number (in parentheses) is the number of students in each category. A graph of the fourth (interaction) table is shown below to help clarify this information.

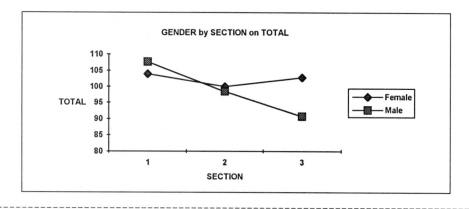

```
                   * * *  A N A L Y S I S   O F   V A R I A N C E  * * *

                  TOTAL
          BY      GENDER
                  SECTION
                             Sum of                  Mean               Signif
     Source of Variation     Squares       DF       Square       F     of F

     Main Effects            1389.964       3       463.321     2.086   .107
        GENDER                324.054       1       324.054     1.459   .230
        SECTION              1040.675       2       520.337     2.342   .101

     2-way Interactions       960.444       2       480.222     2.162   .121
        GENDER   SECTION      960.444       2       480.222     2.162   .121

     Explained               2350.408       5       470.082     2.116   .071

     Residual               21993.306      99       222.155

     Total                  24343.714     104       234.074
```

The answers to the three experimental questions are: (1) There is no significant main effect for **GENDER**: Females ($M = 102.0$) did not score significantly higher than males ($M = 98.29$), $F(1, 99) = 1.459$, $p = .23$. (2) There is a marginally significant main effect for **SECTION**: Results show that those in Section 1 ($M = 105.09$) scored higher than students in Section 3 ($M = 97.33$), $F(2, 99) = 2.342$, $p = .10$. (3) There is no significant **GENDER** by **SECTION** interaction: Despite the lack of statistical significance, we might note that while scores between males and females did not differ much in the first two sections, in the third section females scored much higher ($M = 102.83$) than did males ($M = 90.73$), $F(2, 99) = 2.162$, $p = .12$. These data are displayed on the graph shown above. Definitions of related terms follow:

SUM OF SQUARES: This is the sum of squared deviations from the mean. In a broader sense, explained sum of squares represents the amount of variation in the dependent variable (**TOTAL** in this case) explained by each independent variable or interaction. Residual sum of squares represents the portion of the variance *not* accounted for by the independent variables or their interaction(s). In this example, only about 10% (2350.408/24343.714) of the variation in **TOTAL** is explained by **GENDER**, **SECTION**, and the **GENDER** × **SECTION** interaction. The remaining 90% remains unexplained by these two variables.

DEGREES OF FREEDOM:

    1) **MAIN EFFECTS:** (Levels of **GENDER** − 1) + (Levels of **SECTION** − 1) = (2 − 1)+(3 − 1) = 3.

    2) **GENDER:** (Levels of **GENDER** − 1) = 2 − 1 = 1.

    3) **SECTION:** (Levels of **SECTION** − 1) = 3 − 1 = 2.

    4) **2-WAY INTERACTION:** (Levels of **GENDER** − 1)(Levels of **SECTION** − 1) = (2 − 1)(3 − 1) = 2.

    5) **EXPLAINED:** (DF of Main effects + DF of Interaction) = 3 + 2 = 5.

    6) **RESIDUAL:** (N − Explained DF − 1) = 105 − 5 − 1 = 99.

    7) **TOTAL:** (N − 1) = 105 − 1 = 104.

MEAN SQUARE: Sums of squares divided by degrees of freedom for each category.

F: The mean square for **GENDER** divided by the residual mean square; the mean square for **SECTION** divided by the residual mean square; and the mean square for the **GENDER** × **SECTION** interaction divided by the residual mean square.

SIGNIFICANCE OF F: Likelihood that each result could happen by chance.

Chapter 15

The ANOVA Command:

Three-Way Analysis of Variance and the Influence of Covariates

The previous two chapters Chapter 13 (one-way ANOVA) and Chapter 14 (two-way ANOVA) have given an overview of what analysis of variance attempts to accomplish. A three-way analysis of variance asks similar questions, and we are not going to reiterate here what we have already presented. We will address in this chapter those things that are unique to three-way analysis of variance (as contrasted with one-way or two-way ANOVAs) and also describe what a covariate is and how it can be used with the ANOVA command.

This chapter will be organized in the same manner as all the analysis chapters (Chapters 6-30), but the emphasis will be somewhat different. This introductory portion will deal with the experimental questions that are usually asked in a three-way ANOVA and then explain what a covariate is and how it is typically used. The logical progression for conducting a three-way analysis of variance will conclude this introductory portion. The Step by Step segment will include a step 6 and a step 6a. Step 6 will consist of a three-way ANOVA based on the **GRADES.SYS** file used in previous analyses. **TOTAL** (total points earned) will serve as the dependent variable, and **GENDER, SECTION,** and **LOWUP** (lower- or upper-division student) will be designated as independent variables. Step 6a will be identical except that it will include one covariate, **PREVGPA,** to "partial out" variance based on each student's previous GPA. The output from an analysis of variance is divided into two major sections: (1) The *cell means* portion, which lists the mean and frequency for each category created by the ANOVA; and (2) the ANOVA table, which indicates sums of squares, *F*-values, significance values, and other statistical information. The first portion (the cell means section) of the analysis will be identical whether or not a covariate is used, but the second portion (the ANOVA table) will often be substantially different.

The major difference between this chapter and previous chapters is that in this chapter most of the explaining will occur in the Output section. A three-way or higher-order ANOVA is complex by any standards, and a very thorough and careful explanation of the analysis done here will hopefully assist you in untangling any three-way or higher-order ANOVAs that you might conduct. An almost universally practiced procedure for helping to clarify ANOVA results is to graph the cell means for interactions.   We will create these graphs in this chapter, in fact, even *non*significant interactions will be graphed and related to the appropriate line of output so that you can understand visually why there *is* a significant effect (when one occurs) and why there *isn't* (when a significant effect does *not* occur).   A graph is not normally created for nonsignificant effects, but we hope that inclusion of them here will assist you toward a clearer understanding of the entire output.

THREE-WAY ANALYSIS OF VARIANCE

Restating briefly, the dependent variable for this analysis will be TOTAL, with independent variables of GENDER, SECTION, and LOWUP.   For this analysis (and for any three-way ANOVA) there will be seven possible experimental questions of interest: The first three deal with main effects: (1) Is there a main effect for GENDER (e.g., do females score differently from males on TOTAL points)?   (2) Is there a main effect for SECTION (e.g., do mean TOTAL points earned in one section differ significantly from the other sections)?   and (3) Is there a main effect for LOWUP (e.g., do upper-division students score significantly differently from lower-division students)?   The next three questions deal with two-way interactions: (4) Is there a significant interaction between GENDER and SECTION on TOTAL points?   (5) Is there a significant interaction between GENDER and LOWUP on TOTAL points?   (6) Is there a significant interaction between SECTION and LOWUP on TOTAL points?   The final experimental question concerns whether there is a significant three-way interaction: (7) Is there a significant GENDER by SECTION by LOWUP effect on TOTAL?

SPSS will print cell means for all combinations of variables and compute *F*-values and associated significance values.   These values will indicate if there are significant main effects and/or if there are significant interactions between variables.   As stated in the previous chapter, it is quite possible to have significant main effects but *not* to have significant interaction, just as it is possible to have significant interactions without significant main effects.

THE INFLUENCE OF COVARIATES

The purpose of covariates is to partition out the influence of other variables before conducting the analysis of interest.   A *covariate* could best be defined as a variable that has a substantial correlation with the dependent variable and is included in the experiment to adjust the results for differences existing among subjects before the start of the experiment.   For example, a 1987 study explored the influence of personality traits on the competitive success (a standardized score of fastest racing times) of a sample of runners who ranged in ability from slow fitness runners to world-class athletes.   In addition to a measure of 16 personality traits, each participant's weekly running mileage, weight/height ratio, and age were acquired. The influence of these physiological measures was well known prior to analysis (runners who run more miles, are skinnier, and are younger run faster). In the analysis, all three measures were used as covariates. The purpose was to exclude variance in the dependent variable (fast racing times) that was determined by the weekly mileage, weight/height ratio, and age. This would allow the researcher to see more clearly the influence of the psychological measures without the additional physiological factors included.

In this study PREVGPA will be used as a covariate. In Chapter 10 it was demonstrated that almost 20% of the variance in TOTAL points is accounted for by the previous GPA. Thus if we wish to see the influence of GENDER, SECTION and LOWUP (lower- or upper-division student) *independent* of the influence of the student's previous GPA, then PREVGPA can be included as a covariate. The inclusion of a covariate or covariates does not influence the cell means in the initial output, but it often has substantial influence (usually reduction) on the sum of squares, *F*-values and a corresponding increase of *p*-values in the ANOVA table. These issues will be further clarified in the Output section.

For additional material, two excellent books on analysis of variance are those written by Schulman (1992) and Lindman (1992). Please see the reference section for more detailed information.

THE LOGICAL PROGRESSION FOR COMPUTING THREE-WAY ANOVA

1. Create file of data, or edit (if necessary) an already existing file.
2. Format file by use of **DATA LIST FILE**, **FORMATS**, and **VARIABLE/VALUE LABELS**; then save as a system file.
3. Access file and formats by the **GET FILE** command.
4. Use the **ANOVA** command to conduct analysis of variance.
5. Use the **WITH** connector to include covariates in the analysis, if desired.
6. Use the **STATISTICS** subcommand to access means and frequencies of each cell.
7. View the results and exit the program.
8. Print data, commands, and output.

STEP BY STEP
Three-Way Analysis of Variance

> 1) *Name and create a data file (Chapter 2), or edit (if necessary) an already existing file (Chapter 3).*

> *2) Name variables, locate column positions, format, create VARIABLE/VALUE LABELS, and then save the formatted DATA FILE as a SYSTEM FILE (Chapter 4).*

From the DOS prompt, type:

> *3) dos> **SPSSPC** ⏎   This step gets you into the SPSS system.*

To clear the menu from the top window prior to analyzing data:

> *4) ALT ⎯ M   Positions cursor to begin to create the command file.*

From the extreme upper left corner of the scratch pad (lower window), type:

> *5)* **GET FILE = 'GRADES.SYS'.**   *1*

LINE 1 Accesses the formatted **SYSTEM FILE** to begin to analyze data. All statistical procedures in this book will begin with the **GET FILE** step.

The following lines compute an analysis of variance (ANOVA) with a dependent variable of TOTAL (total points earned in the class) and independent variables of GENDER, SECTION, and LOWUP. Note that the dependent variable is a continuous variable and the independent variables are discrete or categorical.

> *6)* **GET FILE = 'GRADES.SYS'.**   *1*
> **ANOVA VARIABLES = TOTAL BY GENDER(1,2) SECTION(1,3) LOWUP(1,2)/**   *2*
> **STATISTICS = 3.**   *3*

LINE 1 Same as line 1 from step 5 above.
LINE 2 This is the **ANOVA** command line. Note that the dependent variable comes first. The independent variables follow the **BY** connector. This is three-way ANOVA because there are three independent variables. The *range* of the independent variables must be coded in parentheses after the variable names. You may code for only a *subset* of the variable by listing a smaller range if you wish. In this case, there are two levels of **GENDER**, three levels of **SECTION,** and two levels of **LOWUP**. However, if you wished to consider only the first two sections in the analysis, code the section variable as follows: **SECTION(1,2).**
LINE 3 This **STATISTICS** subcommand requests cell means for each category. You almost always want these values when conducting an analysis of variance.

To include a covariate, it is necessary to use the WITH connector. The command file below conducts the same analysis as in step 6 but includes PREVGPA as a covariate.

> *6a)* **GET FILE = 'GRADES.SYS'.**   *1a*
> **ANOVA VARIABLES = TOTAL BY GENDER(1,2) SECTION(1,3) LOWUP(1,2)**
> **WITH PREVGPA/**   *2a*
> **STATISTICS = 3.**   *3a*

LINE **1a**   Same as above.

LINE **2a**   This line is similar to line 2 above except that it includes the **WITH** connector and the covariate **PREVGPA** that follows. Note that the covariate does not *need* to be on the next line (as it is above). For any command line, if it is too long, simply hit the return at a natural break point and continue typing. This line is followed by a slash instead of a period to show that a subcommand follows.

LINE **3a**   This line accesses means and frequencies for each cell. SPSS output will produce a number of tables (nine in this case) to generate main effect and interaction information.

---

7) `F9` `W` `↵`   *to save your command file for future access.*

If file is not already named, enter the file name (e.g., **GRADES.CTL**) at the prompt between the **W** and the **ENTER**.

To run the program, first position cursor at the beginning of the GET FILE line, then:

---

8) `F10` `C`   *to run your program from the cursor.*

After viewing the results:

---

9) `F10` `E` **FINISH** `↵`   *to exit to the DOS prompt.*

To print command files and results:

---

10) dos > **PRINT SPSS.LIS** `↵` `↵`   *(Sometimes the second RETURN is not necessary.)*

OUTPUT
Three-Way Analysis of Variance and Analysis of Covariance

The format in this Output section will differ from most other output sections in this book. The output will be divided into two separate presentations. In the first of these, we show the results of a three-way analysis of variance that does *not* include a covariate. For this first analysis, instead of reproducing the output generated by SPSS we will integrate the cell means portion of the output (the first segment) with the ANOVA table portion (which follows). After each of the nine sections of the cell means portion, the ANOVA line that relates to that portion will follow immediately. For the five tables that involve interactions, a graph of the output will be included to help clarify the relation among the table, the graph, and the ANOVA output. Explanation or clarification will follow after each table/graph/line presentation, rather than at the end of the Output section.

For the second presentation, the output from a three-way analysis of variance *that includes a covariate* will be shown. The tables of cell means and associated graphs (the first presentation) are identical whether or not a covariate is included; so these will not be produced a second time. What we will show is the complete ANOVA table output in the same format as produced by SPSS. To demonstrate how mean square, *F*-, and *p*-values differ when a covariate is included, the ANOVA results *without* the covariate will *also* be included in the same table. The output that does *not* include the covariate will be shown in parentheses and *italicized* so as not to interfere in the interpretation of the original output. Explanation will then follow.

The following OUTPUT is produced by this COMMAND FILE. Interpretation, illustration, and/or definitions follow each portion of output.

```
GET FILE = 'GRADES.SYS'.
ANOVA VARIABLES = TOTAL BY GENDER(1,2) SECTION(1,3) LOWUP(1,2)/
STATISTICS = 3.
```

```
                    * * *  CELL MEANS  * * *

        TOTAL       BY      GENDER  SECTION  LOWUP

TOTAL POPULATION │  100.57 (N = 105) │
```

	Sum of Squares	DF	Mean Square	F	Sig of F
TOTAL	24343.714	104	234.074	-	-

This cell identifies the overall mean for the variable **TOTAL** for the entire sample ($N = 105$). The sum of squares is the total of squared deviations from the grand mean for all subjects. The degrees of freedom is $N - 1$ ($105 - 1 = 104$), and the mean square is the sum of squares divided by the degrees of freedom. There are no *F* or *p* statistics generated for a single value.

Main Effect for GENDER

GENDER	1 = FEMALE	2 = MALE
	102.03 (N = 64)	98.29 (N = 41)

Main Effects	Sum of Squares	DF	Mean Square	F	Sig of F
GENDER	357.083	1	357.083	1.703	.195

The table indicates that 64 females scored an average of 102.03 TOTAL points while 41 males scored an average of 98.29. A visual display (e.g., graph) is rarely needed for main effects. It is clear that females scored higher than males. The degrees of freedom for main effects is determined by the number of levels of the variable minus one. Thus degrees of freedom for GENDER is: $2 - 1 = 1$; for SECTION is: $3 - 1 = 2$; and for LOWUP is: $2 - 1 = 1$. The F-value is determined by dividing the mean square for the variable of interest (GENDER in this case) by the residual mean square. The $F = 1.703$ and $p = .195$ indicate that there is no significant main effect for gender; that is, the scores for females and males do not differ significantly.

Main Effect for SECTION

SECTION	SECTION 1	SECTION 2	SECTION 3
	105.09 (N = 33)	99.49 (N = 39)	97.33 (N = 33)

Main Effects	Sum of Squares	DF	Mean Square	F	Sig of F
SECTION	1063.751	2	531.876	2.537	.085

This table indicates that 33 students from the first section scored a mean of 105.09 points, 39 students from the second section scored a mean of 99.49 points, and 33 students from the third section scored a mean of 97.33 points. An F-value of 2.537 ($p = .085$) indicates that there is a marginally significant main effect for SECTION. Visual inspection indicates that the difference in scores between the first and the third sections is greatest.

Main Effect for LOWUP

LOWUP	1 = LOWER DIV	2 = UPPER DIV
	99.55 (N = 22)	100.84 (N = 83)

Main Effects	Sum of Squares	DF	Mean Square	F	Sig of F
LOWUP	83.844	1	83.844	.400	.529

This result indicates that 22 lower-division students scored a mean TOTAL of 99.55, while 83 upper-division students scored a mean TOTAL of 100.84. A graph, once again, is unnecessary. An F-value of .400 and p of .529 indicate no significant differences for scores of upper-division and lower-division students.

Two-Way Interaction, GENDER by SECTION

SECTION GENDER	SECTION 1	SECTION 2	SECTION 3
1 = FEMALE	103.95 (N = 20)	100.00 (N = 26)	102.83 (N = 18)
2 = MALE	106.85 (N = 13)	98.46 (N = 13)	90.73 (N = 15)

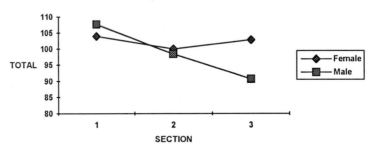

GENDER by SECTION on TOTAL

```
2-way Interactions Sum of Squares  DF   Mean Square    F     Sig of F
GENDER by SECTION       998.992     2     499.496     2.382    .098
```

These results indicate a marginally significant **GENDER** by **SECTION** interaction ($F = 2.382$, $p = .098$). The contents of the six cells identify the mean **TOTAL** score and the number of subjects within each of six categories. One way to visually identify an interaction is to see whether the two or more lines of the graph are parallel. If the lines are parallel, this indicates that there is *no* interaction. There is no *significant* interaction when the lines do not differ significantly from parallel. There is a significant interaction when the two lines *do* differ significantly from parallel. Be careful! Interactions cannot be determined by viewing a graph alone. The vertical and horizontal scales of a graph can be manipulated to indicate a greater effect than actually exists. The related output from the ANOVA table will indicate whether or not there is a significant effect. In the graph above, clearly the "action" is happening in the third section. While there is not much difference in scores between males and females in the first two sections, the difference is much larger in the third section. These data could also be presented with the **GENDER** variable along the horizontal axis and the **SECTION** variable coded to the right. The graphic configuration used is determined by which displays the relationship between variables more clearly.

Two-Way Interaction, GENDER by LOWUP

LOWUP GENDER	LOWER DIV (1)		UPPER DIV (2)	
1 = FEMALE	102.50	(N = 16)	101.88	(N = 48)
2 = MALE	91.67	(N = 6)	99.43	(N = 35)

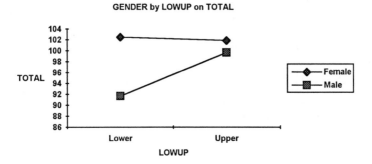

GENDER by LOWUP on TOTAL

2-way Interactions	*Sum of Squares*	*DF*	*Mean Square*	*F*	*Sig of F*
GENDER by LOWUP	427.243	1	427.243	2.038	.157

An *F*-value of 2.038 ($p = .16$) indicates no significant interaction between **GENDER** and **LOWUP**. Note that the two lines *appear* to deviate substantially from parallel, and yet no significance. Two factors influence this: (1) Values on the vertical axis vary only from 86 to 104, while **TOTAL** points vary from 48 to 125. We display only a narrow segment of the actual range, causing an exaggerated illusion of deviation from parallel. (2) The significance of a main effect or interaction is substantially influenced by the sample size. In the case above, two of the cells have only 6 and 16 subjects, decreasing the *power* of the analysis. Lower power means that a greater difference is required to show significance than if the sample size were larger.

Two-Way Interaction, SECTION by LOWUP

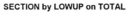

SECTION	LOWUP	LOWER DIV (1)	UPPER DIV (2)
1		109.86 (N = 7)	103.81 (N = 26)
2		90.09 (N = 11)	103.18 (N = 28)
3		107.50 (N = 4)	95.93 (N = 29)

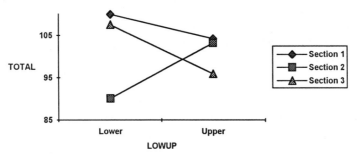

SECTION by LOWUP on TOTAL

2-way Interactions	*Sum of Squares*	*DF*	*Mean Square*	*F*	*Sig of F*
SECTION by LOWUP	1809.362	2	904.681	4.315	.016

Both the ANOVA line (note the $F = 4.315 = .016$ and the graph indicate a significant SECTION by LOWUP interaction. While the first and third sections show lines relatively close to parallel, the second section shows a nearly opposite trend. A reasonable interpretation of the interaction might be: While lower-division students tend to score higher than upper-division students in Sections 1 and 3, the reverse is true in Section 2. The results would be stronger than the $p = .016$ were it not for low cell counts in the three lower-division cells.

Three-Way Interaction, GENDER by SECTION by LOWUP

	LOWUP = 1:	LOWER DIVISION	
GENDER SECTION	SECTION 1	SECTION 2	SECTION 3
1 (FEMALE)	113.20 (N = 5)	93.00 (N = 8)	110.00 (N = 3)
2 (MALE)	101.50 (N = 2)	82.33 (N = 3)	100.00 (N = 1)

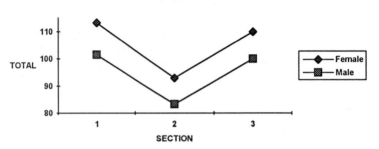

	LOWUP = 2:	UPPER DIVISION	
GENDER SECTION	SECTION 1	SECTION 2	SECTION 3
1 (FEMALE)	100.87 (N = 15)	103.11 (N = 18)	101.40 (N = 15)
2 (MALE)	107.82 (N = 11)	103.30 (N = 10)	90.07 (N = 14)

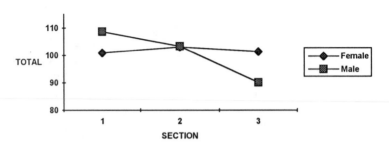

3-way Interactions	Sum of Squares	DF	Mean Square	F	Sig of F
GENDER SECTION LOWUP	171.572	2	85.786	.409	.665

As a starting point, three-way and higher-order interactions are often quite difficult to interpret. The researcher must have a strong conceptual grasp of the nature of the data set and what constitutes meaningful relationships. For the sample listed above, an $F = .409$ and $p = .665$ indicate that the three-way interaction does not even hint at significance. When there is no significant interaction, the researcher would usually not draw graphs. We have included them here to demonstrate one way that you might visually display a three-way interaction. While one might note the almost identical pattern for females and males in the first chart, a more important thing to notice is the very low cell counts for all six cells of the lower division group (5, 8, 3, 2, 3, 1, respectively). Even if the outcome proved to be statistically significant, the low cell count would nullify the usefulness of the results. The degrees of freedom for a three-way interaction is: Number of levels of the first variable minus one, times number of levels of the second variable minus one, times number of levels of the third variable minus one $[(2 - 1) \times (3 - 1) \times (2 - 1) = 2]$.

A THREE-WAY ANOVA THAT INCLUDES A COVARIATE

In this final section of the output, we will show the ANOVA output in the form displayed by SPSS. The cell means and graphs (previous section) will be identical whether or not a covariate or covariates are included. What changes is the sum of squares and, correspondingly, the degrees of freedom (in some cases), the mean squares, *F*-values, and significance values. If the covariate has a substantial influence, the analysis will usually demonstrate lower mean square and *F*-values for most of the main effects and interactions, and higher significance values. In the chart that follows, the boldface material will duplicate the output (which includes **PREVGPA** as a covariate) exactly as SPSS produces it. The results from the ANOVA table for the analysis *without* the covariate will then follow, in parentheses and *italicized*.

The following OUTPUT *is produced by this* COMMAND FILE. * INTERPRETATION follows.*

```
GET FILE = 'GRADES.SYS'.
ANOVA VARIABLES = TOTAL BY GENDER(1,2) SECTION(1,3) LOWUP(1,2) WITH
PREVGPA/
STATISTICS = 3.
        (GET FILE = 'GRADES.SYS'.)
        (ANOVA VARIABLES = TOTAL BY GENDER(1,2) SECTION(1,3) LOWUP(1,2)/)
        (STATISTICS = 3.)
---------------------------------------------------------------------
Page #                          SPSS/PC+                          Date

            TOTAL                   TOTAL)
    BY      GENDER          (BY     GENDER)
            SECTION                 SECTION)
            LOWUP                   LOWUP)
    WITH    PREVGPA         (without covariate)
```

Source of Variation	Sum of Squares	DF	Mean Square	F	Signif of F
Covariates	4549.01	1	4549.01	25.62	.000
	(NA)	*(-)*	*(NA)*	*(NA)*	*(NA)*
PREVGPA	4549.01	1	4549.01	25.62	.000
	(NA)	*(-)*	*(NA)*	*(NA)*	*(NA)*
Main Effects	764.01	4	191.00	1.08	.373
	(1473.81)	*(4)*	*(368.45)*	*(1.76)*	*(.144)*
GENDER	49.12	1	49.12	.28	.600
	(357.08)	*(1)*	*(357.08)*	*(1.70)*	*(.195)*
SECTION	559.22	2	270.61	1.58	.213
	(1063.75)	*(2)*	*(531.88)*	*(2.54)*	*(.085)*
LOWUP	202.11	1	202.11	1.14	.289
	(83.84)	*(1)*	*(83.84)*	*(.40)*	*(.529)*
2-way Interactions	2530.99	5	506.20	2.85	.019
	(3200.59)	*(5)*	*(640.12)*	*(3.05)*	*(.013)*
GENDER SECTION	553.44	2	276.72	1.56	.216
	(998.99)	*(2)*	*(499.50)*	*(2.38)*	*(.098)*
GENDER LOWUP	155.51	1	155.51	.88	.352
	(427.24)	*(1)*	*(427.24)*	*(2.04)*	*(.157)*
SECTION LOWUP	1864.36	2	932.18	5.25	.007
	(1809.36)	*(2)*	*(904.68)*	*(4.32)*	*(.016)*
3-way Interactions	162.57	2	81.29	.46	.634
	(171.57)	*(2)*	*(85.79)*	*(.41)*	*(.665)*
GENDR SCTION LOWUP	162.57	2	81.29	.46	.634
	(171.57)	*(2)*	*(85.79)*	*(.41)*	*(.665)*
Explained	8006.59	12	667.22	3.76	.000
	(4845.97)	*(11)*	*(440.54)*	*(2.01)*	*(.028)*
Residual	16337.13	92	177.58		
	(19497.74)	*(93)*	*(209.65)*		
Total	24343.71	104	234.07		
	(same)	*(same)*	*(same)*		

Some general observations concerning the output (above) are mentioned here, followed by the definition of terms. Note that the covariate **PREVGPA** accounts for a substantial portion of the total variation in the dependent variable **TOTAL**. A rule of thumb for computing the portion of the total variance observed in the dependent variable is to divide the sum of squares for the variable(s) of interest by the total sum of squares. An example: The sum of squares for the covariate **PREVGPA** is 4,549.01. The total sum of squares observed is 24,343.71. 4,549.01/24,343.71 = .187. This indicates that 18.7% of the total variation in the dependent variable **TOTAL** is accounted for by **PREVGPA**. The *explained* variance (third line up from the bottom) is the sum of the sum of squares from all explained sources of variation—covariates, main effects, two-way interactions, and the three-way interaction. The total amount of explained variation is 8,006.59/24,343.71 = .3289. Thus 32.89% of the variation in TOTAL is explained by all covariates, main effects, and interactions, and 67.11% is *residual* or unexplained.

Note also the comparisons of the components of the ANOVA table when comparing analyses with and without a covariate. Since the covariate "consumes" much of the variance, most of the F-values are lower and corresponding p-values (for main effects and interactions) are higher when the covariate is included. This is not strictly true, however. Notice that the main effect for LOWUP and the SECTION × LOWUP interaction show higher F-values and correspondingly lower p-values when the covariate is included.

SUMS OF SQUARES: This is the sum of squared deviations from the mean. In a broader sense, explained sum of squares represents the amount of variation in the dependent variable (TOTAL in this case) explained by each independent variable or interaction. Residual sum of squares represents the portion of the variance *not* accounted for by the covariate(s), independent variables, or their interaction(s).

DEGREES OF FREEDOM:
1. Covariates: 1 degree of freedom for each covariate.
2. Main effects: Sum of the main effects degrees of freedom for each independent variable: $1 + 2 + 1 = 4$.
3. GENDER: (Levels of GENDER − 1): $2 − 1 = 1$.
4. SECTION: (Levels of SECTION − 1): $3 − 1 = 2$.
5. LOWUP: (Levels of LOWUP − 1): $2 − 1 = 1$.
6. Two-way interactions: Sum of the degrees of freedom for the three two-way interactions: $2 + 1 + 2 = 5$.
7. Three-way interactions: The degrees of freedom for the individual three-way interaction (2).
8. Explained: (DF covariates + DF main effects + DF of Interactions): $1 + 4 + 5 + 2 = 12$.
9. Residual: (N − Explained DF − 1): $105 − 12 − 1 = 92$.
10. Total: (N − 1): $105 − 1 = 104$.

MEAN SQUARES: Sum of squares divided by degrees of freedom for each category.

F: The mean square for each main effect or interaction divided by the residual mean square.

SIGNIFICANCE OF F: Likelihood that the associated result could happen by chance.

Chapter 16

The MANOVA Command:

Multivariate T-Tests and Hotelling's T²

This is the first chapter describing a procedure that uses several dependent variables concurrently within the same analysis: Multivariate *T*-tests, using Hotelling's T^2. In SPSS, the MANOVA command performs a Hotelling's T^2. The MANOVA command is perhaps the most complex command in SPSS; this chapter, however, describes how to do multivariate *T*-tests, the simplest of the MANOVA procedures. Chapter 17 extends this discussion by focusing on multivariate analysis of variance and covariance, and Chapter 18 goes on to describe multivariate analysis of variance using within-subjects designs and repeated-measures designs.

As described in earlier chapters, an independent-samples *t*-test indicates whether there is a difference between two separate groups on a particular dependent variable. In our example, it might be interesting to explore differences between women and men on their GPAs (PREVGPA), as well as on their scores on the final exam (FINAL). Sometimes, researchers use two separate *t*-tests to explore these effects. There are times, however, when it may be important to tell whether there is a difference between two groups on several variables simultaneously. Also, if the dependent variables are correlated with each other, it may be desirable to gain statistical power by analyzing the dependent variables concurrently.

One popular approach to examining gender differences on GPAs (PREVGPA) and scores on the final exam (FINAL), is to do two separate *t*-tests. This approach has the advantage of conceptual clarity and ease of interpretation; however, it does have disadvantages. In particular, when several *t*-tests are performed, the experimentwise error increases—that is, the chance that one or more of your findings may be due to chance increases. Furthermore, when dependent variables are correlated with each other, doing separate *t*-tests may not give the most accurate picture of the data.

In response to these and other problems associated with doing multiple *t*-tests, Hotelling's T^2 was developed. It examines the differences between two groups (or between one group and zero) across several dependent variables; that is, it examines whether there are differences among the dependent variables simultaneously. Further analyses allow you to examine the *pattern* of changes in the dependent variables, either by conducting a series of univariate *t*-tests or by using a procedure similar to discriminant analysis.

It is important to remember that, in univariate analysis (when you are working with one dependent variable at a time), $t^2 = F$. Similarly, in multivariate analysis (when you are working with several dependent variables simultaneously), Hotelling's $T^2 = F$. On the computer printouts in this chapter, SPSS lists T^2 values as F's. Also, it is important to be certain that the dependent variables do not exhibit linear dependency on each other: For example, it would be incorrect to analyze class percent (**PERCENT**) and total points received (**TOTAL**) together because the percent for the class depends on the total points received.

THE LOGICAL PROGRESSION FOR COMPUTING MULTIVARIATE T-TESTS

1. Create file of data, or edit (if necessary) an already existing file.
2. Format file by use of **DATA LIST FILE**, **FORMATS**, and **VARIABLE/VALUE LABELS**; then save as a system file.
3. Access file and formats by the **GET FILE** command.
4. Use the **MANOVA** command to conduct a multivariate *T*-test.
5. Use the **PRINT CELLINFO** subcommand, if desired, to access means and correlations of the cells.
6. Use the **PRINT PARAMETERS** subcommand, if desired, to access parameter estimates.
7. Use the **PRINT SIGNIF** subcommand, if desired, to access univariate *t*-tests of the dependent variables.
8. View the results and exit the program.
9. Print data, commands, and output.

STEP BY STEP
Multivariate T-Tests

> 1) *Name and create a data file (Chapter 2), or edit (if necessary) an already existing file (Chapter 3).*

> 2) *Name variables, locate column positions, format, create VARIABLE/VALUE LABELS, and then save the formatted DATA FILE as a SYSTEM FILE (Chapter 4).*

From the DOS prompt, type:

> 3) *dos > SPSSPC* ↵   *This step gets you into the SPSS system.*

To clear the menu from the top window prior to analyzing data:

> 4) ALT ⊢M   *Positions cursor to begin to create the command file.*

From the extreme upper left corner of the scratch pad (lower window), type:

> 5) GET FILE = 'GRADES.SYS'.   1

LINE 1 Accesses the formatted SYSTEM FILE to begin to analyze data. All statistical procedures in this book will begin with the GET FILE step.

The following command file calculates a simple T^2, without any additional statistics. The independent variable is the subjects' gender (GENDER), and the dependent variables examined are subjects' previous GPA (PREVGPA), along with their grade on the final exam (FINAL).

> 6) GET FILE = 'GRADES.SYS'.   1
> MANOVA PREVGPA FINAL BY GENDER(1,2).   2

LINE 1 The same as step 5, line 1 above.
LINE 2 The MANOVA command is the SPSS command used to access multivariate T^2. SPSS lists the dependent variables first. If you have more than two dependent variables, they may be listed here. The independent variable comes after the dependent variables and is separated from them with the word BY. The coding behind the independent variable, **(1,2)** is required.

Note: If you do not include an independent variable, then SPSS/PC+ will test whether the dependent variables are significantly different from zero.

The following command file calculates a T^2, as well as producing a number of additional statistics that are often useful. There are many more subcommands available with the MANOVA command, but we have included only the most frequently used options. See the SPSS/PC+ Advanced Statistics 4.0 Manual for additional options.

> 6a) GET FILE = 'GRADES.SYS'.   1a
> MANOVA PREVGPA FINAL BY GENDER(1,2)/   2a
> PRINT CELLINFO(MEANS COR) PARAMETERS(ESTIM) SIGNIF(UNIV).   3a

LINE 1a The same as above.
LINE 2a The same as step 6, line 2 above, except that it ends here in a (/) instead of a (.) because there is a subcommand following.
LINE 3a If you desire additional statistics, the PRINT subcommand is used and may be followed by any

or all of the following options:

- **CELLINFO(MEANS COR)** produces means for each dependent measure in each of the two cells, as well as correlations between the dependent measures for each of the two cells (e.g., the correlation between **PREVGPA** and **FINAL** for only subjects that are female, as well as for only subjects that are male). If you only want **MEANS** or **COR**relations, then you may list only the one that you wish.
- **PARAMETERS(ESTIM)** produces parameter estimates for each of the dependent variables. This output is similar to the basic output that is given by discriminant analysis (see Chapter 23). If there is an overall significant difference between the dependent variables as predicted by the independent variable, then this information may be useful in interpreting exactly what that difference is.
- **SIGNIF(UNIV)** produces univariate *t*-tests for each of the dependent variables used in the multivariate T^2. This output is often useful in interpreting exactly where a significant difference between two groups lies across several dependent measures. If this is the only additional information that you want besides the simple **MANOVA** command as listed in step 6 above, then you do not need to include it here; it will appear automatically. However, if you request any of the **PRINT** subcommand options, then you should also specify **SIGNIF(UNIV)** if you wish the univariate *t*-tests to print.

Note: Many other subcommands and print options are available within SPSS. The SPSS manuals describe them fully, but they are beyond the scope of this book. If you do need to look at the manuals, however, two things that you are likely to need are **PRINT HOMOGENEITY(ALL)**, to produce tests for univariate and multivariate homogeneity of variance, and **PLOT NORMAL**, to produce normal and detrended normal plots. Both of these commands may be useful in exploring the homogeneity of variance between the various conditions, as well as to examine the normality of the data.

---

7) F9 W ↵   *to save your command file for future access.*

If file is not already named, enter the file name (e.g., **GRADES.CTL**) at the prompt between the **W** and the **ENTER**.

To run the program, first position cursor at the beginning of the GET FILE line, then:

---

8) F10 C   *to run your program from the cursor.*

After viewing the results:

---

9) F10 E FINISH ↵   *to exit to the DOS prompt.*

To print command files and results:

---

10) dos > **PRINT SPSS.LIS** ↵ ↵   *(Sometimes the second RETURN is not necessary.)*

OUTPUT
Multivariate T-Tests

The following OUTPUT *is produced by this* COMMAND FILE. *Interpretation, description and/or definitions follow each segment of output.*

```
GET FILE = 'GRADES.SYS'.
MANOVA PREVGPA FINAL BY GENDER(1,2)/
PRINT CELLINFO(MEANS COR) PARAMETERS(ESTIM) SIGNIF(UNIV).
```

Note: We abbreviated the following printout, since the complete printout takes four long, single-spaced pages. Some sections of the report may not be present unless you specifically request them (using the PRINT subcommand). Because of this, each section of the report is listed separately, along with its interpretation.

CELL MEANS: *PRINT CELLINFO(MEANS)*

```
-------------------------------------------------------------------------
   Cell Means and Standard Deviations
   Variable .. PREVGPA
      FACTOR           CODE              Mean       Std. Dev.       N
      GENDER           FEMALE            2.897        .746          64
      GENDER           MALE              2.595        .763          41
   For entire sample                     2.779        .764         105

   Variable .. FINAL
      FACTOR           CODE              Mean       Std. Dev.       N
      GENDER           FEMALE           62.359       7.490          64
      GENDER           MALE             60.098       8.514          41
   For entire sample                    61.476       7.943         105
-------------------------------------------------------------------------
```

This printout is quite straightforward; the codes refer to the levels of the independent variable.

CORRELATIONS: *PRINT CELLINFO(COR)*

```
-------------------------------------------------------------------------
   Cell Number .. 1      [Female]
   Correlation matrix with Standard Deviations on Diagonal
                    PREVGPA        FINAL
   PREVGPA            .746
   FINAL              .482         7.490

   Determinant of Variance-Covariance matrix =        23.98849
   LOG(Determinant) =                                  3.17757

   Cell Number .. 2      [Male]
   Correlation matrix with Standard Deviations on Diagonal
                    PREVGPA        FINAL
   PREVGPA            .763
   FINAL              .490         8.514
```

```
Determinant of Variance-Covariance matrix =            32.08865
LOG(Determinant) =                                      3.46850

Determinant of pooled Variance-Covariance matrix       27.09104
LOG(Determinant) =                                      3.29920

Multivariate test for Homogeneity of Dispersion matrices
Box's M =                             .89064
F WITH (3,328811) DF =                .29020, P =    .833 (Approx.)
Chi-Square with 3 DF =                .87059, P =    .833 (Approx.)
------------------------------------------------------------------------
```

This printout has several different sections: First printed are correlations between each of the dependent variables for each level of the independent variable, followed by the determinant and logarithm of the determinant of the pooled variance-covariance matrix for the entire sample. Finally listed are tests for homogeneity of the dispersion matrices. Note that if more dependent variables are present, the correlation tables will be longer but interpretation of this output will be the same.

CORRELATION MATRICES: SPSS prints correlation matrices for each of the levels of the independent variable (female = 1 and male = 2 in this example). Multivariate T^2 tests assume that these matrices are the same. Note that on the diagonal elements, standard deviations are printed (e.g. the standard deviation for females' **PINAL** is 7.49).

DETERMINANT OF THE VARIANCE-COVARIANCE MATRICES: Not often used, the determinant provides an indication of how strong a relationship there is among the variables in the correlation matrix. The smaller the number, the more closely the variables are related to each other. This is used primarily by the computer to compute the Box's *M* test (discussed later). The determinant of the pooled variance-covariance matrix refers to both of the variance-covariance matrices present on the printout.

LOG(DETERMINANT): The natural logarithm of the determinant. This is used by the computer (to determine the homogeneity of dispersion matrices) but is not often used by researchers.

MULTIVARIATE TEST FOR HOMOGENEITY OF DISPERSION MATRICES: Box's *M* test examines whether the variance-covariance matrices (also known as dispersion matrices) are the same for both of the cells (i.e., for males and females). To evaluate this test, SPSS calculates an *F* or χ^2 approximation for the *M*; these values, along with their associated *p*-values, are listed in the printout. Significant *p*-values indicate *differences* between the variance-covariance matrices for the two groups; since $p = .83$ in this example, there is not statistical evidence that female and male students have significantly different variance-covariance matrices. This test is very sensitive, however; so even if the test did detect differences between the variance-covariance matrices, this does not necessarily mean that the T^2 value is incorrect.

MULTIVARIATE T²

```
------------------------------------------------------------------------
             * * ANALYSIS   OF   VARIANCE -- DESIGN   1 * *

EFFECT .. GENDER
Multivariate Tests of Significance (S = 1, M = 0, N = 50 )
```

Test Name	Value	Approx. F	Hypoth. DF	Error DF	Sig. of F
Pillais	.04000	2.12480	2.00	102.00	.125
Hotelling's	.04166	2.12480	2.00	102.00	.125
Wilks	.96000	2.12480	2.00	102.00	.125
Roys	.04000				

Univariate F-tests with (1,103) D. F.

Variable	Hypoth. SS	Error SS	Hypoth. MS	Error MS	F	Sig of F
PREVGPA	2.27683	58.39604	2.27683	.56695	4.01591	.048
FINAL	127.84635	6434.34413	127.84635	62.46936	2.04654	.156

This section prints no matter what options are requested unless the **PRINT** subcommand was used without specifying **SIGNIF(UNIV)** (see step 6a). Note: Be certain that you read the table labeled **EFFECT .. GENDER** (or whatever your independent variable is) and *not* the section labeled **EFFECT .. CONSTANT**. It should be noted that although there is no multivariate effect (since the T^2 is not significant), there *is* a univariate effect of **PREVGPA**, indicating that females had significantly higher GPAs than males.

MULTIVARIATE TESTS OF SIGNIFICANCE: Test names and values indicate several methods of testing for differences between the dependent variables due to the independent variable. Traditionally, Hotelling's method is used to compute T^2. In this case there is 1 hypothesis degree of freedom (number of groups − 1) and 103 error degrees of freedom (sample size − hypothesis degrees of freedom − 1).

APPROXIMATE F: Estimate of the *F*-value (remember that $F = T^2$).

HYPOTHESIS DF: Two, since there are two dependent variables.

ERROR DF: Sample size − hypothesis degrees of freedom − 1.

SIGNIFICANCE OF F: *p*-value for the *F*.

UNIVARIATE F-TESTS: For each of the dependent variables, SPSS does a simple *F*-test. If you want *t*-values instead of *F*-values, convert from *F* to *t* (*t* equals the square root of *F*).

HYPOTHESIS SS: The between-groups sum of squares; the sum of squared deviations between the grand mean and each group mean, weighted (multiplied) by the number of subjects in each group.

ERROR SS: The within-groups sum of squares; the sum of squared deviations between the mean for each group and the observed values of each subject within that group.

HYPOTHESIS MS: Hypothesis sum of squares divided by hypothesis degrees of freedom. Since there is only one degree of freedom for the hypothesis, this value is the same as the hypothesis sum of squares.

ERROR MS: Error sum of squares divided by error degrees of freedom.

F: Hypothesis MS divided by Error MS

SIGNIFICANCE OF F: *p*-value for the *F*.

PARAMETER ESTIMATES: **PRINT PARAMETER(ESTIM)**

Estimates for PREVGPA

Parameter		Coeff	Std. Err	t-Value	Sig t	Lower −95% CL− Upper	
CONSTANT	1	2.74579840	.07531	36.45968	.000	2.59644	2.89516
GENDER	2	.15092035	.07531	2.00397	.048	.00156	.30028

estimates for FINAL

Parameter		Coeff	Std. Err	t-Value	Sig t	Lower −95% CL− Upper	
CONSTANT	1	61.2284680	.79053	77.45280	.000	59.66065	62.79629
GENDER	2	1.1309070	.79053	1.43057	.156	−.43692	2.69873

Parameter estimates are provided to help in the interpretation of the overall multivariate

T^2. For each of the dependent variables, parameter estimates are produced that predict the means for the cells. For example, the cell mean for **PREVGPA** is predicted by: constant coefficient ± gender coefficient. Whether the **GENDER** coefficient is added to or subtracted from the constant coefficient depends on the level of gender. Since we have coded female as 1 and male as 2 in this case, we *add* the gender coefficient to get the mean for females and *subtract* the gender coefficient to get the mean for males:

STANDARD ERROR: A measure of the dispersion of the coefficients.

t-VALUE: This *t*-value tests whether the parameter is different from zero. The constant's *t*-value will usually be large, unless the average of the means is near zero. The parameter associated with the independent variable should have a *t*-value identical to the univariate *t* associated with that parameter.

SIGNIFICANCE OF t: The *p*-value associated with the *t*-value.

LOWER AND UPPER 95% CONFIDENCE LIMITS: These values indicate the boundaries of where the parameter coefficients may actually be. For example, although the constant for previous GPA is 2.75, because of random error it may differ somewhat from this value. There is, however, a 95% chance that the actual value is between 2.60 and 2.90.

Chapter 17

The MANOVA Command:
Multivariate Analysis of Variance and Covariance

Chapter 16 discussed multivariate T^2 statistics, which analyze several dependent variables based on one independent variable with two levels (or examines whether the dependent variables are different from zero). This chapter extends the concepts from the previous chapter to multivariate analysis of variance and covariance (MANOVA and MANCOVA), in which one or more independent variables are analyzed with two or more dependent variables. As in the case of the Hotelling's T^2 statistic, all of the dependent measures are analyzed simultaneously. If you wish, you may include covariates in the analysis. If you do, SPSS examines the effects of the independent variables on the dependent variables once the effects of one or more covariates have been removed. Chapter 15 contains a clear definition of *covariate*, describes how it works, and provides an example.

Chapter 18 will extend these ideas further by allowing for within-subjects designs, as well as designs using repeated measures. This chapter will discuss only between-subjects designs.

SPSS uses the MANOVA command to do MANOVAs and MANCOVAs. Stopping for a moment to clarify a typographical convention (and this is consistent throughout all chapters); we use the small caps boldface when referring to a command or variable name (e.g., MANOVA, CORRELATION, FINAL). When we are referring to a procedure or variable in the generic sense, we use normal text (e.g., MANOVA, correlation, final exam score). MANOVA is in many ways the most complex command available within SPSS, and it allows for many options and subcommands. This chapter will focus on the most frequently used options.

MANOVA is an extension of ANOVA; so if you are unfamiliar with ANOVA, you should ground yourself firmly in that procedure (see Chapters 13-15) before attempting to conduct a MANOVA. Just as in univariate analysis of variance (ANOVA), MANOVA produces an F statistic to determine whether there are significant differences between the groups. MANOVA is designed to test for interactions as well as for main effects. Since more than one dependent variable is present, however, multivariate F

statistics involve matrix algebra and examine the differences between all of the dependent variables simultaneously.

For the example in this chapter, the effects of students' section (SECTION) as well as whether they are upper or lower division (LOWUP) are examined in terms of their influence on students' scores on the five quizzes (QUIZ1 to QUIZ5). In addition to this, previous GPA (PREVGPA) will be used as a covariate; that is, the effects of PREVGPA on the dependent variables are removed before the MANOVA itself is performed.

THE LOGICAL PROGRESSION FOR COMPUTING MANOVA

1. Create file of data, or edit (if necessary) an already existing file.
2. Format file by use of **DATA LIST FILE**, **FORMATS**, and **VARIABLE** or **VALUE LABELS**; then save as a system file.
3. Access file and formats by the **GET FILE** command.
4. Use the **MANOVA** command to conduct a multivariate analysis of variance.
5. Use the **WITH** connector to specify covariates, if necessary.
6. Use the **PRINT CELLINFO** subcommand, if desired, to access means and correlations of the cells.
7. Use the **PRINT PARAMETERS** subcommand, if desired, to access parameter estimates.
8. Use the **PRINT SIGNIF** subcommand, if desired, to access univariate t-tests of the dependent variables and step-down F-tests of the dependent variables (using the dependent variables as covariates; see the Output section for more details).
9. View the results and exit the program.
10. Print data, commands, and output.

STEP BY STEP
Multivariate Analysis of Variance (MANOVA)

1) Name and create a data file (Chapter 2), or edit (if necessary) an already existing file (Chapter 3).

2) Name variables, locate column positions, format, create VARIABLE/VALUE LABELS, and then save the formatted DATA FILE as a SYSTEM FILE (Chapter 4).

From the DOS prompt, type:

3) dos > SPSSPC ↵   *This step gets you into the SPSS system.*

To clear the menu from the top window prior to analyzing data:

4) [ALT]─[M]	*Positions cursor to begin to create the command file.*

From the extreme upper left corner of the scratch pad (lower window), type:

5) **GET FILE** = '<u>GRADES</u>.**SYS**'.	1

LINE 1 Accesses the formatted **SYSTEM FILE** to begin to analyze data. All statistical procedures in this book will begin with the **GET FILE** step.

The following lines compute a multivariate analysis of variance (MANOVA) with the five quizzes (QUIZ1 to QUIZ5) as the dependent variables, and with the section number (SECTION) and status (lower- or upper-division) (LOWUP) as the independent variables.

6) **GET FILE** = '<u>GRADES</u>.**SYS**'.	1
MANOVA <u>QUIZ1</u> <u>QUIZ2</u> <u>QUIZ3</u> <u>QUIZ4</u> <u>QUIZ5</u> **BY** <u>SECTION(1,3)</u> <u>LOWUP(1,2)</u>.	2

LINE 1 The same as step 5, line 1 above.
LINE 2 After the **MANOVA** command, list all of the dependent variables that you want to include in the analysis. You may list as few as one (in which case, a univariate ANOVA will be computed) or as many as you wish. The independent variables come after the dependent variables; the word **BY** separates the independent and dependent variables. After each independent variable, list in parentheses the range of values of the independent variable to be analyzed; in this example, there are three sections (from 1 to 3) and two values of the division status variable (1 = lower-division and 2 = upper-division).

The following command file calculates a MANOVA, includes a covariate, and produces a number of additional statistics that are often useful. There are many more subcommands available with the MANOVA command, but we have included only the most frequently used options; see the SPSS/PC+ Advanced Statistics 4.0 Manual *for additional options.*

6a) **GET FILE** = '<u>GRADES</u>.**SYS**'.	1a
MANOVA <u>QUIZ1</u> <u>QUIZ2</u> <u>QUIZ3</u> <u>QUIZ4</u> <u>QUIZ5</u> **BY** <u>SECTION(1,3)</u> <u>LOWUP(1,2)</u>	
WITH <u>PREVGPA</u>/	2a
PRINT CELLINFO(MEANS COR) PARAMETERS(ESTIM)	
SIGNIF(UNIV STEPDOWN).	3a

LINE 1a The same as above.
LINE 2a The same as step 6, line 2 above except it includes the influence of a covariate, **PREVGPA**. This line ends with a slash instead of a period because there is a subcommand following.
LINE 3a Note first of all the mechanics of line 3a. Both lines 2a and 3a occupy more than one line. Standard procedure, if a line is too long, is to hit the return at a normal break and continue typing. If you want statistics that extend beyond those provided by the default, use the **PRINT** subcommand. Any or all of the following options may be used:

- **CELLINFO(MEANS COR)** produces means for each dependent measure in each of the cells, as well as correlations between the dependent measures for each of the cells (e.g., the correlations between the five quizzes for each of the six cells in the design). If you want *only* **MEANS** or **COR**relations, then you may list only the one that you wish.

- **PARAMETERS(ESTIM)** produces parameter estimates for each of the dependent variables. This output is similar to the basic output produced by discriminant analysis (see Chapter 23). If there is a significant difference between the dependent variables as predicted by the independent variables, then this information may be useful in interpreting exactly where those differences lie.

- **SIGNIF(UNIV)** produces univariate *F*-tests for each of the dependent variables. This output is often useful in interpreting exactly where a significant difference between two groups lies across several dependent measures. If this is the only additional information that you want besides the simple **MANOVA** command as listed in step 6 above, then you do not need to include it here; it will appear automatically. However, if you specify any **PRINT** subcommand options, then you should specify this option if you wish univariate *F*-tests.

- **SIGNIF(STEPDOWN)** produces a series of univariate *F* statistics for each of the dependent variables, in the order listed in the **MANOVA** command (line 2a above). For each dependent variable after the first, the previous dependent variables listed are included in the analysis as covariates. In our example, SPSS will first report a univariate *F* statistic of **QUIZ1**, followed by an *F* statistic of **QUIZ2** with **QUIZ1** as a covariate in the analysis, and so forth until SPSS reports an *F* statistic for **QUIZ5** with the effects of **QUIZ1** through **QUIZ4** covaried out. The order that the dependent variables appear in line 2a is important here; so unless you have a clear rationale for examining these statistics with the dependent variables in a particular order, don't try it.

Note: Many other subcommands and print options are available within SPSS. The SPSS manuals describe them fully, but they are beyond the scope of this book. If you do need to look at the manuals, however, two things that you are likely to need are **PRINT HOMOGENEITY(ALL)**, to produce tests for univariate and multivariate homogeneity of variance, and **PLOT NORMAL**, to produce normal and detrended normal plots. Both of these commands may be useful in exploring the homogeneity of variance among the various conditions, as well as in examining the normality of the data. Also, the **ANALYSIS** subcommand may be useful if you wish to test other designs than the full factorial model that we assume you want here; and the **DISCRIM** subcommand may be useful if you want to perform a discriminant analysis on your data without doing a separate procedure (see Chapter 23). Finally, the **RESIDUALS** subcommand is useful if you wish to examine in detail the residuals.

---

7) $\boxed{\text{F9}}$ $\boxed{\text{W}}$ $\boxed{\hookleftarrow}$ *to save your command file for future access.*

If file is not already named, enter the file name (e.g., **GRADES.CTL**) at the prompt between the W and the **ENTER**.

To run the program, first position cursor at the beginning of the GET FILE line, then:

---

8) $\boxed{\text{F10}}$ $\boxed{\text{C}}$ *to run your program from the cursor.*

After viewing the results:

9) F10 E FINISH ↵   *to exit to the DOS prompt.*

To print command files and results:

10) dos > PRINT SPSS.LIS ↵ ↵   *(Sometimes the second RETURN is not necessary.)*

OUTPUT
Multivariate Analysis of Variance (MANOVA):

The following OUTPUT is produced by this COMMAND FILE. INTERPRETATION follows each section of output.

```
GET FILE = 'GRADES.SYS'.
MANOVA QUIZ1 QUIZ2 QUIZ3 QUIZ4 QUIZ5 BY SECTION(1,3) LOWUP(1,2)
WITH PREVGPA/
PRINT CELLINFO(MEANS COR) PARAMETERS(ESTIM) SIGNIF(UNIV STEPDOWN).
```

Note: We abbreviated the following printout, since the complete printout takes 14 pages. Some of the sections of the report may not be present unless you specifically request them (using the **PRINT** subcommand). Because of this, we list each section of the report separately, along with its interpretation. The section labeled "General Interpretation" will be present in all reports. Because any given **PRINT** subcommand may spread its results throughout a printout, some of the sections are repeated in this output section, in order to match the order of the SPSS output.

CELL MEANS AND CORRELATIONS: **PRINT CELLINFO(MEANS COR)**

```
------------------------------------------------------------------------
               CELL NUMBER
Variable         1    2    3    4    5    6
  SECTION        1    1    2    2    3    3
  LOWUP          1    2    1    2    1    2
```

Cell Means and Standard Deviations
Variable .. QUIZ1

FACTOR	CODE	Mean	Std. Dev.	N
SECTION	1			
LOWUP	LOWER DIV	9.429	.976	7
LOWUP	UPPER DIV	7.846	2.493	26
SECTION	2			
LOWUP	LOWER DIV	5.455	2.115	11
LOWUP	UPPER DIV	8.143	1.779	28
SECTION	3			
LOWUP	LOWER DIV	8.000	1.633	4
LOWUP	UPPER DIV	6.690	2.892	29
For entire sample		7.467	2.481	105

(. . . more output of similar format occurs here)

Cell Number .. 2
Correlation matrix with Standard Deviations on Diagonal

	QUIZ1	QUIZ2	QUIZ3	QUIZ4	QUIZ5	PREVGPA
QUIZ1	2.493					
QUIZ2	.799	1.871				
QUIZ3	.861	.750	2.282			
QUIZ4	.871	.714	.834	2.240		
QUIZ5	.655	.763	.592	.631	1.917	
PREVGPA	.033	.168	-.046	.002	.112	.711

Determinant of Variance-Covariance matrix =   7.28270
LOG(Determinant) =   1.98550

(. . . more output of similar format occurs here)

        0 CELLs with only one observation.
        2 CELLs with singular Variance-Covariance matrix.

Determinant of pooled Variance-Covariance matrix   12.18914
LOG(Determinant) =   2.50055

Multivariate test for Homogeneity of Dispersion matrices
Boxs M =   79.30948
F WITH (63,5855) DF =   1.06604,   P = .338 (Approx.)
Chi-Square with 63 DF =   68.01355,   P = .311 (Approx.)

     SPSS numbers each cell in the design. At the beginning of the printout is a legend; this specifies what levels of each independent variable each cell number defines. This is important to know, because at times SPSS refers to a particular cell number rather than to the levels of the independent variables. Cell means and standard deviations (along with sample sizes) appear next for each of the dependent variables, as well as any covariates that may be present. We present only one of the dependent variables here, in order to conserve space.

     Following cell means are correlations for the dependent variables and the covariates. Correlation tables for the dependent variables and any covariates appear, broken down for each cell. Cells are numbered here (note the "Cell Number .. 2"). Refer to the legend at the beginning of the printout to learn what level of each independent variable each cell represents. These correlations are followed by the determinant and logarithm of the pooled variance-covariance matrix. Finally listed are tests for homogeneity of the dispersion matrices.

CORRELATION MATRICES: SPSS prints correlation matrices for each of the levels of the independent variable. MANOVA tests assume that these matrices are the same for each cell of the design. Note that standard deviations are printed on the diagonal elements.

DETERMINANT OF THE VARIANCE-COVARIANCE MATRIX: Not often used, the determinant provides an indication of how strong a relationship there is among the variables in the correlation matrix. The smaller the number, the more closely the variables are related to each other. Determinants are used primarily by the computer to compute the Box's *M* test (see last item in this terms list). The determinant of the pooled variance-covariance matrix refers to a composite of all the variance-covariance matrices present on the printout.

LOG(DETERMINANT): The natural log (ln) of the determinant. The computer uses this, but researchers rarely do.

CELLS WITH ONLY ONE OBSERVATION AND SINGULAR VARIANCE-COVARIANCE MATRICES: Any cells with only one observation or with singular variance-covariance matrices indicate that there may not be enough data to accurately compute MANOVA statistics, or that there may be other problems present in the data, such as linear dependencies (where one variable is dependent on one or more of the other variables). Results from any analysis with only one observation or with singular variance-covariance matrices for some cells should be interpreted with caution.

MULTIVARIATE TEST FOR HOMOGENEITY OF DISPERSION MATRICES: Box's *M* test examines whether the variance-covariance matrices are the same in all cells. To evaluate this test, SPSS calculates an *F* or χ^2 approximation for the *M*. These values, along with their associated *p*-values, appear in the printout. Significant *p*-values indicate *differences* between the variance-covariance matrices for the two groups. This test is very sensitive; so just because it detects differences between the variance-covariance matrices does not necessarily mean that the *F*-values are incorrect.

ANALYSIS INCLUDED WHEN COVARIATES ARE USED

```
--------------------------------------------------------------------------------

EFFECT .. WITHIN CELLS Regression
Multivariate Tests of Significance (S = 1, M = 1 1/2, N = 46 )
Test Name      Value    Approx. F   Hypoth. DF    Error DF   Sig. of F
  Pillais      .10003    2.08960         5.00       94.00       .073
  Hotellings   .11115    2.08960         5.00       94.00       .073
  Wilks        .89997    2.08960         5.00       94.00       .073
  Roys         .10003

Univariate F-tests with (1,98) D. F.
           Square                Adj                                      Sig
Variable  Mult R    Mult R      R-sq    Hypoth MS    Error MS       F     of F
  QUIZ1   .06579    .25650     .05626   35.09634     5.08536    6.90145   .010
  QUIZ2   .07824    .27971     .06883   19.79009     2.37913    8.31821   .005
  QUIZ3   .05953    .24398     .04993   28.02046     4.51747    6.20268   .014
  QUIZ4   .05897    .24283     .04936   28.64873     4.66528    6.14084   .015
  QUIZ5   .07010    .26477     .06061   19.17942     2.59606    7.38790   .008

--------------------------------------------------------------------------------
```

This section analyzes the effect of the covariate or covariates on the dependent measures.

MULTIVARIATE TESTS OF SIGNIFICANCE: Test Names and Values indicate several methods of testing for differences between the dependent variables due to the independent variables. Pillai's method is considered the best test by many, in terms of statistical power and robustness. In this case there are 5 hypothesis degrees of freedom (number of groups − 1) and 94 error degrees of freedom (sample size − number of groups − number of dependent variables).

PRINT SIGNIF(STEPDOWN) WITH A COVARIATE

```
--------------------------------------------------------------------------------

Roy-Bargmann Stepdown F-tests
Variable  Hypoth MS   Error MS   StpDown F   Hypoth DF   Error DF   Sig of F
  QUIZ1   35.09634    5.08536     6.90145        1          98        .010
  QUIZ2    3.40861    1.46034     2.33412        1          97        .130
  QUIZ3     .02637    1.34249      .01964        1          96        .889
  QUIZ4     .14109    1.54927      .09107        1          95        .763
  QUIZ5    1.77206    1.51092     1.17284        1          94        .282

--------------------------------------------------------------------------------
```

The Roy-Bargmann Stepdown F examines the effects of the covariate on each of the dependent variables. Note in this example that the effect of **PREVGPA** (the covariate) on **QUIZ1** (the first dependent variable listed in the **MANOVA** command) is the same here as it was on the previous table of univariate F-tests. For each succeeding dependent variable, however, the effects of all preceding dependent variables are removed; they have been covaried out. Thus the values presented for **QUIZ2** indicate the effect of **PREVGPA** on **QUIZ2**, with any common variance shared by **QUIZ1**, **QUIZ2**, and **PREVGPA** removed from the analysis. In effect, the values presented for **QUIZ2** examine any effects of previous GPA on the second quiz not already accounted for by the effect of previous GPA on **QUIZ1**. Likewise, for example, the values displayed for **QUIZ5** include any effects of previous GPA on **QUIZ5** not accounted for by **PREVGPA**'s correlations with **QUIZ1** through **QUIZ4**. The F-values in this printout are labeled "Stepdown F" to indicate that they refer to any new variance not accounted for by previous variables in the table.

ANALYSES INCLUDED WHEN COVARIATES ARE USED

```
----------------------------------------------------------------------------
Regression analysis for WITHIN CELLS error term
Dependent variable .. QUIZ1
COVARIATE    B    Beta   Std Err  t-Value  Sig of t  Lower -95% CL- Upper
 PREVGPA .7962  .2565     .303    2.627      .010      .195            1.398
----------------------------------------------------------------------------
```

Although we have shown only one dependent variable here, a printout like this will appear for each dependent variable. The ANOVA-like analysis of the effects of the covariates on each dependent variable was listed above; here, the regression analysis of the covariates on each dependent variable is listed.

B: The coefficient(s) for the covariate.

BETA: The standardized regression coefficients. This is the B-value for standardized scores (z-scores) of the variables.

STANDARD ERROR: A measure of the stability of the B-values. It is the standard deviation of the B-value given a large number of samples drawn from the same population.

t-VALUE: B divided by the standard error of B.

SIGNIFICANCE OF t: The probability that these t-values could occur by chance; the probability that B is not significantly different from zero.

LOWER AND UPPER 95% CONFIDENCE LIMITS (CL): Based on the B and the standard error, these values indicate that there is (in this example) a 95% chance that B is between .195 and 1.398.

GENERAL INTERPRETATION

```
----------------------------------------------------------------------------
EFFECT .. SECTION BY LOWUP
Multivariate Tests of Significance (S = 2, M = 1 , N = 46 )
Test Name        Value    Approx F   Hypoth DF   Error DF  Sig. of F
 Pillais         .23848    2.57229     10.00      190.00      .006
 Hotellings      .29250    2.72023     10.00      186.00      .004
 Wilks           .76838    2.64710     10.00      188.00      .005
 Roys            .20499
```

```
Univariate F-tests with (2,98) D. F.
Variable    Hypoth SS    Error SS    Hypoth MS   Error MS      F    Sig of F
  QUIZ1      75.51360    498.36530    37.75680    5.08536    7.42461    .001
  QUIZ2      10.87360    233.15444     5.43680    2.37913    2.28521    .107
  QUIZ3      45.39162    442.71243    22.69581    4.51747    5.02400    .008
  QUIZ4      35.52613    457.19715    17.76307    4.66528    3.80751    .026
  QUIZ5      36.27391    254.41382    18.13695    2.59606    6.98634    .001
```

This section prints, no matter what options you request. Information as presented here will be given for each main effect and interaction possible in your design, as well as for the constant (important statistically, but usually not meaningful in the interpretation). Here, we present the interaction effect of **SECTION** by **LOWUP**; a similar set of multivariate and univariate tables will be produced for each interaction and main effect.

MULTIVARIATE TESTS OF SIGNIFICANCE: Test names and values indicate several methods of testing for differences between the dependent variables due to the independent variables. Pillai's method is often considered to be one of the more robust tests.

APPROXIMATE F: Estimate of the *F*-value.

HYPOTHESIS DF: (Number of DV's − 1) × (Levels of **SECTION** − 1) × (Levels of **LOWUP** − 1).

ERROR DF: Calculated differently for different tests.

SIGNIFICANCE OF F: *p*-value for the *F*.

UNIVARIATE F-TESTS: For each of the dependent variables, SPSS does a simple *F*-test.

HYPOTHESIS SS: The between-groups sum of squares; the sum of squared deviations between the grand mean and each group mean, weighted (multiplied) by the number of subjects in each group.

ERROR SS: The within-groups sum of squares; the sum of squared deviations between the mean for each group and the observed values of each subject within that group.

HYPOTHESIS MS: Hypothesis sum of squares divided by hypothesis degrees of freedom.

ERROR MS: Error sum of squares divided by error degrees of freedom.

F: Hypothesis MS divided by the Error MS.

SIGNIFICANCE OF F: *p*-value for the *F*.

THE STEPDOWN F: *PRINT SIGNIF(STEPDOWN)*

```
Roy-Bargmann Stepdown F-tests
Variable    Hypoth MS   Error MS   StpDown F   Hypoth DF   Error DF   Sig of F
  QUIZ1      37.75680   5.08536    7.42461        2          98        .001
  QUIZ2        .10277   1.46034     .07038        2          97        .932
  QUIZ3        .11765   1.34249     .08764        2          96        .916
  QUIZ4        .85115   1.54927     .54939        2          95        .579
  QUIZ5       8.06777   1.51092    5.33964        2          94        .006
```

The Roy-Bargmann Stepdown *F* is printed below the multivariate and univariate tests of significance for each main effect and interaction. It examines the effects of the main effect or (in the example presented here) interaction on each of the dependent variables, with any covariates' effects on the dependent variable removed. Note in this example that the effect of **SECTION BY LOWUP** on **QUIZ1** (the first dependent variable listed in the **MANOVA** command) is the same here as it was on the previous table of univariate *F*-tests. For each succeeding dependent variable, however, the effects of all preceding dependent variables have been removed; their effects have been covaried out. Thus the values presented for QUIZ2 indicate the effect of SECTION BY LOWUP on QUIZ2, with any common variance shared by QUIZ1 and QUIZ2 removed from the analysis.

The *F*-values in this printout are labeled "Stepdown F" to indicate that they refer to any new variance not accounted for by previous variables in the table.

PARAMETER ESTIMATES: *PRINT PARAMETERS(ESTIM)*

```
-----------------------------------------------------------------------------
 Estimates for QUIZ1 adjusted for 1 covariate
Parameter          Coeff    Std Err    t-Value   Sig. t       Lower -95% CL- Upper
CONSTANT 1      5.29257859    .92244    5.73759    .000     3.46203         7.12313
SECTION   2     1.06489167    .40074    2.65733    .009      .26964         1.86014
          3     -.68958531    .37277   -1.84992    .067    -1.42933          .05016
LOWUP     4     -.07992215    .29252    -.27322    .785     -.66042          .50058
SECTION BY LOWUP
          5      .98314278    .40979    2.39915    .018      .16993         1.79635
          6    -1.33329180    .37100   -3.59380    .001    -2.06952         -.59706
-----------------------------------------------------------------------------
```

Parameter estimates help in the interpretation of the overall multivariate *F*. For each of the dependent variables, parameter estimates are produced that predict the means for the cells. Note that in this example (because the effects of PREVGPA have been removed by including PREVGPA as a covariate), the parameters will not sum to the actual cell means; rather, they will sum to the cell means after they have been adjusted for the covariate.

The parameters for any given main effect or interaction must sum to zero. SPSS does not print all of the possible estimates, but only enough estimates so that the other estimates not printed may be determined. To determine the mean of any particular cell in the design (adjusted for any covariates that may be present), you must sum the constant (parameter 1) plus certain other parameters. Since there are three class sections, SPSS produces *two* parameters for SECTION: The first (1.06), which is added to the constant for the first section; and the second (–.69), which is added to the constant for the second section. Because the parameters must sum to zero, the third section's parameter is –.37 (because 1.06 – .69 – .37 = 0). This indicates that the first section's scores are higher than the second and third sections' scores. Similarly, in examining the effects of being a lower-division student or an upper-division student, the value of .08 should be *subtracted* from the constant for lower-division students and *added* to the constant for upper-division students.

Calculating values for the interaction term is somewhat more involved; the computer produces only enough parameters to define the rest of the parameters; so the two interaction parameters produced in this example (.98 and –1.33) are the parameters for the lower-division Section 1 and lower-division Section 2 cells; the rest must be calculated as shown below. Note that the **bold** numbers are the parameters produced by the computer; the *italicized* numbers were calculated by making each row and column sum to zero:

LOWUP	Section 1	Section 2	Section 3	SUM
Lower division	**.98**	**−1.33**	*.35*	0
Upper division	*−.98*	*1.33*	*−.35*	0
SUM	0	0	0	0

In addition to the parameter estimates, SPSS produces the following output:

STANDARD ERROR: A measure of the dispersion of the coefficients.

t-VALUE: This t-value indicates the size of the parameter coefficient's effect. The constant's t-value will usually be large, unless the average of the means is near zero. The parameter associated with the independent variable should have a t-value identical to the univariate t associated with that parameter.

SIGNIFICANCE OF t: The p-value associated with the t-value.

LOWER AND UPPER 95% CONFIDENCE LIMITS: These values indicate the boundaries of the parameter coefficients.

The MANOVA Command:

Multivariate Analysis of Variance with Repeated Measures and Within-Subjects Factors

The previous two chapters have discussed designs with more than one dependent variable, and either one independent variable with two levels (multivariate T^2, Chapter 16) or multiple independent variables with two or more levels each (MANOVA and MANCOVA, Chapter 17). These analyses have all involved between-subjects designs, in which each subject is tested in only one level of the independent variable(s). There may be times, however, when a within-subjects design is more appropriate. Each subject is tested in more than one level of the independent variable or variables in a within-subjects or repeated-measures design.

This chapter will describe three different within-subjects procedures that MANOVA may compute. The first is a completely within-subjects design, in which each subject experiences every experimental condition and produces values for each cell in the design. Mixed-design analyses are then described, in which one or more of the independent variables are within subjects, and one or more are between subjects. This example also includes a covariate. Finally, doubly multivariate designs are discussed. Doubly multivariate designs are similar to standard within-subjects designs, except that there are multiple dependent variables tested within subjects.

The GRADES.SYS file is again the example. In this chapter, however—in order to demonstrate a within-subjects design—the meaning of QUIZ1 through QUIZ4 will be (perhaps somewhat capriciously) redefined. In particular, instead of being the scores on four different quizzes, QUIZ1 through QUIZ4 will refer to scores on the same quiz taken under four different conditions (or, alternatively, equivalent tests taken under four different conditions). These four conditions are based on a 2 (colors of paper) by 2 (colors of ink) within-subjects design. Students are given the same quiz (or equivalent quizzes) on either blue or red paper, printed in either green or black ink. This design produces the following combinations of paper colors and ink colors, with QUIZ1 through QUIZ4 assigned to each of the cells as noted:

	Ink Color	
Paper Color	**Green**	**Black**
Blue	Blue paper, Green ink QUIZ1	Blue paper, Black ink QUIZ2
Red	Red paper, Green ink QUIZ3	Red paper, Black ink QUIZ4

TRANSFORMED VARIABLES

Although the interpretation of within-subjects MANOVA is not conceptually very different from the interpretation of between-subjects MANOVA, there are several important differences in the way that SPSS handles within-subjects designs. In particular, SPSS does not like working with your *actual* within-subjects variables. Since what we are really interested in is the *differences* among the various dependent variables, SPSS converts the dependent variables that you specify into a *new* set of dependent variables upon which it performs the MANOVA calculations. SPSS handles most of these details automatically, but it is important to realize that the computer is really working with variables that it *derived* from your variables, rather than your variables *themselves*.

SPSS names these variables that it computes T1 through T-whatever, depending on how many conditions are in your design; in our 2 × 2 design, SPSS creates variables T1 through T4. SPSS does a reasonably good job of translating these variable names back to the original variable names, so you don't need to understand the computer's variables in order to identify main effects and interactions. However, in interpreting significant interactions and main effects with within-subjects MANOVA, it is sometimes necessary to understand how SPSS derived the variables that it works with. So SPSS produces a transformation matrix to help you interpret how (in our example) T1 through T4 relate to QUIZ1 through QUIZ4. In this example, the transformation matrix looks something like this:

	Computer's variable name			
Your variable name	T1	T2	T3	T4
QUIZ1	.500	.500	.500	.500
QUIZ2	.500	.500	-.500	-.500
QUIZ3	.500	-.500	.500	-.500
QUIZ4	.500	-.500	-.500	.500

The numbers produced in the transformation matrix won't always be nice round ones like the .500's present in this table, but the basic method of interpretation is similar no matter what the numbers are. In this case, you will notice that:

$$\text{T1} = .500 \times \text{QUIZ1} + .500 \times \text{QUIZ2} + .500 \times \text{QUIZ3} + .500 \times \text{QUIZ4}$$

The exact numbers are not important in interpreting the meaning of **T1**; what is important is that each of the four variables **QUIZ1** through **QUIZ4** are added together to make the computer's new variable **T1**. So, **T1** may be interpreted as the constant effect of **QUIZ1** through **QUIZ4**. **T2** is computed by adding **QUIZ1** and **QUIZ2**, and subtracting **QUIZ3** and **QUIZ4**; this is the difference between the mean of blue paper and the mean of red paper. **T2**, therefore, is a test of the main effect of paper color. **T3** is computed by adding **QUIZ1** and **QUIZ3**, and subtracting **QUIZ2** and **QUIZ4**; this is the difference between the mean of green ink and the mean of black ink. So, **T3** is a test of the main effect of ink color. **T4** examines the paper color by ink color interaction.

LOGICAL PROGRESSION FOR COMPUTING WITHIN-SUBJECTS MANOVA

1. Create file of data, or edit (if necessary) an already existing file.
2. Format file by use of **DATA LIST FILE, FORMATS,** and **VARIABLE** or **VALUE LABELS**; then save as a system file.
3. Access file and formats by the **GET FILE** command.
4. Use the **COMPUTE** command, if needed, to prepare for the use of a covariate.
5. Use the **MANOVA** command to conduct multivariate analysis of variance.
6. Specify between-subjects independent variables, if necessary.
7. Specify covariates, if necessary.
8. Use the **WSFACTORS** subcommand to specify the within-subjects variables.
9. Use the **MEASURE** subcommand to specify doubly multivariate analyses, if applicable.
10. Use the **PRINT CELLINFO** subcommand, if desired, to access means and correlations of the cells.
11. Use the **PRINT SIGNIF** subcommand, if desired, to access univariate t-tests of the dependent variables.
12. Use the **PRINT TRANSFORM** subcommand to print a transformation matrix.
13. View the results and exit the program.
14. Print data, commands, and output.

STEP BY STEP
Within-Subjects MANOVA

> 1) *Name and create a data file (Chapter 2), or edit (if necessary) an already existing file (Chapter 3).*

> 2) *Name variables, locate column positions, format, create VARIABLE/VALUE LABELS, and then save the formatted DATA FILE as a SYSTEM FILE (Chapter 4).*

From the DOS prompt, type:

> 3) *dos* > **SPSSPC** $\boxed{\leftarrow}$ *This step gets you into the SPSS system.*

To clear the menu from the top window prior to analyzing data:

> 4) $\boxed{\text{ALT}}$-$\boxed{\text{M}}$ *Positions cursor to begin to create the command file.*

From the extreme upper left corner of the scratch pad (lower window), type:

> 5) **GET FILE = 'GRADES.SYS'.**   *1*

LINE 1 Accesses the formatted SYSTEM FILE to begin to analyze data. All statistical procedures in this book will begin with the GET FILE step.

This command instructs SPSS to perform a 2 (color of paper) × 2 (color of ink) within-subjects analysis of variance, with QUIZ1 through QUIZ4 referring to the cells of the model as presented in the table in the introductory section of this chapter.

> 6) **GET FILE = 'GRADES.SYS'.**   *1*
> **MANOVA QUIZ1 QUIZ2 QUIZ3 QUIZ4/**   *2*
> **WSFACTORS PAPERCOL(2) INKCOLOR(2)/**   *3*
> **PRINT CELLINFO(MEANS COR) TRANSFORM.**   *4*

LINE 1 The same as step 5, line 1 above.

LINE 2 MANOVA is the command used to conduct within-subjects analysis of variance. After the MANOVA command, list all of the dependent variables used in the design (one for each cell).

LINE 3 The WSFACTORS subcommand informs SPSS what the independent variables are in your design. These are *not* names of variables that currently exist; they are *new* variable names that will only be used by the MANOVA command. In this case, we have defined the two independent variables as PAPERCOL (the color of the paper on which the quiz was printed) and INKCOLOR (the color of the ink with which the quiz was printed). The numbers in parentheses refer to the number of levels of each independent variable (in this case, there are two paper colors, and two ink colors). Variables listed later in the WSFACTORS subcommand should be the ones that change most rapidly in the list of variables in line 2. By way of explanation, observe the chart that follows:

Quiz number	Paper color	Ink color
1	blue	green
2	blue	black
3	red	green
4	red	black

Note that the ink color changes more rapidly than paper color as we move from **QUIZ1** to **QUIZ4**. Thus the ink color variable (**INKCOLOR**) will go last in the **WSFACTORS** line, and the slower-changing variable (**PAPERCOL**) will come earlier. We demonstrate with only two variables with two levels each, but the same rationale applies with a greater number of variables that have more than two levels.

LINE **4 PRINT** instructs SPSS to produce additional output. **CELLINFO(MEANS COR)** produces means for each dependent measure, as well as correlations between the dependent measures. If you wish only **MEANS** or **COR**relations, then you may list only the one that you want. **TRANSFORM** produces a transformation matrix; this may be useful in interpreting the output.

Step 6a illustrates a mixed design, in which some of the factors are within-subjects and some are between-subjects. In this case, a 2 (ink color) × 2 (gender of subject) MANOVA is performed, using previous GPA as a covariate.

```
6a)  GET FILE = 'GRADES.SYS'.                                          1a
     COMPUTE PGPA1 = PREVGPA.                                          2a
     COMPUTE PGPA2 = PREVGPA.                                          3a
     MANOVA QUIZ1 QUIZ2 BY GENDER (1,2) WITH PGPA1 PGPA2/             4a
     WSFACTORS INKCOLOR(2)/                                            5a
     PRINT CELLINFO(MEANS COR) TRANSFORM.                              6a
```

LINE **1a** The same as above.

LINES **2a-3a** If you are using a covariate in a within-subjects design, there must be a separate covariate variable name for each within-subjects cell. In our example, this indicates that there must be a separate covariate for **QUIZ1** and **QUIZ2**. Since we really want the *same* covariate for each cell, these **COMPUTE** commands create new variables (labeled **PGPA1** and **PGPA2**), both equal to **PREVGPA**, used as covariates for **QUIZ1** and **QUIZ2**.

LINE **4a MANOVA** is the command used to conduct within-subjects analysis of variance. After the **MANOVA** command, list all of the dependent variables used in the design (one for each within-subjects cell). The between-subjects independent variable(s) are listed after the word **BY**; the numbers in parentheses refer to the lowest and highest values that the independent variable may take (in this case, **GENDER** may range from 1 = female to 2 = male). Include any covariates after the word **WITH**; there must be one covariate for each level of the within-subjects factor(s). If you want to use the same covariate in each level (as we do here), create new variables as illustrated in lines 2a and 3a above.

LINE **5a** The **WSFACTORS** subcommand informs SPSS what the within-subjects independent variables are in your design. These are *not* names of variables that currently exist; they are *new* variable names that will be used only by the **MANOVA** command. In this case, we have defined the within-subjects independent variable as **INKCOLOR** (the color of the ink with which the quiz was printed). The number in parentheses refers to the number of levels of the independent variable. As described under sequence step 6, line 3, variables listed later in the **WSFACTORS** subcommand should be the ones that change most rapidly in the list of dependent variables.

LINE **6a PRINT** instructs SPSS to produce additional output. **CELLINFO(MEANS COR)** produces means for each dependent measure, as well as correlations between the dependent measures. If you want only **MEANS** or **COR**relations, then you may list only the one that you want. **TRANSFORM** produces a transformation matrix; this may be useful in interpreting the output.

Step 6b illustrates a doubly multivariate design, in which there are two or more dependent variables measured in different levels of one or more within-subjects factors. In this example, QUIZ1 and QUIZ2 are short-answer quizzes, and QUIZ3 and QUIZ4 are multiple-choice quizzes. QUIZ1 and QUIZ3 were taken in the green-ink color condition, and QUIZ2 and QUIZ4 were taken in the black-ink color condition.

```
6b) GET FILE = 'GRADES.SYS'.                                          1b
    MANOVA QUIZ1 QUIZ2 QUIZ3 QUIZ4/                                   2b
    WSFACTORS INKCOLOR(2)/                                            3b
    MEASURE ESSAY MC/                                                 4b
    PRINT CELLINFO(MEANS) SIGNIF(UNIV) TRANSFORM.                     5b
```

LINE **1b** The same as above.

LINE **2b** After the **MANOVA** command, list all of the dependent variables used in the design (for each within-subjects cell and each dependent variable). Group the dependent measures first and then group the variables by the conditions of the within-subjects independent variables.

LINE **3b** The **WSFACTORS** subcommand informs SPSS what the independent variables are in your design. These are *not* names of variables that currently exist; they are *new* variable names that will be used only by the **MANOVA** command. In this case, we have defined the within-subjects independent variable as **INKCOLOR** (the color of the ink with which the quiz was printed). The number in parentheses refers to the number of levels of the independent variable. As mentioned in sequence step 6, line 3, variables listed later in the **WSFACTORS** subcommand should be the ones that change most rapidly in the list of dependent variables.

LINE **4b** The **MEASURE** subcommand labels each of the dependent variables listed in line 2b. In this case, **QUIZ1** and **QUIZ2** refer to essay quizzes, and **QUIZ3** and **QUIZ4** are multiple-choice quizzes. SPSS doesn't do a very good job of labeling your output based on this subcommand, but it is useful to help you keep track of what SPSS is doing.

LINE **5b** **PRINT** instructs SPSS to produce additional output. **CELLINFO(MEANS COR)** produces means for each dependent measure, as well as correlations between the dependent measures. If you want only **MEANS** or **COR**relations, then you may list only the one that you want. **SIGNIF(UNIV)** produces univariate *F*-tests for each of the dependent variables; these, along with the transformation matrix produced by **TRANSFORM,** may be useful in interpreting the output.

```
7)  F9  W  ↵          to save your command file for future access.
```

If file is not already named, enter the file name (e.g., **GRADES.CTL**) at the prompt between the W and the **ENTER**.

To run the program, first position cursor at the beginning of the GET FILE line, then:

```
8)  F10  C           to run your program from the cursor.
```

After viewing the results:

9) F10 E **FINISH** ↵   *to exit to the DOS prompt.*

To print command files and results:

10) *dos* > **PRINT SPSS.LIS** ↵ ↵   *(Sometimes the second RETURN is not necessary.)*

OUTPUT
Within-Subjects MANOVA

Most of the output from MANOVA using within-subjects design is similar to the output for between-subjects designs (Chapter 17); so in order to conserve space, we present only representative portions of the complete output here, including all of the essential output and focusing on material that is unique to within-subjects designs.

Also, because there are three example analyses done in this chapter, we use subheadings to distinguish among the three types of analyses demonstrated: Within-subjects designs (step 6), mixed designs (step 6a), and doubly multivariate designs (step 6b). Output from the within-subjects example (step 6) will always be given, and output from the other two examples will be included only if it differs noticeably in content or interpretation from the within-subjects design.

COMMAND FILES

Within-Subjects Designs (step 6)

```
GET FILE = 'GRADES.SYS'.
MANOVA QUIZ1 QUIZ2 QUIZ3 QUIZ4/
WSFACTORS PAPERCOL(2) INKCOLOR(2)/
PRINT CELLINFO(MEANS COR) TRANSFORM.
```

Mixed Designs (step 6a)

```
GET FILE = 'GRADES.SYS'.
COMPUTE PGPA1 = PREVGPA.
COMPUTE PGPA2 = PREVGPA.
MANOVA QUIZ1 QUIZ2 BY GENDER (1,2) WITH PGPA1 PGPA2/
WSFACTORS INKCOLOR(2)/
PRINT CELLINFO(MEANS COR) TRANSFORM.
```

Doubly Multivariate Designs (step 6b)

```
GET FILE = 'GRADES.SYS'.
MANOVA QUIZ1 QUIZ2 QUIZ3 QUIZ4/
WSFACTORS INKCOLOR(2)/
MEASURE ESSAY MC/
PRINT CELLINFO(MEANS COR) SIGNIF(UNIV) TRANSFORM.
```

CELL MEANS AND CORRELATIONS: **PRINT CELLINFO(MEANS COR)**

Within-Subjects Designs (step 6)

Variable	Mean	Std Dev	N
QUIZ1	7.467	2.481	105
QUIZ2	7.981	1.623	105
QUIZ3	7.981	2.308	105
QUIZ4	7.800	2.280	105

Means, standard deviations, and sample sizes are presented for each condition in the design. If between-subjects factors are present, then SPSS will print each within-subjects condition's means for each between-subjects condition. Note that correlations are not printed for purely within-subjects designs.

The interpretation of the correlation matrices is identical to those presented in Chapter 17, with one exception: If you are using covariates, then the correlation matrices may be singular without necessarily producing any problems in the MANOVA interpretation.

TRANSFORMATION MATRICES

In analyzing within-subjects designs, SPSS converts your variables into new variables that it uses to analyze the data. These new variables are linear combinations of your variables; the transformation matrix provides a record of how SPSS computed the new variables from your variables. This may be useful in interpreting main effects and interactions.

Within-Subjects Designs (step 6)

```
Orthonormalized Transformation Matrix (Transposed)
              T1        T2        T3        T4
QUIZ1        .500      .500      .500      .500
QUIZ2        .500      .500     -.500     -.500
QUIZ3        .500     -.500      .500     -.500
QUIZ4        .500     -.500     -.500      .500
```

Each of the four variables **QUIZ1** through **QUIZ4** is added together to make the computer's new variable **T1**: **T1** = .5(**QUIZ1**) + .5(**QUIZ2**) + .5(**QUIZ3**) + .5(**QUIZ4**). Thus, **T1** may be interpreted as the constant effect of **QUIZ1** through **QUIZ4**. Any test that is labeled as testing **T1** will examine whether the sum of **QUIZ1** through **QUIZ4** is not equal to zero. **T2** is computed by adding **QUIZ1** and **QUIZ2**, and subtracting **QUIZ3** and **QUIZ4**. This is the difference between the mean of blue paper and the mean of red paper. **T2**, therefore, is a test of the main effect of paper color. **T3** is computed by adding **QUIZ1** and **QUIZ3**, and subtracting **QUIZ2** and **QUIZ4**. This is the difference between the mean of green ink and the mean of black ink. So, **T3** is a test of the main effect of ink color. **T4** = .5(**QUIZ1**) − .5(**QUIZ2**) − .5(**QUIZ3**) + .5(**QUIZ4**); this examines the paper color × ink color interaction.

Mixed-Subjects Designs (step 6a)

```
-------------------------------------------------------------------------
Orthonormalized Transformation Matrix (Transposed)
                   T1           T2           T3           T4
QUIZ1            .707         .707         .000         .000
QUIZ2            .707        -.707         .000         .000
PGPA1           .000         .000         .707         .707
PGPA2           .000         .000         .707        -.707
-------------------------------------------------------------------------
```

In this case, **T1** = **QUIZ1** + **QUIZ2**; so **T1** is the constant effect. **T2** = **QUIZ1** − **QUIZ2**; as a difference score, **T2** tests for a main effect of ink color. **T3** is the sum of **PGPA1** + **PGPA2** (just as a reminder, **PGPA1** and **PGPA2** are identical values used as covariates for **QUIZ1** and **QUIZ2**); this variable is used in analyzing the previous GPA covariate. **T4** = **PGPA1** − **PGPA2**; however, since they are identical, **T4** = 0. **T4** is not used in the analysis for this reason.

Doubly Multivariate Designs (step 6b)

```
-------------------------------------------------------------------------
Orthonormalized Transformation Matrix (Transposed)
                   T1           T2           T3           T4
QUIZ1            .707         .707         .000         .000
QUIZ2            .707        -.707         .000         .000
QUIZ3           .000         .000         .707         .707
QUIZ4           .000         .000         .707        -.707
-------------------------------------------------------------------------
```

Since this doubly multivariate design consists of two dependent variables (**QUIZ1** and **QUIZ2** representing scores on an essay quiz and **QUIZ3** and **QUIZ4** representing scores on a multiple-choice quiz), **T1** and **T3** are constant effects of the essay and multiple-choice variables, respectively. **T2** is the effect of ink color on the essay quizzes, and **T4** is the effect of ink color on the multiple-choice quizzes.

MAIN EFFECTS AND INTERACTIONS

Within-Subjects Designs (step 6)

```
-------------------------------------------------------------------------
  Note..  TRANSFORMED variables are in the varieties column.
          These TRANSFORMED variables correspond to the
          'PAPERCOL BY INKCOLOR' WITHIN-SUBJECT effect.

Tests involving 'PAPERCOL BY INKCOLOR' Within-Subject Effect.
 Tests of Significance for T4 using UNIQUE sums of squares
```

Source of Variation	SS	DF	MS	F	Sig of F
WITHIN CELLS	144.06	104	1.39		
PAPERCOL BY INKCOLOR	12.69	1	12.69	9.16	.003

```
-------------------------------------------------------------------------
```

SPSS will present information similar to that given here for each main effect and interaction possible in your design, as well as for the constant (important statistically, but usually not meaningful in the interpretation). Here, we present the interaction effect of paper color by ink color. Since the interaction is significant ($p = .003$), the means of the cells must be examined to interpret the interaction effect, either by examining the means themselves, or by performing additional t-tests. In this case the means demonstrate an interaction shown in the figure below: Black ink produces higher quiz scores than green ink, when the quiz is printed on blue paper; however, green ink produces higher quiz scores than black ink when the quiz is printed on red paper.

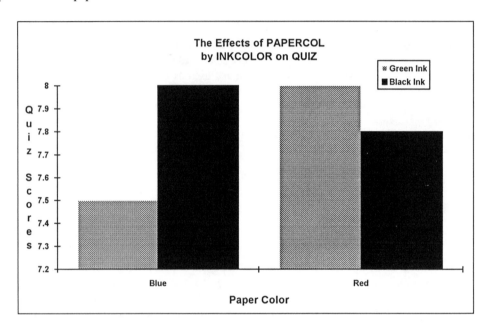

NOTE..: The note SPSS produces is to remind you that the computer is actually testing variables created as linear combinations from your variables. SPSS prints both the test being performed in terms of your variable names (in this case, the **PAPERCOL** by **INKCOLOR** interaction) and as the transformed variable that is being tested. In this example, the test of **T4** is presented to examine the interaction effect.

PAPER COLOR BY INKCOLOR SS: The between-groups sum of squares; the sum of squared deviations between the grand mean and each group mean, weighted (multiplied) by the number of subjects in each group.

WITHIN-CELLS SS: The within-groups sum of squares; the sum of squared deviations between the mean for each group and the observed values of each subject within that group.

PAPERCOL BY INKCOLOR DF: (Number of levels in independent variable #1 − 1) × (Number of levels in independent variable #2 − 1), etc.

WITHIN CELLS DF: Sample size − hypothesis degrees of freedom − 1.

PAPERCOL BY INKCOLOR MS: Hypothesis sum of squares divided by hypothesis degrees of freedom. Since there is only 1 degree of freedom for the hypothesis, this value is the same as the hypothesis sum of squares.

WITHIN CELLS MS: Within-cells sum of squares divided by within-cells degrees of freedom.

F: Hypothesis MS divided by error MS.

SIGNIFICANCE OF F: p-value for the F.

Mixed-Subjects Designs (step 6a)

```
-------------------------------------------------------------------------
Tests of Between-Subjects Effects.
 Tests of Significance for T1 using UNIQUE sums of squares

   Source of Variation         SS      DF      MS      F   Sig of F
   WITHIN CELLS             680.55    102     6.67
   REGRESSION                53.08      1    53.08    7.96    .006
   CONSTANT                 489.80      1   489.80   73.41    .000
   GENDER                      .74      1      .74     .11    .740


 Regression analysis for WITHIN CELLS error term
 Dependent variable .. T1


 COVARIATE    B    Beta   Std Err  t-Value  Sig of t  Lower -95%  CL- Upper
 T3        .6742  .2690     .239    2.821     .006     .195              1.148
-------------------------------------------------------------------------
```

Most of the interpretation of mixed-subjects designs is the same as the interpretation of within-subjects designs. The between-subjects effects are listed together, along with the effects of any covariates. The REGRESSION *Source of Variation* refers to the effects of the covariates on the dependent variables. A regression analysis is included that (in this example) indicates the effects of **T3** (the previous GPA) on **T1** (the scores on QUIZ1 and QUIZ2). Interpretation of the *Source of Variation* table is the same as for within-subjects designs (above). The interpretation of the regression analysis follows.

B: The coefficient(s) for the covariate for each dependent variable.

BETA: The standardized regression coefficients. This is the *B*-value for standardized scores (*z*-scores) of the variables.

STANDARD ERROR: A measure of the stability of the *B*-values. It is the standard deviation of the *B*-value given a large number of samples drawn from the same population.

t-VALUE: *B* divided by the standard error of *B*.

SIGNIFICANCE OF T: The probability that these *t*-values could occur by chance; the probability that the covariate's effects are equal to zero.

LOWER AND UPPER 95% CONFIDENCE LIMITS (CL): Based on the *B* and the standard error, these values indicate that there is (in this example) a 95% chance that *B* is between .195 and 1.148.

Note: If you are using covariates, SPSS will probably produce a warning that looks something like this:

```
-------------------------------------------------------------------------
* W A R N I N G  * For WITHIN CELLS error matrix, these covariates
*                 * appear LINEARLY DEPENDENT on preceding
*                 * variables ...
                         T4
                  1 D.F. will be returned to this error term.
-------------------------------------------------------------------------
```

As long as you are using a covariate, this message may be ignored.

Doubly Multivariate Designs (step 6b)

```
-------------------------------------------------------------------------
Tests involving 'INKCOLOR' Within-Subject Effect.

Mauchly sphericity test, W =          .95125
Chi-Square approx. =                  5.14785 with 2 D. F.
Significance =                         .076

Greenhouse-Geisser Epsilon =          .95352
Huynh-Feldt Epsilon =                 .97087
Lower-bound Epsilon =                 .50000

EFFECT .. INKCOLOR
Multivariate Tests of Significance (S = 1, M = 0, N = 50 1/2)

Test Name        Value   Approx. F  Hypoth DF   Error DF  Sig. of F
Pillais         .08623    4.86001       2.00     103.00       .010

Univariate F-tests with (1,104) D. F.

Variable  Hypoth SS   Error SS   Hypoth MS   Error MS     F     Sig. of F
T2        13.88571   175.11429   13.88571   1.68379   8.24670      .005
T4         1.71905   111.78095    1.71905   1.07482   1.59939      .209
-------------------------------------------------------------------------
```

MAUCHLY'S SPHERICITY TEST is a test of multivariate normality. SPSS computes a χ^2 approximation for this test, along with its significance level. If the significance level associated with Mauchly's sphericity test is small (i.e., $p < .05$) then the data may not be spherically distributed. This may indicate that assumptions of spherically distributed data are being violated. On the other hand, it may be that the data is fine, because the test is very sensitive for large samples.

If assumptions of sphericity are violated, then you may wish to adjust the degrees of freedom for the multivariate tests of significance by multiplying them by GREENHOUSE-GEISSER'S EPSILON (multiply both degrees of freedom, and look up the F-value in a table with the new degrees of freedom). The Greenhouse-Geisser's Epsilon is an attempt to adjust the F-value when the assumptions of sphericity are not met. The HUYNH-FELDT EPSILON is a refinement of the Greenhouse-Geisser epsilon, since Greenhouse-Geisser may adjust the degrees of freedom too much when you are working with small samples. In this example, the assumptions are not violated ($p > .05$); so no adjustments need to be made.

MULTIVARIATE TESTS OF SIGNIFICANCE: Results from the INKCOLOR effect are analyzed. Test names and values indicate several methods of testing for differences between the dependent variables due to the independent variable. Pillai's test is one of the most common and is the only one we report in our example (to conserve space).

APPROXIMATE F: Estimate of the F-value.

SIGNIFICANCE OF F: p-value for the F.

UNIVARIATE F-TESTS: For each of the dependent variables, SPSS does a simple (univariate) F-test. Note that the dependent variables presented here refer to the transformed variables used by SPSS, rather than your variables; in this case, T2 refers to the effect of the essay quizzes, and T4 refers to the effect of the multiple-choice quizzes.

HYPOTHESIS MS: The between-groups sum of squares; the sum of squared deviations between the grand mean and each group mean, weighted (multiplied) by the number of subjects in each group.

ERROR SS: The within-groups sum of squares; the sum of squared deviations between the mean for each group and the observed values of each subject within that group.

HYPOTHESIS MS: Hypothesis sum of squares divided by hypothesis degrees of freedom. Since there is only one degree of freedom for the hypothesis, this value is the same as hypothesis sum of squares.

ERROR MS: Error sum of squares divided by error degrees of freedom.

F: Hypothesis MS divided by Error MS.

SIGNIFICANCE OF F: *p*-value for the *F*.

Chapter 19

The REGRESSION Command:

Simple Linear Regression and Curvilinear Regression

The **REGRESSION** command is designed to do either simple regression (Chapter 19) or multiple regression (Chapter 20). We split the command into two chapters largely for the sake of clarity. If the reader is unacquainted with *multiple* regression, this chapter, on simple regression, will serve as an introduction. Several things will be covered in the introductory portion of this chapter: (a) the concept of predicted values and the regression equation, (b) the relationship between bivariate correlation and simple regression, (c) the proportion of variance explained in one variable by another, (d) a test for curvilinear relationships, and (e) the logical progression for conducting simple or curvilinear regression.

Several words of caution are appropriate here: First, a number of thick volumes have been written on regression analysis. We are in no way attempting in a few pages to duplicate those efforts. The introductions of these two chapters are designed to give only an overview and a conceptual feel for the regression procedure. Second, in this chapter (and Chapter 20) we are describing how to conduct regression that considers curvilinear tendencies in the data, in addition to the standard linear relationships. We suggest that those less acquainted with regression spend the time to thoroughly understand *linear* regression before attempting the much less frequently used tests for curvilinear trends.

PREDICTED VALUES AND THE REGRESSION EQUATION

There are many times when, given information about one characteristic of a particular phenomenon, we have some idea as to the nature of another characteristic. Consider the height and weight of adult humans. If we know that a person is 7 feet (214 cm) tall, we would suspect (with a fair degree of certainty) that this person probably weighs more than 200 pounds (91 kg). If a person is 4 feet 6 inches (137 cm) tall, we would suspect that such a person would weigh less than 100 pounds (45 kg). There is a wide variety of phenomena in which, given information about one variable, we have some clues about characteristics of another: IQ and academic success, oxygen uptake and ability to run a fast mile, percentage of fast-twitch muscle fibers and speed in a 100-

meter race, type of automobile one owns and monetary net worth, average daily caloric intake and body weight, feelings of sympathy toward a needy person and likelihood of helping that person. Throughout a lifetime humans make thousands of such inferences (e.g., he's fat, he must eat a lot). Sometimes our inferences are correct, other times not. Simple regression is designed to help us come to more accurate inferences. It cannot guarantee that our inferences are accurate or correct, but it can determine the likelihood or probability that our inferences are sound; and given a value for one variable, it can predict the most likely value for the other variable based on available information.

To illustrate regression, we will introduce our example at this time. While it would be possible to use the **GRADES.SYS** file to illustrate simple regression (e.g. the influence of previous GPA on final points), we have chosen to create a new data set that is able to demonstrate both linear regression and curvilinear regression. The new file is called **ANXIETY.SYS** and consists of a data set in which 73 students are measured on their level of pre-exam anxiety on a *none*(1) to *severe*(10) scale, and then measured on a 100-point exam. The hypothesis for a linear relationship might be that those with very low anxiety will do poorly because they don't care much and that those with high anxiety will do better because they are motivated to spend more time in preparation. The dependent (criterion) variable is **EXAM**, and the independent (predictor) variable is **ANXIETY**. In other words we are attempting to predict the exam score from the anxiety score. Among other things that regression accomplishes, it is able to create a *regression equation* to calculate a person's *predicted* score on the exam based on his or her anxiety score. The regression equation follows the model of the general equation designed to predict a student's *true* or actual score.

$$\text{EXAM}_{(true)} = \text{some CONSTANT} + \text{a coefficient} \times \text{ANXIETY} + \text{RESIDUAL}$$

That is, the true **EXAM** score is equal to a **CONSTANT** plus some weighted number (coefficient) times the **ANXIETY** score plus the **RESIDUAL**. The inclusion of the **RESIDUAL** term is to acknowledge that *predicted* values in the social sciences are almost never exactly correct and that to acquire a *true* value requires the inclusion of a term that adjusts for the discrepancy between the predicted score and the actual score. This difference is called the *residual*. For instance, the equation based on our data set (with constant and coefficient generated by the regression procedure) follows:

$$\text{EXAM}_{(true)} = 64.247 + 2.818(\text{ANXIETY}) + \text{RESIDUAL}$$

To demonstrate the use of the equation, we will insert the anxiety value for subject #24, who scored 6.5 on the anxiety scale.

$$\text{EXAM}_{(true)} = 64.247 + 2.818(\textbf{6.5}) + \text{RESIDUAL}$$

$$\text{EXAM}_{(true)} = 82.56 + \text{RESIDUAL}$$

The 82.56 is the student's *predicted* score based on his 6.5 anxiety score. We know that the actual exam score for subject 24 was 94. We can now determine the value of the **RESIDUAL** (how far off our predicted value was), but we can do this only *after* we know the true value of the dependent variable (**EXAM** in this case). The residual is simply the true value minus the predicted value (94 − 82.56), or 11.44. The equation with all values inserted now looks like this:

$$94 = 82.56 + 11.44$$

We have included a brief description of the residual term because you will see it so frequently in the study of statistics, but we now turn our attention to the issue of predicted values based on a calculated regression equation. We will return to the issue of residuals later. The regression equation for the predicted value of **EXAM** is:

$$\text{EXAM}_{(\text{predicted})} = 64.247 + 2.818(\text{ANXIETY})$$

To demonstrate computation, subjects 2, 43, and 72 scored 1.5, 7.0, and 9.0 anxiety points, respectively. Computation of the predicted scores for each of the three follows. Following the predicted value is the actual score achieved by the three subjects (in parentheses), to demonstrate how well (or poorly) the equation was able to predict the true scores:

Subject 2: $\text{EXAM}_{(\text{predicted})} = 64.247 + 2.818(\textbf{1.5}) = \textbf{68.47}$ (actual score was 52)
Subject 43: $\text{EXAM}_{(\text{predicted})} = 64.247 + 2.818(\textbf{7.0}) = \textbf{83.97}$ (actual score was 87)
Subject 72: $\text{EXAM}_{(\text{predicted})} = 64.247 + 2.818(\textbf{9.0}) = \textbf{89.61}$ (actual score was 71)

We notice that for subject 2, the predicted value was much too high (68.47 vs. 52); for subject 43, the predicted value was quite close to the actual score (83.97 vs. 87); and for subject 72, the predicted value was also much too high (89.61 vs. 71). From this limited observation we might conclude that the ability of our equation to predict values is pretty good for midrange **ANXIETY** scores, but much poorer at the extremes. Or, we may conclude that there are factors other than a measure of the subject's pre-exam anxiety that influence his or her exam score. The issue of *several* factors influencing a variable of interest will be addressed in the next chapter.

SIMPLE REGRESSION, CORRELATION, AND AMOUNT OF VARIANCE EXPLAINED

We are not left at the mercy of our intuition to determine whether or not a regression equation is able to do a good job of predicting scores. The output generated by the **REGRESSION** command calculates four different values that are of particular interest to the researcher:

1. SPSS generates a score that measures the strength of relationship between the dependent variable (**EXAM**) and the independent variable (**ANXIETY**). This score is designated with a capital R and is simply our old friend, the bivariate correlation (r).

The capital R is used (rather than a lower case r) because the REGRESSION command is usually used to compute *multiple* correlations (that is, the strength of relationship between several independent variables and a single dependent variable). For a description of correlation, please refer to Chapter 11.

2. Along with the computation of R, SPSS prints out a probability value (p) associated with R to indicate the significance of that association. Once again, a $p < .05$ is generally interpreted as indicating a statistically significant correlation. If $p > .05$, the strength of association between the two variables is usually not considered statistically significant; or the relationship between the two constructs is considered weak.

3. R square (or R^2) is simply the square of R, but it has special significance. The R^2 value is the proportion of variance in one variable accounted for (or explained) by the other variable. For the relationship between ANXIETY and EXAM, SPSS calculated values of $R = .48794$ ($p < .0001$) and $R^2 = .23808$. The R square value indicates that 23.8% of the variance in the EXAM score is accounted for by pretest ANXIETY. The standard disclaimers must be inserted here: With a correlation, be cautious about inferring causation. In this case the *direction* of causation is safe to assume because an exam score cannot influence *pre*-exam anxiety.

4. SPSS calculates the constant and the coefficient (called B-values) for the regression equation. As already noted, the constant and coefficient computed for the regression equation identifying the relationship between ANXIETY and EXAM were 64.247 and 2.818, respectively.

TESTING FOR A CURVILINEAR RELATIONSHIP

Most knowledgeable people would consider it foolishness to think that higher pretest anxiety will produce higher scores on an exam. A widely held position is that very low level anxiety will result in poor scores (due to lack of motivation) and that as anxiety scores increase, motivation to do well increases and higher scores result. However, there comes a point when additional anxiety is detrimental to performance, and at the top end of the anxiety scale there would once again be a decrease of performance. Regression analysis (whether it be simple or multiple) measures a *linear* relationship between independent variable(s) and the dependent variable. In the fictional data set presented earlier there is a fairly strong linear relationship between ANXIETY and the EXAM score ($R = .484$, $p < .0001$). But perhaps the regression equation would generate more accurate predicted values (yielding a better "fit" of the data) if a quadratic equation were employed that included an ANXIETY-squared (ANX^2) term.

Usually, before one tests for a curvilinear trend, there needs to be evidence (theoretical or computational) that such a relationship exists. Frankly, in the social sciences, curvilinear trends happen in only a limited number of circumstances, but they can be critical to understanding the data when they do occur. To demonstrate, we produce the scatter plot showing the relationship between the standardized predicted values and the standardized residuals. Please don't give up in despair! Look at the chart; then in the paragraph that follows we'll describe what it means and why we use it.

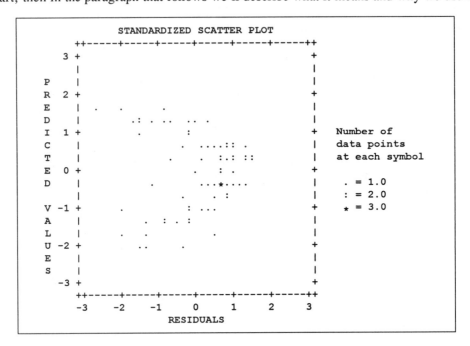

First off, you know what predicted values are, and you also know what residuals are, from having read the previous three pages. On the graph, the predicted values are on the vertical axis and the residuals are on the horizontal axis. For instance, on the three subjects we measured earlier, the predicted values were 68.47, 83.97, and 89.61, respectively. The residuals (absolute values of the predicted score minus the actual score) for the same three people are 16.47, 3.03, and 18.61, respectively. But the scales on the graph range from –3 to +3. That is because the sets of scores have been *standardized*. Standardization means that a distribution is changed to z-scores, with a mean of zero (0) and a standard deviation of one (1.0). This is done so that both sets of values are measured on the same *scale*, or *metric*. When variables are on the same scale, it buffers against skewed distributions, and allows a clearer picture of the relationships among variables.

But why don't we simply create a scatter plot comparing **EXAM** scores with **ANXIETY** scores? The reason is that many curvilinear trends are not possible to see visually from a scatter plot of the primary variables. The plotting of the residuals with the predicted scores usually gives a much clearer indication of nonlinear tendencies. Note in the scatter plot graph the U-shaped distribution of dots that opens to the left. This pattern indicates that a curvilinear trend exists and should be tested for. If there is no recognizable pattern to the dots, then we may assume that the *linear* equation would not be improved by measuring for curvilinear tendencies.

Using the **REGRESSION** command, it is possible to calculate an equation that tests for a nonlinear trend. The quadratic regression equation produced by SPSS follows:

$$\text{EXAM}_{(\text{predicted})} = 30.377 + 18.926(\text{ANXIETY}) + -1.521(\text{ANXIETY})^2$$

Now substituting the **ANXIETY** values for the same subjects (2, 43, and 72); let us see if the *quadratic* equation is able to do a better job of predicting actual **EXAM** scores than did the *linear* regression equation presented earlier:

Subject 2: EXAM $_{(\text{pred})}$ = 30.337 + 18.928(**1.5**) + -1.521(**7.0**)^2 = **55.31**   (actual score, 52)
Subject 43: EXAM $_{(\text{pred})}$ = 30.337 + 18.928(**7.0**) + -1.521(**7.0**)^2 = **88.30**   (actual score, 87)
Subject 72: EXAM $_{(\text{pred})}$ = 30.337 + 18.928(**9.0**) + -1.521(**9.0**)^2 = **77.49**   (actual score, 71)

A quick check of the results from the linear equation demonstrates the substantially superior predictive ability of the quadratic equation. Note the chart below:

Subject	Actual	Linear	Quadratic
2	52	68.47	55.31
43	87	83.97	88.30
72	71	89.61	77.49

Furthermore a scatter plot (below) of the standardized predicted values of **EXAM** and the standardized residuals no longer yields a detectable pattern of data.

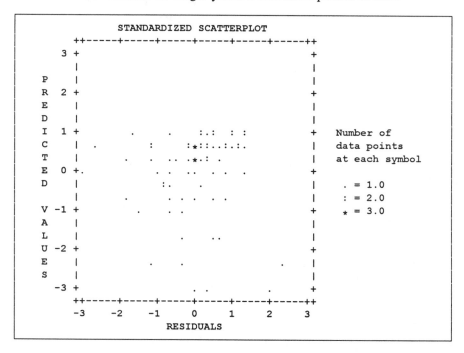

To produce a quadratic or higher-order equation is not difficult, and the procedure that tests for a curvilinear relationship is explained in the Step by Step section. A more extensive discussion of curvilinear regression may be found in Kerlinger and Pedhazur (1973).

A number of additional books are available that cover both simple and multiple regression. Several that the authors feel are especially good include: Chatterjee and Price (1991); Gonick and Smith (1993); Schulman (1992); Sen and Srivastava (1990); and Weisberg (1985). Please see the reference section for more detailed information on these books.

THE LOGICAL PROGRESSION FOR CONDUCTING REGRESSION ANALYSIS

1. Create file of data, or edit (if necessary) an already existing file.
2. Format file by use of **DATA LIST FILE**, **FORMATS**, and **VARIABLE/VALUE LABELS**; then save as a system file.
3. Access file and formats by the **GET FILE** command.
4. Use the **COMPUTE** command to create quadratic or higher-order variables, if desired.
5. Use the **REGRESSION** command to access regression analysis.
6. Use the **VARIABLES** subcommand to identify which variables will be used.
7. Use the **DEPENDENT** subcommand to identify which is the dependent variable.
8. Use the **METHOD** subcommand to specify entry procedure.
9. Use the **SCATTERPLOT** subcommand to produce a scatter plot between the predicted values and the residuals.
10. View the results and exit the program.
11. Print data, commands, and output.

STEP BY STEP
Simple and Curvilinear Regression Analysis

> 1) *Name and create a data file (Chapter 2), or edit (if necessary) an already existing file (Chapter 3).*

> 2) *Name variables, locate column positions, format, create VARIABLE/VALUE LABELS, and then save the formatted DATA FILE as a SYSTEM FILE (Chapter 4).*

From the DOS prompt, type:

> 3) *dos > SPSSPC* ⏎   *This step gets you into the SPSS system.*

To clear the menu from the top window prior to analyzing data:

4)	ALT — M	*Positions cursor to begin to create the command file.*

From the extreme upper left corner of the scratch pad (lower window), type:

5)	GET FILE = 'ANXIETY.SYS'.	1

LINE **1** Accesses the formatted SYSTEM FILE to begin to analyze data. All statistical procedures in this book will begin with the GET FILE step.

To access the simplest regression analysis between EXAM and ANXIETY (with EXAM as the dependent or criterion variable and ANXIETY as the independent or predictor variable), create the following command file.

```
6) GET FILE = 'ANXIETY.SYS'.                          1
   REGRESSION VARIABLES = EXAM ANXIETY/             2
   DEPENDENT = EXAM/                                 3
   METHOD = ENTER.                                   4
```

LINE **1** Same as step 5, line 1 above.

LINE **2** The REGRESSION command instructs SPSS to conduct regression analysis. The **VARIABLES** subcommand identifies the two variables of interest. Note that both the dependent and independent variables are included.

LINE **3** This line identifies which of the two variables is the dependent (criterion) variable.

LINE **4** The METHOD subcommand identifies which method you wish to utilize to conduct regression. For simple regression, any method will accomplish the same thing, but the line is required to conduct the analysis. Chapter 20 will describe different options for *multiple* regression.

Note: There are a number of additional options that may be used to modify the analysis or the output. For sake of greater simplicity in this chapter, we will present these options in Chapter 20 only.

To conduct an analysis that creates a regression equation that checks for curvilinear trends between EXAM and ANXIETY and also accesses a scatter plot of the standardized predicted values with the standardized residuals, create the following command file:

```
6a) GET FILE = 'ANXIETY.SYS'.                         1a
    COMPUTE ANXIETY2 = ANXIETY**2.                   2a
    REGRESSION VARIABLES = EXAM ANXIETY ANXIETY2/   3a
    DEPENDENT = EXAM/                                4a
    METHOD = ENTER/                                  5a
    SCATTERPLOT (*PRED *RESID).                      6a
```

LINE **1a** Same as line 1 from step 6 above.

LINE **2a** To test for a curvilinear trend, it is necessary to compute a new variable that is the square of the independent variable. For this analysis, this new variable is named ANXIETY2. The ANXIETY**2 is the format for raising a variable to the second power (see Chapter 5). Note that the **COMPUTE** line ends with a period, not a slash. If you wished to check for a cubic trend you would need to enter a *new* line, **COMPUTE ANXIETY3 = ANXIETY**3.** and include this new variable in the variable lists. A cubic equation is almost never used in the social sciences, but SPSS is quite capable of analyzing such an equation if it is appropriate.

LINE **3a** Note the inclusion of three variables in this line now, as the **ANXIETY2** variable is included. This is now no longer simple regression because there are two (not one) predictor variables; it is now designated as *multiple regression.*

LINE **4a** This designates the dependent variable and is identical to step 6, line 3 above.

LINE **5a** The method line is identical to step 6, line 4 above, except that it is followed by a slash instead of a period because a subcommand follows.

LINE **6a** This line is optional. The **SCATTERPLOT** subcommand instructs SPSS to create a scatter plot between the standardized predicted values (***PRED**) and residuals (***RESID**). Other scatter plots may be created by listing any two variables in your analysis within the parentheses.

---

7) | F9 | W | ↵ | *to save your command file for future access.*

If file is not already named, enter the file name (e.g., **ANXIETY.CTL**) at the prompt between the **W** and the **ENTER**.

To run the program, first position cursor at the beginning of the GET FILE line, then:

---

8) | F10 | C | *to run your program from the cursor.*

After viewing the results:

---

9) | F10 | E | FINISH | ↵ | *to exit to the DOS prompt.*

To print command files and results:

---

10) *dos* > PRINT SPSS.LIS | ↵ | ↵ | *(Sometimes the second RETURN is not necessary.)*

OUTPUT
Simple and Curvilinear Regression Analysis

The following OUTPUT is produced by this COMMAND FILE. INTERPRETATION follows.

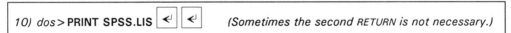

```
GET FILE = 'ANXIETY.SYS'.
REGRESSION VARIABLES = EXAM ANXIETY/
DEPENDENT = EXAM/
METHOD = ENTER.
```

Note: We do not include the scatterplot of predicted values and residuals here because they were demonstrated in some detail in the introduction of this chapter.

```
--------------------------------------------------------------------------
          * * * *  M U L T I P L E    R E G R E S S I O N  * * * *

Equation Number 1    Dependent Variable:  EXAM         Method:  Enter

Variables entered on Step number 1:         ANXIETY

Multiple R              .48794
R Square                .23808
Adjusted R Square       .22735
Standard Error        12.21533

Analysis of Variance
                      DF    Sum of Squares    Mean Square
Regression             1        3310.47579    3310.47579
Residual              71       10594.20915     149.21421

F =   22.18606        Signif F =   .0000

------------------- Variables in the Equation-------------------
Variable            B        SE B      Beta         T     Sig T
ANXIETY        2.817771    .598226   .487938     4.710    .0000
(Constant)    64.246977   3.602481              17.834    .0000
--------------------------------------------------------------------------
```

MULTIPLE R: Since there is only one independent variable, this number is the bivariate correlation (r) between **EXAM** and **ANXIETY**.

R SQUARE: The **R SQUARE** value identifies the proportion of variance in **EXAM** accounted for by **ANXIETY**. In this case 23.8% of the variance in **EXAM** is explained by **ANXIETY**.

ADJUSTED R SQUARE: **R SQUARE** is an accurate value for the sample drawn but is considered an optimistic estimate for the population value. The **ADJUSTED R SQUARE** is considered a better population estimate.

STANDARD ERROR: The standard deviation of the expected values for the dependent variable, **EXAM**.

REGRESSION: Statistics relating to the explained portion of the variance.

RESIDUAL: Statistics relating to the *un*explained portion of the variance.

DF: Degrees of freedom: For regression, the number of independent variables (1 in this case). For the residual, the number of subjects (73) minus the number of independent variables (1), minus 1: ($73 - 1 - 1 = 71$).

SUM OF SQUARES: For regression this is the within-groups sum of squares; for residual, the between-groups sum of squares. Note that in this case there is a larger portion of unexplained variance than there is of explained variance, a reality also reflected in the R^2 value.

MEAN SQUARE: Sum of squares divided by degrees of freedom.

F: Mean square regression divided by mean square residual.

SIGNIF F: Likelihood that this result could occur by chance.

B: Coefficient and constant for the linear regression equation: $\text{EXAM}_{(pred)} = \mathbf{64.247 + 2.818(ANXIETY)}$.

SE B: Standard error of B: A measure of the stability or sampling error of the B-values. It is the standard deviation of the B-values given a large number of samples drawn from the same population.

BETA: The standardized regression coefficients. This is the B-value for standardized scores (z-scores) of the variable **ANXIETY**. This value will always vary between ± 1.0.

T: B divided by the standard error of B.

SIG T: Likelihood that this result could occur by chance.

A REGRESSION ANALYSIS THAT TESTS FOR A CURVILINEAR TREND

The following OUTPUT *is produced by this* COMMAND FILE. INTERPRETATION *follows.*

```
GET FILE = 'ANXIETY.SYS'.
COMPUTE ANXIETY2 = ANXIETY**2.
REGRESSION VARIABLES = EXAM ANXIETY ANXIETY2/
DEPENDENT = EXAM/
METHOD = ENTER.
```

----

    * * * * M U L T I P L E   R E G R E S S I O N * * * *

Equation Number 1   Dependent Variable: EXAM   Method: Enter

Variables entered on Step number 1:   ANXIETY2
                Step Number 2   ANXIETY

Multiple R	.80070
R Square	.64112
Adjusted R Square	.63086
Standard Error	8.44321

Analysis of Variance

	DF	Sum of Squares	Mean Square
Regression	2	8914.53850	4457.26925
Residual	70	4990.14644	71.28781

F = 62.52499   Signif F = .0000

------------------ Variables in the Equation-------------------

Variable	B	SE B	Beta	T	Sig T
ANXIETY2	-1.521209	.171571	-2.860644	-8.866	.0000
ANXIETY	18.925629	1.863206	3.277247	10.158	.0000
(Constant)	30.377097	4.559942		6.662	.0000

    The terms described previously also apply to *this* output. Notice the high multiple *R*-value (.80), indicating a very strong relationship between the independent variable (ANXIETY) and its square (ANXIETY2) and the dependent variable, EXAM. An R^2-value of .641 indicates that 64.1% of the variance in EXAM is accounted for by ANXIETY and its square. The *F* and associated *p*-values (Signif F, Sig T) reflect the strength of the relationship between both independent variables and EXAM (F, and Signif F), and between each individual independent variable and EXAM (T and Sig T). In Chapter 20 we will address in some detail the influence of several variables (there are two here) on a dependent variable. Also note that while the betas always vary between ±1 for linear equations, they extend beyond that range in this quadratic equation. Beneath the *B* in the lower table are the coefficients for the regression equation. Note that in the introduction, the regression equation we tested had a constant of 30.377, an ANXIETY coefficient of 18.926, and an (ANXIETY)^2 coefficient of –1.521. (Remember your Algebra I class? A quadratic equation with a negative coefficient of the x^2 term describes a parabola that opens downward.)

Chapter 20

The REGRESSION Command:

Multiple Regression Analysis

Multiple regression is the natural extension of simple regression presented in Chapter 19. In simple regression, we measured the amount of influence one variable (the independent or predictor variable) had on a second variable (the dependent or criterion variable). We also computed the constant and coefficient for a regression equation designed to predict the value of the dependent variable, based on the value of the independent variable. While simple regression shows the influence of *one* variable on another, multiple regression analysis shows the influence of *two or more* variables on a designated dependent variable.

Another way to consider multiple regression analysis is from the viewpoint of a slope-intercept form of an equation. When a simple correlation between two variables is computed, the intercept and slope of the *regression line* (or line of best fit) may be requested. Those are the numbers that are used in the regression equation to compute the predicted values mentioned above. We describe here a simple regression equation as a vehicle for introducing multiple regression analysis. To assist in this process we present a new example based on a file called **HELPING1.SYS**. This system file is related to a study of helping behavior; it is real data derived from a sample of 81 subjects.

THE REGRESSION EQUATION

We earlier (Chapter 10) explained and demonstrated correlation between **PREVGPA** (students' previous GPAs) and **TOTAL** (the total number of points earned by students) and included slope/intercept information about the regression line. In this chapter we introduce the new set of data mentioned above. Two of the variables used to illustrate simple regression are **ZHELP** (a measure of total amount of time spent helping a friend with a problem, measured in *z*-scores) and **SYMPATHY** (the amount of sympathy felt by the helper in response to the friend's problem, measured on a *little*(1) to *much*(7) scale). Although correlation is often bidirectional, in this case **ZHELP** is designated as the dependent variable (that is, one's sympathy influences how much help is given *rather* *than* the amount of help influencing one's sympathy). A significant correlation ($r = .45514$, $p < .0001$) was computed, demonstrating a substantial relationship between the amount of sympathy one feels and the amount of help given. In addition, the intercept value (-1.892) and the slope ($.498$) were also calculated for a regression equation showing the relationship between the two variables. From these numbers we can create the formula to determine the *predicted value* of **ZHELP**:

$$\text{ZHELP}_{(\text{predicted})} = -1.892 + .498(\text{SYMPATHY}) \quad \text{or} \quad Z_p = -1.892 + .498S$$

If a person measured 5.6 on the **SYMPATHY** scale, the predicted value for that person for **ZHELP** would be .897. In other words, if a person measured fairly high in sympathy (5.6 in this case), it is anticipated that he or she would give quite a lot of help (a z-score of .897 indicates almost one standard deviation more than the average amount of help). The sequence below illustrates the computation of this number:

$$Z_p = -1.892 + .498(\mathbf{5.6}) \quad \rightarrow \quad Z_p = -1.892 + 2.789 \quad \rightarrow \quad Z_p = \mathbf{.897}$$

Multiple regression analysis is similar but allows *more than* one independent variable to have an influence on the dependent variable.

In this example, two other measures were also significantly correlated with **ZHELP**: **ANGER** (Angry or irritated emotions felt by the helper toward the needy friend, on a *none*(1) to *much*(7) scale), and **EFFICACY** (self-efficacy, or the helper's belief that he or she had the resources to be of help to the friend, on a *little*(1) to *much*(7) scale). The multiple regression analysis generated the following B values (The B can be roughly translated as the *slope* or *weighted constant* for the variable of interest.): $B_{(\text{sympathy})} = .4941$, $B_{(\text{anger})} = .2836$, and $B_{(\text{efficacy})} = .4125$, and the constant (intercept) $= -4.3078$. From these numbers a new equation may be generated to determine the predicted value for **ZHELP**:

$$\text{ZHELP}_{(\text{predicted})} = -4.3078 + .4941(\text{SYMPATHY}) + .2836(\text{ANGER}) + .4125(\text{EFFICACY})$$

Inserting numbers from an actual subject, subject 9 in this case:

$$Z_p = -4.3078 + .4941(\mathbf{3.5}) + .2836(\mathbf{1.0}) + .4125(\mathbf{2.9}) \quad = \quad -1.09$$

This result suggests that this person who measured midrange on sympathy (3.5), low in anger (1.0), and low in self-efficacy (2.9) would be expected to give little help (a z-score of -1.09 is more than one standard deviation below average). Subject 9's *actual* **ZHELP** score was $-.92$. The prediction in this case was fairly close to accurate.

A *positive* value for one of the B coefficients indicates that a higher score on the associated variable will increase the value of the dependent variable (e.g., more sympathy yields more help). A *negative* coefficient on a predictor variable would *decrease* the value of the dependent variable. The greater the B-value (absolute values), the greater the influence on the value of the dependent variable. The smaller the B-value (absolute values) the less influence that variable has on the dependent variable.

However, *B*-values often cannot be compared directly because different variables may be measured on different scales, or have different *metrics*. To resolve this difficulty, SPSS also generates a standardized score called *Beta* (β), which allows for direct comparison of the relative strengths of relationships between variables. β varies between ±1.0 and can be interpreted in a manner similar to a bivariate correlation.

In the previous equation, we find, as expected, that higher SYMPATHY and higher EFFICACY scores correlated with higher ZHELP scores. Contrary to intuition, we find that more ANGER also correlated positively with ZHELP. Why this is true is a matter of discussion and interpretation of the researcher. When an unexpected result occurs, the researcher would be well advised to recheck those data to ensure that variables were coded and entered correctly. SPSS gives no clues as to why analyses turn out the way they do.

MULTIPLE REGRESSION AND R²: THE AMOUNT OF VARIANCE EXPLAINED

In multiple regression analysis, any number of variables *may* be used as predictors, but many variables are not necessarily the ideal. It is important to find variables that *significantly* influence the dependent variable. SPSS has procedures by which only *significant* predictors will be entered into the regression equation. With a regression procedure called FORWARD, a dependent variable and any number of predictor (independent) variables are designated. REGRESSION will first compute which predictor variable has the highest bivariate correlation with the dependent variable. SPSS will then create a regression equation with this one selected independent variable. This means that after the first step, a regression equation has been calculated that includes the designated dependent variable and *only one* independent variable. Then REGRESSION will enter the second variable, which explains the greatest amount of *additional* variance. This second variable will be included only if it explains a *significant* amount of additional variation. After this second step, the regression equation has the same dependent variable but now has *two* predictor variables. Then, if there is a third variable that significantly explains more of the variance, it too will be included in the regression equation. This process will continue until no additional variables significantly explain additional variance. By default, REGRESSION will cease to add new variables when *p* drops below the .05 level of significance. The researcher, however, has the option to designate a different level of significance as a criterion for entry into the equation if desired.

The measure of the strength of relationship between the independent variables (note, plural) and the dependent variable is designated with a capital *R* and is usually referred to as *multiple R*. This number squared (R^2) yields a value that represents the proportion of variation in the dependent variable that is explained by the independent variables. In the regression analysis that produced the regression equation shown above, the value of multiple *R* was .616, and the R^2 was .380. This indicates that 38% of the variance in ZHELP was accounted for by SYMPATHY, ANGER, and EFFICACY. See the Output section of this chapter for more information about multiple *R*.

CURVILINEAR TRENDS, MODEL BUILDING, AND REFERENCES

Regression, like correlation, measures for *linear* relationships. In the previous chapter we described the procedure to test for a *curvilinear* relationship. The same process operates with multiple regression. If there is theoretical or statistical evidence that one or more of the predictor variables demonstrates a curvilinear association with the dependent variable, then a quadratic (the variable squared) factor may be added as a predictor. Please refer to the previous chapter for an explanation of this process.

A final critical item concerns model building, that is, conducting a regression analysis that is conceptually sound. Certain fundamental criteria are necessary for creating a reliable model:

1. Your research must be thoughtfully crafted and carefully designed. The arithmetic of regression will not correct for either meaningless relationships or serious design flaws. Regrettably, many details of what constitutes research that is "thoughtfully crafted and carefully designed" extend well beyond the scope of this book.

2. The sample size should be large enough to create meaningful correlations. There are no hard rules concerning acceptable sample size, but as N drops below 50, the validity of your results become increasingly questionable.

3. Your data should be examined carefully for outliers or other abnormalities.

4. The predictor variables should be approximately normally distributed, ideally with skewness and kurtosis values between ±1. However, good results can often be obtained with an *occasional* (!!) deviation from normality among the predictor variables, or even the inclusion of a discrete variable (such as gender). A normal distribution for the dependent variable is also urged; but discriminant analysis (Chapter 23) uses a *discrete* measure as the criterion variable in a regression procedure.

5. Be keenly aware of the issue of linear dependency between the predictor variables. Never use two variables one of which is partially or entirely dependent upon the other (such as points on the final and total points in the class). Also avoid variables that are conceptually very similar (such as worry and anxiety). To compute a matrix of correlations between potential predictor variables is always wise. Variables that correlate higher than $r = .5$ should be scrutinized carefully before both are included in a regression analysis. The power and interpretability of results are substantially compromised when variables that are linearly dependent are included in the analysis.

Multiple regression analysis is not a simple procedure. Like analysis of variance, a number of thick volumes have been written on the topic, and we are in no way attempting to duplicate those efforts. It is suggested that, before you attempt to conduct multiple regression analysis, you take a course in the subject. A number of books are available that cover both simple and multiple regression. Several that the authors feel are especially good include: Chatterjee and Price (1991); Gonick and Smith (1993); Schulman (1992); Sen and Srivastava (1990); and Weisberg (1985). Please see the reference section for more detailed information on these books.

The purpose of the previous four pages has been to remind you of the rationale behind regression if you have been away from it for a while. The purpose of the pages that follow is to explain step by step how to conduct multiple regression analysis with SPSS and how to interpret the output.

THE LOGICAL PROGRESSION FOR CONDUCTING MULTIPLE REGRESSION ANALYSIS

1. Create file of data, or edit (if necessary) an already existing file.
2. Format file by use of **DATA LIST FILE**, **FORMAT**, and **VARIABLE/VALUE LABELS**; then save as a **SYSTEM FILE**.
3. Access file and formats by the **GET FILE** command.
4. Use the **REGRESSION** command to access multiple regression analysis.
5. Use the **DESCRIPTIVES** subcommand to request correlations or other statistics.
6. Use the **SELECT** subcommand to select a *portion* of the data for analysis.
7. Use the **VARIABLES** subcommand to identify which variables will be used.
8. Use the **STATISTICS** subcommand to access statistics other than those provided by the default.
9. Use the **CRITERIA** subcommand to enter significance values other than the defaults for variables to be entered or removed.
10. Use the **DEPENDENT** subcommand to identify the dependent variable.
11. Use the **METHOD** subcommand to identify whether you wish forced entry, forced removal, forward, backward, or stepwise procedure(s).
12. Use the **SCATTERPLOT** subcommand to produce a scatter plot between the predicted values and the residuals.
13. Use the **RESIDUALS** subcommand to conduct tests and further analyze data.
14. View the results and exit the program.
15. Print data, commands, and output.

The data we use by way of example are from the study already discussed on pages 163-167. The file name is **HELPING.SYS**, $N = 81$. The following variables will be used in the description: All variables except **ZHELP** are measured on a *little*(1) to *much*(7) scale.

ZHELP: The dependent variable. The standardized score (z-score) for the amount of help given by a person to a friend in need on a –3 to +3 scale.

SYMPATHY: Feelings of sympathy aroused in the helper by the friend's need.

ANGER: Feelings of anger or irritation aroused in the helper by the friend's need.

EFFICACY: Self-efficacy of the helper in relation to the friend's need.

SEVERITY: Helper's rating of how severe the friend's problem was.

EMPATEND: Empathic tendency of the helper as measured by a personality test.

STEP BY STEP
Multiple Regression Analysis

Due to the complexity of formatting and explaining the **REGRESSION** procedure, a brief overview will be presented here to clarify. The first five steps will be identical to previous chapters and contain basic information about how to enter data, format data, and get into the SPSS system. The step-6 portion will be divided into two parts (6 and 6a). Step 6 will be the *simplest possible* default forward regression procedure, followed by explanation of the procedure and an example of the results in the Output section. Step 6a will include a number of (frequently) important options. One command file that includes all of these options will be presented. Fairly extensive discussion will explain each line, identify whether a particular procedure is required or optional, and include other important considerations and variations.

> *1)* *Name and create a data file (Chapter 2), or edit (if necessary) an already existing file (Chapter 3).*

> *2)* *Name variables, locate column positions, format, create VARIABLE/VALUE LABELS, and then save the formatted DATA FILE as a SYSTEM FILE (Chapter 4).*

From the DOS prompt, type:

> *3)* *dos>* **SPSSPC** ↵   *This step gets you into the SPSS system.*

To clear the menu from the top window prior to analyzing data:

> *4)* ALT ‐ M   *Positions cursor to begin to create the command file.*

From the extreme upper left corner of the scratch pad (lower window), type:

> *5)* **GET FILE = 'HELPING1.SYS'.**   *1*

LINE **1** Accesses the formatted **SYSTEM FILE** to begin to analyze data. All statistical procedures in this book will begin with the **GET FILE** step.

The following command file conducts a FORWARD regression analysis with a dependent variable of ZHELP and independent variables of SEVERITY, SYMPATHY, ANGER, EMPATEND, and EFFICACY.

> *6)* **GET FILE = 'HELPING1.SYS'.**   *1*
> **REGRESSION VARIABLES = SEVERITY SYMPATHY ANGER EMPATEND**
> **EFFICACY ZHELP/**   *2*
> **DEPENDENT = ZHELP/**   *3*
> **METHOD = FORWARD/**   *4*

LINE 1 Same as line 1 in step 5 above.

LINE 2 The **REGRESSION** command accesses the procedure. The **VARIABLES** subcommand identifies which variables will be used in the equation. Note that both dependent *and* independent variables are listed. Always end this line with a slash.

LINE 3 The **DEPENDENT** subcommand identifies **ZHELP** as the dependent variable.

LINE 4 **METHOD** identifies **FORWARD** as the procedure we will use to enter variables into the equation. Significance to enter is .05, the default, which means that if the first variable significantly explains variance in the dependent variable, and if succeeding variables significantly explain additional variance (at the $p < .05$) level, each variable that meets this criteria will be entered into the equation—that is, included as a predictor variable.

The command file that follows contains a number of additional options to those presented in step 6. This is not an exhaustive list, but frequently used options are included. If you wish a complete description of __all__ options, refer to the SPSS/PC+ Statistics 4.0 Manual.

```
6a)  GET FILE = 'HELPING1.SYS'.                                    1a
     REGRESSION DESCRIPTIVES = CORR/                               2a
     SELECT ETHNIC EQ 1/                                           3a
     VARIABLES = SEVERITY SYMPATHY ANGER EMPATEND EFFICACY ZHELP/  4a
     STATISTICS = DEFAULTS CHA BCOV F/                             5a
     CRITERIA = PIN(.10) POUT(.20)/                                6a
     DEPENDENT = ZHELP/                                            7a
     METHOD = STEPWISE/                                            8a
     SCATTERPLOT (*PRED *RESID)/                                   9a
     RESIDUALS.                                                    10a
```

LINE 1a Same as above.

LINES 2a-9a Concerning *order* of steps 2a-9a: The order shown above should be the order you follow. Commands that are designated as *optional* may simply be deleted if you do not wish those functions. The lines designated as *required* must be included in the order shown.

LINE 2a **REGRESSION** is required. **DESCRIPTIVES** is optional. If you write only **DESCRIPTIVES/** (without equals sign or options), this will access the default: mean, standard deviation, and correlation matrix. If you type **DESCRIPTIVES =** followed by one or more options, SPSS will print only the options you request and exclude the default options. Options that are available are in the following table.

Descriptive Option	Result
MEAN	Mean, printed by default
STDDEV	Standard deviation, printed by default
CORR	Correlations, printed by default
N	N used for computing statistics
COV	Covariance matrix
ALL	All statistics

LINE 3a **SELECT** is optional. This subcommand will select a subset of your data for analysis. The **ETHNICIT EQ 1** (above) selects the ethnic group coded 1—Caucasian in the HELPING1.SYS file. In applying this command, use the following letter codings:

Letter Code	Meaning
EQ	Equal to (=)
NE	Not equal to (≠)
LT	Less than (<)
LE	Less than or equal to (≤)
GT	Greater than (>)
GE	Greater than or equal to (≥)

Other examples: **ETHNICIT GT 1** would run an analysis for all non-Caucasian subjects. **GENDER EQ 1** would run analysis for all females.

LINE **4a** This is the same as line 2 shown above. This **VARIABLES** line is required.

LINE **5a** The **STATISTICS** line is optional. If this command is not included at all, by default the following items will be included in the output: R, R^2, Adjusted R^2; an ANOVA table including degrees of freedom, sums of squares, mean squares, F-value for R, and the significance of F; regression coefficients including B, standard error of B, β, t-value for β, and two-tailed significance levels of t; and statistics for variables not in the equation, including β (value if the variable were entered), t-value for β, significance of t, the partial correlation with the dependent variable (after other variables are already in the equation), and the minimum tolerance. Other statistics are available. In the line above, **CHA** requests R^2 change, F-value for R^2 change, and associated significance values. **BCOV** accesses a variance-covariance matrix of included variables. **F** requests that F-values rather than t-values be included in the output. There are more, many more. See the *SPSS/PC+ Statistics 4.0 Manual* for a complete list.

LINE **6a** The **CRITERIA** line is optional. If it is not included, by default SPSS will use values of $p \leq .05$ to enter and $p \geq .10$ to remove when using **FORWARD**, **BACKWARD**, or **STEPWISE** methods of regression. If you wish different values, use the line 6a format to request such. The line above requests a p to enter (**PIN**) of .10 and a p to remove (**POUT**) of .20.

LINE **7a** The **DEPENDENT** subcommand is required. You may list more than one dependent variable, in which case SPSS will run a separate analysis for each dependent variable listed, using all other variables on the variable list (line 4a) as predictors.

LINE **8a** The **METHOD** line is required. There are five options under **METHOD**:

FORWARD: This method will enter variables one at a time, based on the designated significance value to enter. The process ceases when there are no additional variables that explain a significant portion of additional variance.

BACKWARD: This method enters *all* independent variables at one time and then removes variables one at a time based on a preset significance value to remove. In the above file, the value to remove (**POUT**) is .20. The default is .10. When there are no more variables that meet the requirement for removal, the process ceases.

STEPWISE: This method combines both **FORWARD** and **BACKWARD** procedures. Due to the complexity of intercorrelations, the variance explained by certain variables will change when new variables enter the equation. Sometimes a variable that qualified to enter loses some of its predictive validity when other variables enter. If this takes place, the **STEPWISE** method will remove the "weakened" variable. **STEPWISE** is probably the most frequently used of the regression methods, but some researchers feel that such an "automatic" procedure should be used with caution and not replace sound research methodology.

ENTER: This is the forced entry option. SPSS will enter at one time all specified variables regardless of significance values.

REMOVE: This is the forced removal option. SPSS will remove at one step all designated variables. Unlike the other four options, which will use all independent variables by default, REMOVE must have a variable list designated. The format for such a line is: METHOD = REMOVE VARIABLES = SEVERITY ANGER/

Note: For all five methods a separate variable list *may* be included if you desire variables other than *all independent variables*. Designate such variables in the same format shown for REMOVE.

LINE 9a This line is optional. The SCATTERPLOT subcommand instructs SPSS to create a scatter plot between the standardized predicted values (*PRED) and residuals (*RESID). Other scatter plots may be created by listing any two variables in your analysis within the parentheses. Chapter 19 gives a detailed description of this process.

LINE 10a The RESIDUALS subcommand is optional and has the power to summon up a frightening array of data. The default is accessed when the word RESIDUALS is used without specifying *which* residuals you wish. The default includes histograms of the standardized residuals, a normal probability plot of standardized values, a list of outliers—the 10 most extreme values in the data file—and the Durbin-Watson test statistic for unselected cases. A complete list of RESIDUAL options is listed in the *SPSS/PC+ Statistics 4.0 Manual*.

---

7) F9 W ↵   *to save your command file for future access.*

If file is not already named, enter the file name (e.g., **HELPING1.CTL**) at the prompt between the **W** and the **ENTER**.

To run the program, first position cursor at the beginning of the GET FILE line, then:

---

8) F10 C   *to run your program from the cursor.*

After viewing the results:

---

9) F10 E FINISH ↵   *to exit to the DOS prompt.*

To print command files and results:

---

10) dos> PRINT SPSS.LIS ↵ ↵   *(Sometimes the second RETURN is not necessary.)*

OUTPUT
Multiple Regression Analysis

The following OUTPUT *is produced by this* COMMAND FILE. INTERPRETATION *follows.*

```
GET FILE = 'HELPING1.SYS'.
REGRESSION VARIABLES = SEVERITY SYMPATHY ANGER EMPATEND EFFICACY ZHELP/
DEPENDENT = ZHELP/
METHOD = FORWARD.
```

Note: We show only the final pages of output here.

```
-------------------------------------------------------------------------
            * * * *  M U L T I P L E   R E G R E S S I O N  * * * *

Equation Number 1       Dependent Variable:    ZHELP

Method:    Forward        Criteria:    PIN = .0500      POUT = .1000

Variable(s) Entered on Step Number 3:   EFFICACY

Multiple R            .61608   Analysis of Variance    Sum of
R Square             .37955                      DF    Squares   Mean Square
Adjusted R Square    .35538   Regression          3   47.65387     15.88462
Standard Error      1.00582   Residual           77   77.89864      1.01167

                       F =   15.70138   Significance of F =   .0000

------------------- Variables in the Equation -------------------

Variable              B          SE B       Beta        T      Sig T
SYMPATHY          .494061      .100057     .451147     4.938    .0000
ANGER             .283631      .082726     .310032     3.429    .0010
EFFICACY          .412490      .131605     .284380     3.134    .0024
(Constant)      -4.307819      .731990

---------------- Variables not in the Equation ----------------

Variable       Beta In    Partial   Min Tolerance      T      Sig T
SEVERITY       .077133    .089961        .843997      .787     .4335
EMPATEND       .119020    .144096        .885808     1.269     .2082
-------------------------------------------------------------------------
```

PIN: Probability value to enter a variable into the regression equation. In this case $p = .05$, the default value.

POUT: Probability value to remove an already entered variable from the regression equation. In this case $p = .10$, the default value.

MULTIPLE R: The multiple correlation between the dependent variable ZHELP and the three variables in the regression equation, SYMPATHY, ANGER, and EFFICACY.

R SQUARE: The R^2 value identifies the portion of the variance accounted for by the independent variables; that is, approximately 38% of the variance in ZHELP is accounted for by SYMPATHY, ANGER, and EFFICACY.

ADJUSTED R SQUARE: R^2 is an accurate value for the sample drawn but is considered an optimistic estimate for the *population* value. The Adjusted R^2 is considered a better population estimate and is useful when comparing the R^2 values between models with different numbers of independent variables.

STANDARD ERROR: **STANDARD ERROR** is the standard deviation of the expected value of (in this case) ZHELP. Note that this value shrinks as each new variable is added to the equation (see output from next section).

DEGREES OF FREEDOM: For regression, the number of independent variables in the equation. For residual, N, minus the number of independent variables entered, minus 1: $81 - 3 - 1 = 77$.

SUM OF SQUARES: The regression sum of squares corresponds to the between-group sum of squares in ANOVA, and the residual sum of squares corresponds to the within-group sum of squares in ANOVA. Note that in this case there is a larger portion of <u>un</u>explained variance than there is of explained variance, a reality also reflected in the **R SQUARE** value.

MEAN SQUARE: Sums of squares divided by the degrees of freedom.

F: Mean squares regression divided by mean squares residual.

SIGNIFICANCE OF F: Probability that this F-value could occur by chance. The present results show that the likelihood of the given correlation occurring by chance is less than 1 in 10,000.

B: The coefficients and constant for the regression equation that measures predicted values for ZHELP:

$$\text{ZHELP}_{\text{(predicted)}} = -4.307819 + .494061(\text{SYMPATHY}) + .283631(\text{ANGER}) + .35538(\text{EFFICACY})$$

STANDARD ERROR OF B: A measure of the stability or sampling error of the B-values. It is the standard deviation of the B-value given a large number of samples drawn from the same population.

BETA (β): The standardized regression coefficients. This is the B-value for standardized scores (z-scores) of the variables. These values will vary strictly between plus-and-minus 1.0.

T: B divided by the standard error of B. This holds for both variables in the equation and those variables *not* in the equation.

SIGNIFICANCE OF T: The probability that these t-values could occur by chance.

BETA IN: The beta values for the *excluded* variables if these variables were actually in the regression equation.

PARTIAL: The partial correlation coefficient with the dependent variable ZHELP, adjusting for variables already in the regression equation. For example, the simple correlation (r) between ZHELP and SEVERITY is .292. After SYMPATHY, ANGER, and EFFICACY have "consumed" much of the variance, the <u>partial</u> correlation between ZHELP and SEVERITY is only .089. EMPATEND, on the other hand, shrinks only a little, from .157 to .144.

MINIMUM TOLERANCE: Tolerance is a commonly used measure of colinearity. It is defined as $1 - R_i^2$, where R_i is the R-value of variable i when variable i is predicted from all other independent variables. A low tolerance value (near 0) indicates extreme collinearity—the given variable is almost a linear combination of the other independent variables. A high value (near 1) indicates that the variable is relatively independent of other variables. This measure deals with the issue of linear dependence that was discussed in the Introduction. When variables are included that are linearly dependent, they inflate the standard errors, thus weakening the power of the analysis. It also conceals other problems, such as curvilinear trends in the data.

Note: Definitions below apply to the output that follows.

R SQUARE CHANGE: This is simple subtraction of the R^2 value for the given line minus the R^2 value from the previous line. Note that $.09324 = .30040 - .20715$ (within rounding error). The number (.09324) indicates that the inclusion of the second variable (ANGER) explains an additional 9.3% of the variance.

F CHANGE: This is the F-value associated with the additional variance explained by a new variable. Note that the **OVERALL F** (next to the last line) is by no means the sum of the **F CHANGE** values. This is because with each new variable added, the degrees of freedom also increases, reducing the **OVERALL F** value.

SIGNIF OF F CHANGE: Significance associated with the F-change values.

REGRESSION ANALYSIS INCLUDING THE F-CHANGE OPTION

The following OUTPUT is produced by this COMMAND FILE. INTERPRETATION follows.

```
GET FILE = 'HELPING1.SYS'.
REGRESSION VARIABLES = SEVERITY SYMPATHY ANGER EMPATEND EFFICACY ZHELP/
STATISTICS = DEFAULTS CHA/
DEPENDENT = ZHELP/
METHOD = FORWARD.
```

Note: This output is a greatly condensed version of the SPSS output (which requires 12 pages) to demonstrate the changes in the variables from step to step as new variables are entered into the regression equation.

```
-----------------------------------------------------------------------
        * * * *  M U L T I P L E   R E G R E S S I O N  * * * *
Dependent Variable:   ZHELP
```

Statistic	Step # Variables in Equation	Step #1 SYMPATHY	Step #2 SYMPATHY ANGER	Step #3 SYMPATHY ANGER EFFICACY
Multiple R		.45514	.54808	.61608
R Square		.20715	.30040	.37955
Adjusted R Square		.19711	.28246	.35538
Standard Error		1.12252	1.06119	1.00582
R Square Change		.20715	.09324	.07916
F Change		20.64063	10.39600	9.82381
Signif F Change		.0000	.0018	.0024
Analysis of Variance				
DEGREES of FREEDOM	Regression	1	2	3
	Residual	79	78	77
SUM of SQUARES	Regression	26.00829	37.71541	47.65387
	Residual	99.54421	87.83710	77.89864
MEAN SQUARES	Regression	26.00829	18.85770	15.88462
	Residual	1.26005	1.12612	1.01167
Overall F		20.64063	16.74578	15.70138
Signif of Overall F		.0000	.0000	.0000

```
-----------------------------------------------------------------------
```

First, all statistical terms are defined in the previous two pages. The only change in the command file from two pages earlier is the inclusion of the **STATISTICS = DEFAULTS CHA/**. This line requests, in addition to a variety of default statistics, three change measures: *R*-square change, *F* change, and significance of *F* change. These values are shown on lines 5, 6, and 7 of the output listed above. The purpose of displaying the output from the three steps in this format is to allow you to see how the computed values change as each new variable is added. Note for instance how the multiple *R*, the *R* square, and the adjusted *R* square *increase* in value with the addition of each new variable. Note also how the standard error, *R*-square change, and *F* change *decrease* in value with the addition of new variables. Similar patterns may be noted for degrees of freedom, sum of squares, and mean squares.

Chapter 21

The FACTOR Command:

Factor Analysis

Over the past 30 or 40 years, factor analysis has gained increasing acceptance and popularity. Raymond B. Cattell drew attention to the procedure when he used factor analysis to reduce a list of more than 4,500 trait names to fewer than 200 questions that measured 16 different personality traits in his personality inventory called the *16 Personality Factor Questionnaire* (16PF). Cattell's use of factor analysis underlines its primary usefulness, that is, to take a large number of observable instances to measure an unobservable construct or constructs. For instance: "Attends loud parties," "talks a lot," "appears comfortable talking with just about anyone," and "is usually seen with others" are four behaviors that can be observed that may measure an unobservable construct called "outgoing". Factor analysis is most frequently used to identify a small number of factors (e.g., outgoing) that may be used to represent relationships among sets of interrelated variables (e.g., the four descriptors).

Four basic steps are required to conduct a factor analysis:
1. calculate a correlation matrix of all variables to be used in the analysis,
2. extract factors,
3. rotate factors to create a more understandable factor structure,
4. interpret results.

The first three steps are covered in this introduction. For step 4, we give a conceptual feel of how to interpret results, but most of the explanation will take place in the Output section.

CREATE A CORRELATION MATRIX

Calculating a correlation matrix of all variables of interest is the starting point for factor analysis. This starting point provides some initial clues as to how factor analysis works. Even at this stage it is clear that factor analysis is derived from some combinations of intercorrelations among descriptor variables. It is not necessary to type in a correlation matrix for factor analysis to take place. If you are starting from raw data (as we have in all chapters up to this point), the **FACTOR** command will automatically create a correlation matrix as the first step. In many instances, however, the researcher may not have the raw data, but only a correlation matrix. Because of this need, step 6b in the Step by Step section shows how to conduct factor analysis after typing a correlation matrix into the command file.

FACTOR EXTRACTION

The purpose of the factor-extraction phase is to extract the factors. *Factors* are the underlying constructs that describe your set of variables. Mathematically, this procedure is similar to a forward run in multiple regression analysis. As you recall (Chapter 20), the first step in multiple regression is to select and enter the *independent* variable that significantly explains the greatest amount of variance observed in the *dependent* variable. When this is completed, the next step is to find and enter the independent variable that significantly explains the greatest *additional* amount of variation in the dependent variable. Then the procedure selects and enters the variable that significantly explains the *next* greatest additional amount of variance and so forth, until there are no variables that significantly explain further variance.

With factor analysis the procedure is similar, and a conceptual understanding of the factor-extraction phase could be gained by rewriting the previous paragraph and omitting *"dependent variable"*, *"significantly"*; and changing *independent variable* to *variables* (plural). Factor analysis does not begin with a dependent variable. It starts with a measure of the total amount of variation observed (similar to total sum of squares) in all variables that have been designated for factor analysis. Please note that this "variation" is a bit difficult to understand conceptually (Whence all this variance floating about? How does one see it? smell it? grasp it? but I digress . . .), but it is quite precise mathematically. The first step in factor analysis is for the computer to select the combination of variables whose shared correlations explain the greatest amount of the total variance. This is called Factor 1. Factor analysis will then extract a second factor. This is the combination of variables that explains the greatest amount of the variance that remains, that is, variation *after* the first factor has been extracted. This is called Factor 2. This procedure continues for a third factor, fourth factor, fifth factor, and so on, until as many factors have been extracted as there are variables.

In the default SPSS procedure, each of the variables is initially assigned a *communality* value of 1.0. Communalities are designed to show the proportion of variance that the factors contribute to explaining a particular variable. These values range from 0 to 1, with 0 indicating that common factors explain none of the variance in a particular variable, and 1 indicating that all the variance in that variable is explained by the common factors. However, for the default procedure at the initial extraction phase, each variable is assigned a communality of 1.0.

After the first factor is extracted, SPSS prints an eigenvalue to the right of the factor number (e.g., Factor number = 1; eigenvalue = 5.13312). Eigenvalues are designed to show the proportion of variance accounted for by each factor (*not* each *variable* as do communalities). The first eigenvalue will always be largest (and always be greater than 1.0) because the first factor (by the definition of the procedure) always explains the greatest amount of total variance. It then lists the percent of the variance accounted for by this factor (the eigenvalue divided by the number of variables), and this is followed by a cumulative percent. For each successive factor, the eigenvalue printed will be smaller than the previous one, and the cumulative percent (of variance explained) will total 100% after the final factor has been extracted. The absence of the word *significantly* is demonstrated by the fact that the **FACTOR** command extracts as many factors as there are variables, regardless of whether or not subsequent factors explain a significant amount of additional variance.

FACTOR SELECTION and ROTATION

The factors extracted by SPSS are almost never *all* of interest to the researcher. If you have as many factors as there are variables, you have not accomplished what factor analysis was created to do. The goal is to explain the phenomena of interest with fewer than the original number of variables, usually substantially fewer. Remember Cattell? He started with 4,500 descriptors and ended up with 16 traits.

The first step is to decide *which* factors you wish to retain in the analysis. The common-sense criterion for retaining factors is that each retained factor must have some sort of face validity or theoretical validity; but prior to the rotation process, it is often impossible to interpret what each factor means. Therefore, the researcher usually selects a mathematical criterion for determining which factors to retain. The SPSS default is to keep any factor with an eigenvalue larger than 1.0. If a factor has an eigenvalue less than 1.0 it explains less variance than an original variable and is usually rejected. (Remember, SPSS will print out as many factors as there are variables, and usually for only a few of the factors will the eigenvalue be larger than 1.0.) There are other criteria for selection (such as the scree plot), or conceptual reasons (based on your knowledge of the data) that may be used. The procedure for selecting a number other than the default will be described in the Step by Step section.

Once factors have been selected, the next step is to rotate them. Rotation is needed because the original factor structure is mathematically correct but is difficult to interpret. The goal of rotation is to achieve what is called *simple structure*, that is, high *factor loadings* on one factor and low loadings on all others. Factor loadings vary between ± 1.0 and indicate the strength of relationship between a particular variable and a particular factor, in a way similar to a correlation. For instance, the phrase "enjoys loud parties" might have a high loading on an "outgoing" factor (perhaps > .6) and have a low loading on an "intelligence" factor (perhaps < .1). This is because an enjoys-loud-parties statement is thought to be related to outgoingness, but unrelated to intelligence. Ideally, simple structure would have variables load entirely on one factor and not at all on the others. On the second graph (below), this would be represented by all asterisks being *on* the rotated factor lines. In social science research, however, this never happens, and the goal is to rotate the axes to have data points as close as possible to the rotated axes. The following graphs are good representations of how an unrotated structure and a rotated structure might look. SPSS will print out graphs of your factor structure (after rotation) and include a table of coordinates for additional clarity.

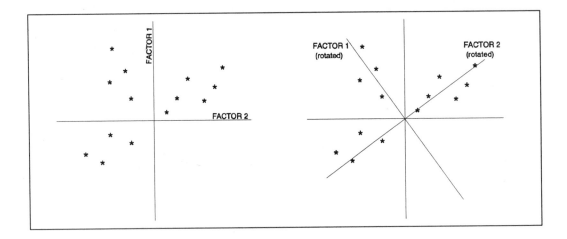

Rotation does not alter the mathematical accuracy of the factor structure, just as looking at a picture from the front rather than from the side does not alter the picture, and changing the measure of height in inches to height in centimeters does not alter how tall a person is. Rotation was originally done by hand, and the researcher would position the axes in the location that appeared to create the optimal factor structure. Hand rotation is not possible with SPSS, but there are several mathematical procedures available to rotate the axes to the best simple structure. Varimax is the default procedure used by SPSS, but there are several others (mentioned in the Step by Step section).

Oblique Rotations: Varimax rotations are called *orthogonal rotations* because the axes that are rotated remain at right angles to each other. Sometimes it is possible to achieve a better simple structure by diverging from perpendicular. The **OBLIMIN** procedure allows the researcher to deviate from orthogonal to achieve a better simple structure. Conceptually, this deviation means that factors are no longer uncorrelated with each other. This is not necessarily disturbing, because few factors in the social sciences *are* entirely uncorrelated. The use of oblique rotations can be quite tricky, and (here we insert our standard disclaimer) you should not attempt to use them unless you have a clear understanding of what you are doing. Let's expand: You should probably not attempt to conduct factor analysis *at all* unless you have had a course in it and/or have a clear conceptual understanding of the procedure. The technique for setting the opening value (δ) for **OBLIMIN** is described in the Step by Step section.

INTERPRETATION

In an ideal world, each of the original variables will load highly (e.g., > .5) on one of the factors and low (e.g., < .2) on all others. Furthermore, the factors that have the high loadings will have excellent face validity and appear to be measuring some underlying construct. In the real world, this rarely happens. There will often be two or three irritating variables that end up loading on the "wrong" factor, and often a variable will load onto two or three different factors. The output of factor analysis requires considerable understanding of your data, and it is rare for the arithmetic of factor analysis alone to produce entirely clear results. In the Output section we will clarify with a real example. The example will be introduced in the following paragraphs.

We draw our example from real data, the **HELPING2.SYS** file. Note that this is a different file from that used in Chapter 20 (**HELPING1.SYS**). It measures many of the same variables as the previous file but is much larger ($N = 517$). In the **HELPING2.SYS** file, self-efficacy (belief that one has the ability to help effectively) was measured by 15 questions, each paired with an amount-of-help question that measured a particular type of helping. An example of one of the paired questions follows:

9a) Time spent expressing sympathy, empathy, or understanding.						
none	0-15	15-30	30-60	1-2	2-5	_____
	minutes	minutes	minutes	hours	hours	hours
9b) Did you believe you were capable of expressing sympathy, empathy, or understanding to your friend?						
1	2	3	4	5	6	7
not at all			some		very much so	

There were three categories of help represented in the 15 questions: six questions measured empathic types of helping, four questions measured informational types of helping, four questions measured instrumental ("doing things") types of helping, and the fifteenth question was open-ended to allow any additional type of help given to be inserted. This means that there were the same number of efficacy questions (15) that measured efficacy for the same three categories of helping and a fifteenth efficacy question that related to the open-ended help question. Factor analysis was conducted on the 15 self-efficacy questions to see if the results would yield the three categories of self-efficacy that were originally created.

A final word: In the Step by Step section, there will be three step-6 variations. Step 6 will be the simplest default factor analysis that is possible. Step 6a will be a command file that describes all variations on factor analysis that we present in this chapter. Step 6b will demonstrate how to conduct a factor analysis from a correlation matrix read into the command file. All three will conduct a factor analysis on the 15 questions that measure self-efficacy in the **HELPING2.SYS** file.

For additional information on factor analysis, the best textbook on the topic known by the authors is by Comrey and Lee (1991). Please see the reference section for additional information about this book.

THE LOGICAL PROGRESSION FOR CONDUCTING FACTOR ANALYSIS

1. Create file of data, or edit (if necessary) an already existing file.
2. Format file by use of **DATA LIST FILE**, **FORMATS**, and **VARIABLE/VALUE LABELS**; then save as a system file.
3. Access file and formats by the **GET FILE** command.
4. Use the **FACTOR** command to conduct factor analysis.
5. Use the **MISSING** subcommand to instruct SPSS how to deal with missing values.
6. Use the **PRINT** subcommand to identify which results you wish to have displayed.
7. Use the **FORMAT** subcommand to designate how you want your output to be displayed.
8. Use the **PLOT** subcommand to request scree plots or paired-factor plots.
9. Use the **CRITERIA** subcommand to identify the number of factors you wish to retain for rotation.
10. Use the **ROTATION** subcommand to select the type of rotation procedure you wish.
11. View the results and exit the program.
12. Print data, commands, and output.

STEP BY STEP
Factor Analysis

> 1) Name and create a data file (Chapter 2), or edit (if necessary) an already existing file (Chapter 3).

> 2) Name variables, locate column positions, format, create VARIABLE/VALUE LABELS, and then save the formatted DATA FILE as a SYSTEM FILE (Chapter 4).

From the DOS prompt, type:

> 3) dos > **SPSSPC** ⏎   *This step gets you into the SPSS system.*

To clear the menu from the top window prior to analyzing data:

4)	ALT ⊦ M	*Positions cursor to begin to create the command file.*

From the extreme upper left corner of the scratch pad (lower window), type:

5) **GET FILE** = 'HELPING2.SYS'.	*1*

LINE 1 Accesses the formatted SYSTEM FILE to begin to analyze data. All statistical procedures in this book will begin with the GET FILE step.

To conduct a factor analysis of the 15 self-efficacy questions (EFFIC1 to EFFIC15), type the following two lines into the command file:

6) **GET FILE** = 'HELPING2.SYS'.	*1*
FACTOR VARIABLES = EFFIC1 **TO** EFFIC15.	*2*

LINE 1 Same as line 1 from step 5 (above).
LINE 2 Yes, folks, this single line will conduct an entire factor analysis. The default procedures include:

1. Calculate a correlation matrix from the raw data.
2. Extract 15 factors by the principal-components method.
3. Select as factors to be rotated all factors that have an eigenvalue greater than 1.0.
4. Rotate the selected factors to a Varimax solution.
5. Print out the factor transformation matrix.

Since the 15 efficacy questions are in order in the system file, the TO connector may be used to indicate all 15 variables. If they were not in order, then it would be necessary to type each of the included variables, with a space between each.

This command file conducts a factor analysis and includes a number of optional procedures.

6a) **GET FILE** = 'HELPING2.SYS'.	*1a*
FACTOR VARIABLES = EFFIC1 **TO** EFFIC15/	*2a*
MISSING = LISTWISE/	*3a*
PRINT = INITIAL CORRELATION KMO EXTRACTION ROTATION/	*4a*
FORMAT = SORT/	*5a*
PLOT EIGEN ROTATION (1 2) (1 3) (1 4) (2 3) (2 4) (3 4)/	*6a*
CRITERIA = FACTORS(4)/	*7a*
ROTATION = VARIMAX/	*8a*
ROTATION = OBLIMIN.	*9a*

LINE 1a Same as above.
LINE 2a This step is necessary. Identifying the variables used in the factor analysis will always be the second line when you start from the GET FILE = format. This is identical to line 2 above except it is followed by a slash instead of a period because a subcommand follows.
LINE 3a This step is optional. Several options are possible concerning missing values: (a) Omit this

line and SPSS will omit any subject who has any missing values for any variables (the default). (b) Replace **LISTWISE** (same as the default) with the word **PAIRWISE** to include cases with complete data for each pair of variables (does not delete all data for a subject with missing values). (c) The word **MEANSUB** will replace each missing value by the mean for that variable. For other options, see the *SPSS/PC+ Statistics 4.0 Manual*.

LINE **4a** This step is optional. If this line is omitted, by default SPSS will output **INITIAL** (the initial factor extraction table), **EXTRACTION** (the factor loadings for each of the variables for the initial extraction), and **ROTATION** (factor loadings for each variable after rotating to a Varimax solution). If you use the **PRINT** subcommand, SPSS will output *only* what you designate after the equals sign. In other words, if you want the default output, you must include the words **INITIAL**, **EXTRACTION**, and **ROTATION**. In the line above, we have included **CORRELATION** (this will print out the correlation matrix of the 15 variables) and **KMO** (this is a measure of the sampling adequacy and a test of sphericity or multivariate normality). Other options are described in the *SPSS/PC+ Statistics 4.0 Manual*.

LINE **5a** This step is optional. The **SORT** subcommand allows for easier reading and interpretation of the final output of the rotated solution. It selects the highest factor loading of each variable for each factor and then lists only the highest factor loading under each factor heading and orders them from largest to smallest. See the output for an example.

LINE **6a** This step is optional. This step requests two different kinds of plots. **EIGEN** accesses the scree plot that produces a line graph of the eigenvalues and is used to determine which factors to keep for rotation. The **ROTATION** accesses the pairwise factor plots *after* rotation. This is similar to the second plot we showed in the introductory section. You must designate which plots you wish. We have requested plots showing Factor 1 paired with Factor 2, Factor 1 paired with Factor 3, Factor 1 paired with 4, 2 with 3, 2 with 4, and 3 with 4. This can be tricky because you don't know at the command file stage how many factors will be rotated. The SPSS default is as follows: If (assuming the plots listed above were requested) only three factors were retained, SPSS would simply omit any requested plot that included a "4". If more than four factors were retained, SPSS would display only the plots requested. Final note: Since we have requested both orthogonal (**VARIMAX**) and oblique (**OBLIMIN**) rotations, SPSS will produce two complete sets of graphs: Graphs that show the factor structure after the varimax rotation, and a set of graphs to show the factor structure after the oblique rotations.

LINE **7a** This step is optional. This is the step that identifies the *number* of factors you wish to retain for rotation. If you omit this line, SPSS will simply use the default (any factor with an eigenvalue larger than 1.0). The number in parentheses following **FACTORS** requests that four factors be retained for rotation. Since there were four factors with eigenvalues larger than 1.0, this line is requesting the default.

LINE **8a** This step is optional. If there are no **ROTATION** subcommands present, **VARIMAX** will be used to rotate the factors. In other words, the line above will not influence the analysis in any way, because it requests the default. Other options include **EQUAMAX** or **QUARTIMAX**. See the *SPSS/PC+ Statistics 4.0 Manual* for a description of these procedures.

LINE **9a** This step is optional. The final step of the present file requests oblique rotations to create a better simple structure. This step is truly optional. There are times when it does *not* produce better results than orthogonal rotations. A thorough understanding of factor analysis, the oblique rotation procedure, and your data is critical before attempting this step. The default delta (δ) value is 0. You may request a different starting delta (δ) value by use of an additional **CRITERIA** subcommand. See the *SPSS/PC+ Statistics 4.0 Manual* for specifications on this procedure.

The next command file shows how to conduct a factor analysis by reading a CORRELATION MATRIX into the command file. We show here only the simplest factor analysis, but any of the additional steps shown in step 6a can be included after the VARIABLES = line.

6b) **DATA LIST MATRIX FREE/**   *1b*
　　EFFIC1 EFFIC2 EFFIC3 EFFIC4 EFFIC5 EFFIC6 EFFIC7 EFFIC8 EFFIC9 EFFIC10
　　EFFIC11 EFFIC12 EFFIC13 EFFIC14 EFFIC15.   *2b*
　　N 517.   *3b*
　　BEGIN DATA.   *4b*
　　1.000
　　　.331 1.000
　　　.486　.296 1.000
　　　.435　.182　.419 1.000
　　　.268　.522　.218　.131 1.000
　　　.494　.282　.491　.309　.201 1.000
　　　.359　.338　.370　.335　.294　.454 1.000
　　　.297　.311　.275　.287　.386　.222　.334 1.000
　　　.222　.354　.144　.076　.353　.316　.213　.247 1.000
　　　.361　.178　.363　.487　.175　.288　.393　.294　.055 1.000
　　　.333　.165　.292　.324　.114　.336　.427　.323　.089　.404 1.000
　　　.309　.247　.200　.223　.220　.426　.314　.202　.332　.151　.309
　　1.000
　　　.467　.093　.437　.429　.058　.329　.288　.239　.129　.583　.428
　　　.253 1.000
　　　.322　.183　.250　.343　.161　.271　.147　.232　.228　.346　.305
　　　.290　.430 1.000
　　　.279　.243　.251　.237　.220　.270　.237　.229　.173　.357　.256
　　　.219　.279　.364 1.000   *5b*
　　END DATA.   *6b*
　　FACTOR READ = COR TRIANGLE/   *7b*
　　VARIABLES = EFFIC1 TO EFFIC15.   *8b*

LINE **1b** Indicates that a list of variables follows this line and that a matrix will be read as the data for analysis. The slash following indicates that the variable names will follow.

LINE **2b** We are no longer reading from a system file, and the name of all variables must be listed here. Once these variables are listed, note that in line 8b the **TO** connector may be used. End the variable section with a period.

LINE **3b** This is the format for indicating the number of subjects or cases. End with a period.

LINE **4b** This is the statement included when data are typed into the command file (rather than accessing a data file or a system file). End with a period.

LINE **5b** This is the correlation matrix of the 15 efficacy questions in the **HELPING2.SYS** file. Note the following when typing in a matrix:

- Start from the left margin and line up columns by decimals.
- Leave at least one space between correlation values.
- If lines toward the end of the matrix are too long, return and continue typing on the next line as shown above.
- No punctuation (periods or slashes) are included except for decimal points.

Note the curious lack of any *negative* correlations. This is an oddity of our data set. Apparently no measure of efficacy on one variable is negatively correlated with efficacy on any other variable. If you do have negative values (as you usually will), include the minus sign in front of the appropriate correlations. Remember that the underlining simply indicates that this is data from an example.

LINE 6b Indicates the end of the data; finish with a period.

LINE 7b Instructs SPSS to read a correlation triangle; end with a slash.

LINE 8b This line identifies variables to use in the factor analysis. Following this line, any of the additional options from step 6a may be included. The output of this command file will be identical (within rounding error) to step 6 (above).

7) ┌──────────────┐
    │ F9 │ W │ ↵ │   *to save your command file for future access.*
    └──────────────┘

If file is not already named, enter the file name (e.g., **HELPING2.CTL**) at the prompt between the **W** and the **ENTER**.

To run the program, first position cursor at the beginning of the GET FILE line, then:

8) ┌──────────┐
    │ F10 │ C │   *to run your program from the cursor.*
    └──────────┘

After viewing the results:

9) ┌────────────────────────┐
    │ F10 │ E │ FINISH │ ↵ │   *to exit to the DOS prompt.*
    └────────────────────────┘

To print command files and results:

10) *dos>* **PRINT SPSS.LIS** │ ↵ │ │ ↵ │   *(Sometimes the second RETURN is not necessary.)*

OUTPUT
Factor Analysis

The following OUTPUT *is produced by this* COMMAND FILE. INTERPRETATION *follows each section of output.*

```
GET FILE = 'HELPING2.SYS'.
FACTOR VARIABLES = EFFIC1 TO EFFIC15/
PRINT = INITIAL KMO EXTRACTION ROTATION/
FORMAT = SORT/
PLOT = EIGEN ROTATION (1 2).
```

- - - - FACTOR ANALYSIS - - - -

Kaiser-Meyer-Olkin Measure of Sampling Adequacy = .87149
Bartlett Test of Sphericity = 1321.6964, Signif = .00000
Extraction 1 for Analysis 1, Principal-Components Analysis (PC)
        Initial Statistics:

Variable	Communality	Factor	Eigenvalue	Pct of Var	Cum Pct
EFFIC1	1.00000	1	5.13312	34.2	34.2
EFFIC2	1.00000	2	1.68167	11.2	45.4
EFFIC3	1.00000	3	1.05454	7.0	52.5
EFFIC4	1.00000	4	1.02764	6.9	59.3
EFFIC5	1.00000	5	.88526	5.9	65.2
EFFIC6	1.00000	6	.75858	5.1	70.3
EFFIC7	1.00000	7	.62782	4.2	74.5
EFFIC8	1.00000	8	.62352	4.2	78.6
EFFIC9	1.00000	9	.58902	3.9	82.5
EFFIC10	1.00000	10	.52957	3.5	86.1
EFFIC11	1.00000	11	.49415	3.3	89.4
EFFIC12	1.00000	12	.45801	3.1	92.5
EFFIC13	1.00000	13	.42943	2.9	95.3
EFFIC14	1.00000	14	.39770	2.7	98.0
EFFIC15	1.00000	15	.29998	2.0	100.0

KAISER-MAYER-OLKIN: A measure of whether your distribution of values is adequate for conducting factor analysis. A measure $> .9$ is generally thought of as excellent, $> .8$ as good, $> .7$ as acceptable, $> .6$ as marginal, $> .5$ as poor, and $< .5$ as unacceptable.

BARTLETT TEST OF SPHERICITY: This is essentially a measure of the multivariate normality of your set of distributions. A significance value $< .05$ suggests that these data do not differ significantly from normal.

PRINCIPAL-COMPONENTS ANALYSIS: The default method of factor extraction used by SPSS. Other options are available (e.g., maximum likelihood, using an EXTRACTION = ML/ subcommand).

VARIABLE: All variables used in the factor analysis are listed here.

COMMUNALITY: The default procedure assigns each variable a communality of 1.00. Different communalities may be requested. See the manual for details.

FACTOR: The number of each factor extracted. Note that the first two columns provide information about the *variables*, and the last four provide information about the *factors*.

EIGENVALUE: The proportion of variance explained by each factor.

PCT OF VAR: The percent of variance explained by each factor, the eigenvalue divided by the sum of the communalities (15 in this case). **CUM PCT** is the sum of each step of the previous column.

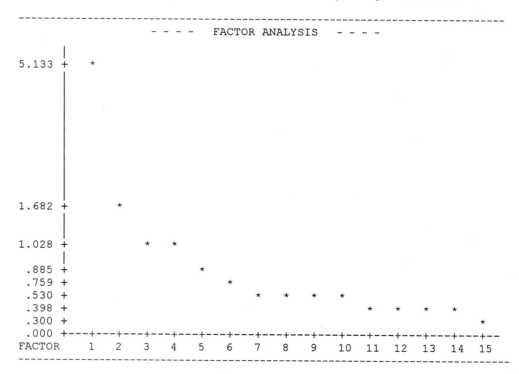

```
-----------------------------------------------------------------------------
                    - - - -    FACTOR ANALYSIS    - - - -
          |
 5.133 +     *
          |
          |
          |
          |
          |
          |
          |
          |
 1.682 +        *
          |
 1.028 +           *    *
          |
  .885 +                 *
  .759 +                    *
  .530 +                       *    *    *    *
  .398 +                                         *    *    *    *
  .300 +                                                             *
  .000 +---+---+---+---+---+---+---+---+---+---+---+---+---+---+---+--
FACTOR    1   2   3   4   5   6   7   8   9  10  11  12  13  14  15
-----------------------------------------------------------------------------
```

This is called a **SCREE PLOT**. It plots the eigenvalues on a bicoordinate plane. It derives its name from the *scree* that is deposited at the base of a landslide. The scree plot is sometimes used to select how many factors to rotate to a final solution. The traditional construct for interpretation is that the scree should be ignored and that only factors on the steep portion of the graph should be selected and rotated. The SPSS default is to select and rotate any factor with an eigenvalue greater than 1.00. Since the default procedure is followed in this example, four (4) factors are selected for rotation.

SPSS will next print out the *unrotated* factor structure. This is rarely of interest to the researcher and, to save space, is not included here. The *rotated* factor structure is displayed next. Note that due to the **FORMAT = SORT/** line in the command file, the factor loadings are sorted in two ways: (a) The highest factor loadings for each factor are selected and listed in separate blocks, and (b) within each block, the factor loadings are sorted from largest to smallest.

To aid in the interpretation of the rotated factor matrix, next to each efficacy variable (**EFFIC1** to **EFFIC15**) the three categories of efficacy are designated:

[Emot]	Efficacy for emotional types of helping
[Inf]	Efficacy for informational types of helping
[Instr]	Efficacy for instrumental types of helping
[----]	The open-ended question

```
----------------------------------------------------------------------
             - - - -   FACTOR ANALYSIS   - - - -

Varimax Rotation 1,  Extraction 1, Analysis 1 --Kaiser Normalization
                    Varimax converged in 10 iterations.
Rotated Factor Matrix

                    FACTOR 1    FACTOR 2    FACTOR 3    FACTOR 4
EFFIC3  [Instr]      .70244      .18090      .02194      .15303
EFFIC4  [Emot]       .64411      .08779      .30150     -.04378
EFFIC7  [Emot]       .63511      .34516     -.09001      .20538
EFFIC10 [Emot]       .62615      .13312      .47208     -.18616
EFFIC13 [Emot]       .61842     -.10041      .50581      .07107
EFFIC1  [Emot]       .61709      .19709      .16230      .29517
EFFIC11 [Inf]        .57348      .04706      .27422      .12529

EFFIC5  [Inf]        .05902      .82762      .08119      .12825
EFFIC2  [Inf]        .16719      .73770      .02421      .23398
EFFIC8  [Inf]        .31273      .59622      .22591     -.05706

EFFIC14 [Emot]       .16316      .04516      .77922      .25387
EFFIC15 [----]       .15667      .25095      .62422      .11266

EFFIC12 [Instr]      .21482      .06421      .19180      .73811
EFFIC9  [Instr]     -.08126      .41802      .17996      .63100
EFFIC6  [Instr]      .57364      .08871     -.00921      .60429
----------------------------------------------------------------------
```

The initial reaction of the researcher who conducted this analysis was "pretty good factor structure!" The first factor is composed primarily of variables that measure efficacy for *emotional* types of helping. One question from instrumental helping ("To what extent did you have the ability to listen carefully, to appraise or to clarify your friend's situation?") and one from informational helping ("Did you believe you were capable of reducing tension and helping your friend get his/her mind off of the problem?") were included in the first factor. Conceptually it is not difficult to see why these two items might load onto the same factor as efficacy for emotional helping.

Factor 2 is composed entirely of the remaining three measures of efficacy for *informational* types of giving. Factor 4 is composed entirely of the remaining three measures of efficacy for *instrumental* types of helping. Factor 3 is a rather strange factor and would likely not be used. Included is the measure of efficacy for *other* types of helping—a measure that the majority of subjects did not answer. The other variable, EFFIC14, is a somewhat strange measure that a number of subjects seemed confused about. It dealt with efficacy for helping the friend reduce self-blame. In many problem situations self-blame was not an issue.

This is the type of thinking a researcher does when attempting to interpret the results from a factor analysis. The present output seems to yield a fairly interpretable pattern of three types of efficacy: Efficacy for emotional types of helping, efficacy for instrumental types of helping, and efficacy for informational types of helping. Factor 3, the strange one, would likely be dropped. Because the two variables in Factor 3 also have factor loadings on the other three factors, the researcher may omit these two variables and run the factor analysis again with just the 13 variables, to see if results differ.

```
--------------------------------------------------------------------------
                - - - -   FACTOR ANALYSIS   - - - -
Factor Transformation Matrix:

            FACTOR 1    FACTOR 2    FACTOR 3    FACTOR 4
FACTOR 1     .73253      .40546      .41863      .35179
FACTOR 2    -.44084      .73618     -.19490      .42040
FACTOR 3    -.11288     -.53791      .01662      .83525
FACTOR 4    -.50628      .06556      .85878     -.04329
--------------------------------------------------------------------------
```

If you multiply the 4 × 4 factor transformation matrix (above) by the original (unrotated) 4 × 15 factor matrix, the result would be the *rotated* factor matrix.

```
--------------------------------------------------------------------------
                - - - -   FACTOR ANALYSIS   - - - -

Horizontal Factor 1  Vertical Factor 2    Symbol   Variable   Coordinates

                     |                       1      EFFIC1    .617   .197
                     |                       2      EFFIC2    .167   .738
                  5 2|                        3      EFFIC3    .702   .181
                     |                       4      EFFIC4    .644   .088
                  8  |                        5      EFFIC5    .059   .828
                     |                       6      EFFIC6    .574   .089
          9          |                       7      EFFIC7    .635   .345
                     |            7           8      EFFIC8    .313   .596
          15         |        1               9      EFFIC9   -.081  .418
                     |       10 3            10      EFFIC10   .626   .133
          |1412      |       11 4            11      EFFIC11   .573   .047
----------------------+----------------------  12      EFFIC12   .215   .064
                     |                      13      EFFIC13   .618  -.100
                     |         13            14      EFFIC14   .163   .045
                     |                      15      EFFIC15   .157   .251
                     |
                     |
                     |
                     |
                     |
                     |
--------------------------------------------------------------------------
```

This is a plot of the factor loadings from Factor 1 and Factor 2. Notice that you can read the identical values (shown in the table to the right) on the rotated factor matrix in the Factor 1 and Factor 2 columns. There are six possible graphs in a four-factor solution. We have shown only one to conserve space. Notice that variables 5, 2, and 8 have the highest factor loadings on Factor 2 (the vertical axis) and relatively low loadings on Factor 1. Also notice that variables 1, 3, 4, 7, 10, 11, and 13 have high loadings on Factor 1 (the horizontal axis) and low loadings on Factor 2. Variables 9, 12, 14, and 15 don't have high loadings on either Factor 1 or Factor 2. SPSS prints out these graphs only after rotation has taken place.

Chapter 22

The CLUSTER Command:

Cluster Analysis

Description of any procedure is often most effectively accomplished by comparison to another procedure. To clarify an understanding of CLUSTER ANALYSIS, we will compare it to FACTOR ANALYSIS. Cluster analysis is in some ways similar to factor analysis (Chapter 21), but it also differs in several important ways. If you are unfamiliar with factor analysis, please read through the introduction of Chapter 21 before attempting this chapter. The introductory paragraphs of this section will compare and contrast cluster analysis with factor analysis. Following this, the sequential steps of the cluster analysis procedure will be identified, along with a description of the data set used as an example to aid in the understanding of each step of the process. This introductory section will conclude with the logical progression for conducting cluster analysis.

CLUSTER ANALYSIS AND FACTOR ANALYSIS COMPARED AND CONTRASTED

Cluster analysis and factor analysis are similar in that both procedures take a larger number of cases or variables and reduce them to a smaller number of factors (or clusters) based on some sort of similarity that members within a group share. However, the statistical procedure underlying each type of analysis and the ways that output is interpreted are often quite different:

1. Factor analysis is used to reduce a larger number of *variables* to a smaller number of factors that describe these variables. While it is possible for the CLUSTER command to group *variables* into larger clusters (described in step 5 of this section and demonstrated in the Step by Step section), the SPSS procedure is primarily designed to use variables as criteria for grouping (agglomerating) *subjects* or *cases* (not variables) into groups, based on each subject's (or case's) scores on a given set of variables. For instance: With a data set of 500 subjects measured on 15 different types of helping

behavior (the variables), factor analysis might be used to extract factors that describe 3 or 4 categories or types of helping based on the 15 help variables. Cluster analysis is more likely to be used with a data set that includes, for instance, 21 cases (such as brands of VCRs) with perhaps 15 variables that identify characteristics of each of the 21 VCRs. Rather than the *variables* being clustered (as in factor analysis), the cases (VCRs here) would be clustered into groups that shared similar features with each other. The result might be three or four clusters of brands of VCRs that share similarities such as price, quality of picture, extra features, reliability of the product, and so on.

2. A large number of variables and/or cases (e.g., 1,000 subjects with 100 variables) can be used fairly comfortably to conduct factor analysis on a PC. In cluster analysis, if the researcher moves beyond 100 cases with 10 to 15 variables each, the memory demands required to conduct cluster analysis expand geometrically, and "Not sufficient memory to conduct cluster analysis" is a frequently observed error message.

3. The statistical procedures involved are radically different for each process. Factor analysis analyzes all variables at each factor extraction step to calculate the variance that each variable contributes to that factor. Cluster analysis calculates a *similarity* or a *distance* measure between each subject or case and every other subject or case (you can see why a large *N* would create an unmanageable number of pairwise comparisons), and then it groups the two subjects/cases that have the greatest similarity or the least distance into a cluster of two. Then it computes the similarity or distance measures all over again and either combines the next two subjects/cases that are closest or (if the distance is smaller) combines the next case with the cluster of two already formed (yielding either two clusters of two cases each, or one cluster of three cases). This process continues until all cases are grouped into one large cluster containing all cases. The researcher decides at which stage to stop the clustering process.

4. As SPSS has configured the **CLUSTER** command, it is better suited for use in business, sociology, or political science (e.g., categories of the 25 best-selling brands of TVs; classification of 40 communities based on several demographic variables; groupings of the 30 most populous cities based on age, SES, and political affiliation) than for use in psychology. Psychologists are more often trying to find similarities between variables or underlying causes for phenomena than trying to divide their subjects into groups via some sort of mathematical construct; and when psychologists *are* trying to divide subjects into groups, discriminant analysis (Chapter 23) often accomplishes the process more efficiently than does cluster analysis.

5. It is possible to use cluster analysis to accomplish something similar to factor analysis—that is, cluster variables (rather than subjects or cases) into similar groups. In order to do so, the researcher must read into the command file a matrix of similarity values (such as a correlation or a covariance matrix), and the **CLUSTER** command will then combine variables in the same way that it normally combines cases. It is often of interest, when working with an appropriate data set, to see how cluster analysis and factor analysis group variables differently. This procedure is illustrated in the Step by Step section of this chapter.

THE EXAMPLE, AND PROCEDURES FOR CONDUCTING CLUSTER ANALYSIS

Cluster analysis goes through a sequence of procedures to come up with a final solution. To assist understanding, before we describe these procedures we will introduce the example constructed for this analysis and use it to clarify each step. Cluster analysis would not be appropriate for either the GRADES.SYS file or the HELPING.SYS file. In each data set the cases are subjects, and there is little rationale for wanting to cluster subjects. We turn instead to a data set that is more appropriate for cluster analysis. This is the only chapter in which these data will be used. It consists of a modified analysis from the magazine *Consumer Reports* on the quality of the top 21 brands of VCRs. The system file associated with this data set will be called VCR.SYS. While this began as factual information, we have "doctored" the data to help create a clearer cluster structure and thus serve as a more convincing example. Because of this, the brand names in the data set are also fictional.

Step 1: Select variables to be used as criteria for cluster formation. In the VCR.SYS file, cluster analysis will be conducted based on the following variables (listed in the order shown in the first Output display): Price, picture quality (5 measures), reception quality (3 measures), audio quality (3 measures), ease of programming (1 measure), number of events (1 measure), number of days for future programming (1 measure), remote control features (3 measures), and extras (3 measures).

Step 2: Select the procedure for measuring distance or similarity between each case or cluster (initially, each case is a cluster of one, the 21 brands of VCRs). The SPSS default for this measure is called the *squared Euclidean distance*, and it is simply the sum of the squared differences for each variable for each case. For instance, Brand A may have scores of 2, 3, 5 for the three audio ratings. Brand B may have ratings of 4, 3, 2, for the same three measures. Squared Euclidean distance for these three measures would be $(2 - 4)^2 + (3 - 3)^2 + (5 - 2)^2 = 13$. In the actual analysis, these squared differences would be summed for all 21 variables for each brand, yielding a numeric measure of the distance between each pair of brands. SPSS provides for the use of measures other than squared Euclidean distance to determining distance or similarity between clusters. These are described in the *SPSS/PC+ Statistics 4.0 Manual*.

A question that may come to mind is, will the cluster procedure be valid if the scales of measurement for the variables are different? In the VCR.SYS file, most measures are rated on a 5-point scale from *much poorer than average*(1) to *much better than average*(5). But the listed prices fluctuate between $200 and $525, and events, days, and extras are simply the actual numbers associated with those variables. The solution suggested by SPSS is to standardize all variables—that is, change each variable to a *z*-score (with a mean of 0 and a standard deviation of 1). This will give each variable equal weight. If all variables are already in the same metric, or if you wish to retain the weighting of the original values, then it is not necessary to change to *z*-scores.

Step 3: Form clusters. There are two basic methods for forming clusters, agglomerative and divisive. For agglomerative hierarchical clustering, SPSS groups cases into progressively larger clusters until all cases are in one large cluster. In divisive hierarchical clustering, the opposite procedure takes place. All cases are grouped into one large cluster, and clusters are split at each step until the desired number of clusters is achieved. The agglomerative procedure is the SPSS default and will be presented here.

Within the agglomerative framework, there are several options of mathematical procedures for combining clusters. The default procedure is called the *average linkage within groups*. SPSS computes the smallest average distance between all group pairs and combines the two groups that are closest. Note that in the initial phase (when all clusters are individual cases), the average distance is simply the computed distance between pairs of cases. Only when actual clusters are formed does the term *average* distance apply. The procedure begins with as many clusters as there are cases (21 in the **VCR.SYS** file). At step one, the two cases with the smallest distance between them are clustered. Then SPSS computes distances once more and combines the two that are next closest. After the second step you will have either 18 individual cases and one cluster of 3 cases, or 17 individual cases and two clusters of two cases each. This process continues until all cases are grouped into one large cluster. Other methods of clustering cases are described in the *SPSS/PC+ Statistics 4.0 Manual*.

Step 4: Interpreting results. Similarly to factor analysis, interpretation and number of clusters to accept as a final solution are largely a matter of the interpretation of the researcher. In the **VCR.SYS** file a three-cluster solution seemed best. There appeared to be three primary qualities that differentiated among groups: The first group was highest in price ($M = \$511.67$), highest in picture quality ($M = 5.00$), and had the greatest number of additional features ($M = 10.8$). The second group contained VCRs that were moderate in price, medium to low on picture quality, and had a smaller number of additional features (\$400.00, 3.00, and 7.8, respectively). The third group contained the budget models (\$262.22, 2.78, and 3.0). The other variables did not seem to contribute to the clustering in any systematic way.

The order followed for the description of cluster analysis in the Step by Step section will be similar to that followed in the chapters that present the more complex statistical procedures. Sequence steps 1-5 and 7-10 will be identical to other chapters. There will be three versions of step 6. The first (step 6) will be the simplest default procedure for conducting cluster analysis. The second (step 6a) will include a number of additional available options to tailor your program to fit your particular needs or to produce additional desired output. The last presentation (step 6b) will show how to conduct cluster analysis of variables (rather than subjects or cases) by reading into the command file a matrix of similarity values (correlations in this case). As usual, the reader will be referred to the *SPSS/PC+ Statistics 4.0 Manual* for additional options that extend beyond the scope of this book.

The best resource on cluster analysis known to the authors is by Brian S. Everitt (1993). Please see the reference section for additional information about this book.

THE LOGICAL PROGRESSION FOR CONDUCTING CLUSTER ANALYSIS

1. Create file of data, or edit (if necessary) an already existing file.
2. Format file by use of **DATA LIST FILE**, **FORMATS**, and **VARIABLE/VALUE LABELS**; then save as a **SYSTEM FILE**.
3. Access file and formats by the **GET FILE** command.
4. Use the **DESCRIPTIVES** command to access certain information about the nature of the variables.
5. Use the **OPTIONS** subcommand to change all variables to z-scores to generate equal metrics for cluster analysis.
6. Use the **FORMATS** command to create an acceptable format for the z-scores.
7. Use the **CLUSTER** command to conduct cluster analysis.
8. Use the **ID** subcommand to identify cases or subjects by name.
9. Use the **METHOD** subcommand to identify criteria for clustering cases.
10. Use the **PRINT** subcommand to request analyses of the cluster structure after a specific number of steps or after a certain number of clusters have been formed, to request a matrix of distances or similarities, or to suppress all tables.
11. Use the **PLOT** subcommand to request horizontal icicle plots or dendograms (the vertical icicle plot is printed by default).
12. View the results and exit the program.
13. Print data, commands, and output.

STEP BY STEP
Cluster Analysis

---

1) *Name and create a data file (Chapter 2), or edit (if necessary) an already existing file (Chapter 3).*

---

2) *Name variables, locate column positions, format, create VARIABLE/VALUE LABELS, and then save the formatted DATA FILE as a SYSTEM FILE (Chapter 4).*

From the DOS prompt, type:

---

3) *dos* > **SPSSPC** | ← | *This step gets you into the SPSS system.*

To clear the menu from the top window prior to analyzing data:

4) ALT ─ M	*Positions cursor to begin to create the command file.*

From the extreme upper left corner of the scratch pad (lower window), type:

5) **GET FILE** = 'VCR.SYS'.	*1*

LINE 1 Accesses the formatted **SYSTEM FILE** to begin to analyze data. All statistical procedures in this book will begin with the **GET FILE** step.

This command file presents the simplest possible cluster analysis. Although steps 2, 3, and 4 (changing all variables to z-scores) are not technically necessary to conduct cluster analysis, their inclusion underlines the importance of the variables having equal metrics to conduct a meaningful investigation.

6) **GET FILE** = 'VCR.SYS'.	*1*
DESCRIPTIVES VARIABLES = PRICE TO EXTRAS3/	*2*
OPTIONS = 3.	*3*
FORMATS ZPRICE TO ZEXTRAS3(F8.6).	*4*
CLUSTER ZPRICE TO ZEXTRAS3.	*5*

LINE 1 Same as step 5, line 1 above.

LINE 2 This line prints out the default descriptives (mean, standard deviation, maximum, minimum, and *N*) for all variables used in cluster analysis. While this step is not technically necessary, it identifies the nature of your variables so you can decide if changing to z-scores is necessary. If metrics of each variable are already identical (they aren't here), then end this line with a period (.) and omit lines 3 and 4. A word of caution: If any variable has a standard deviation of zero (meaning all values for that variable are the same for every subject), cluster analysis will not run. It is necessary to eliminate that variable before using the **CLUSTER** procedure.

LINE 3 **OPTIONS** = **3** changes all variables to z-scores. It also renames each variable by adding a **Z** to the front of each variable name. If the added **Z** extends the variable name to 9 characters, then the final letter of the variable name is dropped. Note before conducting this analysis whether this procedure will create identical variable names (e.g., **FEATURE1**, **FEATURE2** would change to **ZFEATURE**, **ZFEATURE**). An error message will flash if this happens.

LINE 4 It is important to include a formats statement to allow space for up to six decimals to accommodate the z-scores without losing information.

LINE 5 This is the line that conducts the default cluster analysis. The output will include a table of the "agglomeration schedule using average linkage between groups," and a vertical icicle plot (see Output section) to illustrate the previous table.

This command file presents a cluster analysis that includes options for a number of additional specifications and outputs. Each sequence step is identified as necessary or optional and descriptions of each line follow the command file. Optional items may simply be deleted (with attention to period (.) or slash (/) following the previous line) if that procedure is not desired.

```
6a) GET FILE = 'VCR.SYS'.                                          1a
     DESCRIPTIVES VARIABLES = PRICE TO EXTRAS3/                    2a
     OPTIONS = 3.                                                  3a
     FORMATS ZPRICE TO ZEXTRAS3(F8.6).                            4a
     CLUSTER ZPRICE TO ZEXTRAS3/                                   5a
     ID = BRAND/                                                   6a
     METHOD = COMPLETE/                                            7a
     PRINT = SCHEDULE CLUSTER(3,5) DISTANCE/                       8a
     PLOT = VICICLE HICICLE DENDOGRAM.                            9a
```

LINES 1a-5a Identical to lines 1-5 in sequence step 6 above, except that line 5a ends with a slash instead of a period to indicate that a subcommand follows.

LINE 6a Optional, but very desirable. This step will print the name of each case (the brand of VCR in this case), rather than just the sequence number, in all outputs. Of course, a **BRAND** variable must be included in the original data file with the name of each brand included for each case.

LINE 7a This step is optional. It requests SPSS to use the *complete linkage* procedure to cluster variables. If this step is omitted, SPSS will use the **BAVERAGE** (or average linkage between groups) method. Additional methods include **WAVERAGE** (average linkage within groups) and **SINGLE** (single linkage or nearest neighbor). Other methods are available, and each of these clustering procedures may be used with the default method for measuring similarities, the squared Euclidean distance. A more complete description of each method is found in the *SPSS/PC+ Statistics 4.0 Manual*.

LINE 8a This step is optional. If this step is omitted, SPSS will print out the **SCHEDULE** (a table of step-by-step clustering and the distance coefficient between each linked group at each step—see Output) by default. If the **PRINT** subcommand is used, it is *necessary* to request **SCHEDULE** if you wish to include it in your output. **CLUSTER(m,n)** is used if you wish to display a limited range of the output. In the command file above, the designated range **(3,5)** requests a printout of the cluster structure when 3, 4, and 5 clusters have formed. Any numbers (less than or equal to the number of cases) may be included here. **DISTANCE** will print out a matrix of differences or similarities between each pair of cases—that is, an $(N - 1) \times (N - 1)$ matrix. If the **PRINT** subcommand were not used, this matrix of distances would be printed by default. However, if you use the **PRINT** subcommand, you must request it specifically. The cluster command provides several different measures of distance and one measure of similarity. These must be accessed through the **MEASURE** subcommand (see the *SPSS/PC+ Statistics 4.0 Manual* for details).

LINE 9a This step is optional. If this line is omitted, a **VICICLE** plot (vertical icicle plot) will be printed by default. If you use the **PLOT** subcommand, however, you must specifically request the **VICICLE** plot. The **HICICLE** plot is the horizontal icicle plot. It is identical to the vertical icicle plot, except that case names are listed in a column to the left (rather than at the top) and the histogram is horizontal. The vertical plot is generally preferred because it can display up to 25 cases on one page, while the horizontal plot can manage no better than 15 without a page break. The **DENDOGRAM** provides a tree-type graphical display of the step-by-step clustering process. See the Output section for an example.

You can conduct a procedure similar to factor analysis (clustering variables rather than cases/subjects) by reading in a matrix of similarities. There are several methods for computing similarities (e.g., correlations, covariances, or other weighted composites—the manual does not describe these) that may be used for this type of input. What is shown here is a correlation matrix of the efficacy measures that were used in the factor analysis chapter (Chapter 21).

```
6b)  DATA LIST MATRIX FREE/                                                    1b
     EFFIC1 EFFIC2 EFFIC3 EFFIC4 EFFIC5 EFFIC6 EFFIC7 EFFIC8 EFFIC9 EFFIC10
     EFFIC11 EFFIC12 EFFIC13 EFFIC14 EFFIC15.                                   2b
     N 517.                                                                     3b
     BEGIN DATA.                                                               4b
     1.000
      .331 1.000
      .486  .296 1.000
      .435  .182  .419 1.000
      .268  .522  .218  .131 1.000
      .494  .282  .491  .309  .201 1.000
      .359  .338  .370  .335  .294  .454 1.000
      .297  .311  .275  .287  .386  .222  .334 1.000
      .222  .354  .144  .076  .353  .316  .213  .247 1.000
      .361  .178  .363  .487  .175  .288  .393  .294  .055 1.000
      .333  .165  .292  .324  .114  .336  .427  .323  .089  .404 1.000
      .309  .247  .200  .223  .220  .426  .314  .202  .332  .151  .309
     1.000
      .467  .093  .437  .429  .058  .329  .288  .239  .129  .583  .428
      .253 1.000
      .322  .183  .250  .343  .161  .271  .147  .232  .228  .346  .305
      .290  .430 1.000
      .279  .243  .251  .237  .220  .270  .237  .229  .173  .357  .256
      .219  .279  .364 1.000                                                   5b
     END DATA.                                                                 6b
     CLUSTER EFFIC1 TO EFFIC15/                                                7b
     READ = TRIANGLE SIMILAR.                                                  8b
```

LINE **1b** This line tells the computer that a list of variables will follow and that a matrix will be read as the data for analysis. The slash that follows precedes the list of variable names.

LINE **2b** We are no longer reading from a system file, and the name of all variables must be listed here. Once these variables are listed, note that in line 7b the **TO** connector may be used to indicate any consecutive subset (or all) of these variables. End the variable section with a period.

LINE **3b** This is the format for indicating the number of subjects or cases. End with a period.

LINE **4b** This is the statement used when data is included in the command file. End with a period.

LINE **5b** This is the correlation matrix of the 15 efficacy questions in the HELPING2.SYS file. Note the following when typing in a matrix:

  • Start from the left margin and line up columns by decimals.
  • Leave at least one space between correlation values.
  • If lines toward the end of the matrix are too long, return and continue typing on the next line as shown above.
  • No punctuation (periods or slashes) are included, except for decimal points.

Note the lack of any *negative* correlations. For conducting cluster analysis with a correlation matrix, omit all negative signs unless you wish clusters of *positive* correlations only. Remember that the underlining simply indicates that this is data from an example.

LINE **6b** Indicates the end of the data. End with a period.

LINE 7b Instructs SPSS to conduct cluster analysis with the 15 efficacy questions. This line is always followed by a slash because the following line instructs the computer how to read the matrix of data.

LINE 8b The **READ** subcommand identifies the data as triangular in format and indicates that the values are similarities (rather than distances).

Note: This command file represents the simplest possible cluster analysis that reads a matrix of similarities as data. If you wish to request other options (e.g., step 6a, lines 6a-9a), replace the period following **SIMILAR** with a slash and type additional lines of input.

7) `F9` `W` `↵`   *to save your command file for future access.*

If file is not already named, enter the file name (e.g., **VCR.CTL**) at the prompt between the **W** and the **ENTER**.

To run the program, first position cursor at the beginning of the GET FILE line, then:

8) `F10` `C`   *to run your program from the cursor.*

After viewing the results:

9) `F10` `E` **FINISH** `↵`   *to exit to the DOS prompt.*

To print command files and results:

10) *dos>* **PRINT SPSS.LIS** `↵` `↵`   *(Sometimes the second RETURN is not necessary.)*

OUTPUT
Cluster Analysis

The following OUTPUT is produced by this COMMAND FILE. INTERPRETATION follows each portion of output.

```
GET FILE = 'VCR.SYS'.
LIST.
DESCRIPTIVES VARIABLES = PRICE TO EXTRAS3/
OPTIONS = 3.
FORMATS ZPRICE TO ZEXTRAS3(F8.6).
CLUSTER ZPRICE TO ZEXTRAS3/
ID = BRAND/
METHOD = COMPLETE/
PLOT = VICICLE DENDOGRAM.
```

```
------------------------------------------------------------------------
* * * H I E R A R C H I C A L    C L U S T E R    A N A L Y S I S * * *

              P P P P P R R R          F        R R R  E   E   E
              I I I I E E E A A E E              E E E  X   X   X
            P C C C C C C C C U U A V            M M M  T   T   T
            R T T T T T E E E D D T E            D O O  R   R   R
            I U U U U U P P P I I U N            A T T  A   A   A
            C R R R R R T T T O O R T            Y E E  S   S   S
BRAND       E 1 2 3 4 5 1 2 3 1 2 3 E S          S 1 2  1   2   3
```

BRAND	PRICE	PICTUR1	PICTUR2	PICTUR3	PICTUR4	PICTUR5	RECEPT1	RECEPT2	RECEPT3	AUDIO1	AUDIO2	AUDIO3	FEATURE	FEATURES	REMDAYS	REMOTE1	REMOTE2	REMOTE3	EXTRAS1	EXTRAS2	EXTRAS3
SONNY	520	5	5	5	5	5	4	3	3	5	3	3	5	8	31	4	4	4	13	13	13
ANGLER	535	5	5	5	5	5	3	4	3	5	4	4	4	6	365	3	4	4	12	12	12
MITTENSUB	515	5	5	5	5	5	4	3	3	5	3	3	5	8	28	4	4	4	13	13	13
SINGBO	470	5	5	5	5	5	3	3	3	3	3	4	4	6	365	2	4	4	7	7	7
WHACKACHY	525	5	5	5	5	5	2	4	3	4	3	4	4	6	365	4	3	3	11	11	11
SILVERMOON	370	4	4	4	4	4	3	3	3	5	4	5	5	6	365	3	4	4	8	8	8
EXPERTSEE	430	4	4	4	4	4	5	3	4	4	5	4	4	8	365	4	4	4	8	8	8
FROMSHEEBA	505	5	5	5	5	5	3	4	2	4	4	4	4	8	365	3	3	3	9	9	9
POTASONIC1	450	3	3	3	3	3	3	3	3	4	4	4	4	8	30	3	3	3	8	8	8
CLIMAX	365	4	4	4	4	4	2	3	3	4	4	4	3	8	365	4	2	2	4	4	4
POTASONIC2	435	3	3	3	3	3	3	3	3	4	3	4	4	4	30	4	4	4	9	9	9
MAGNESIA	265	3	3	3	3	3	3	4	2	4	4	4	3	8	365	4	4	4	3	3	3
DULL	200	3	3	3	3	3	3	4	2	4	4	4	4	8	365	3	3	3	3	3	3
BURSTINGSTAR	380	2	2	2	2	2	3	3	3	4	4	4	4	4	30	4	4	4	6	6	6
VCJ	420	3	3	3	3	3	2	4	3	4	4	4	4	8	365	2	3	2	6	6	6
ARC	335	2	2	2	2	2	5	4	3	5	3	4	5	8	365	3	2	3	8	8	8
MAGNETOX	205	3	3	3	3	3	3	4	1	3	4	3	3	8	365	4	4	4	3	3	3
RECALLAKING	200	3	3	3	3	3	3	4	2	3	4	4	4	8	365	3	3	3	4	4	4
PAULSANG	205	2	2	2	2	2	3	2	4	4	4	3	4	6	365	3	4	2	2	2	2
EG	275	2	2	2	2	2	3	4	2	4	4	4	3	8	365	3	3	3	2	2	2
RASES	225	2	2	2	2	2	3	4	2	4	4	4	3	8	365	3	4	2	0	0	0

```
------------------------------------------------------------------------
```

This is simply the data file with brand names to the left and variable names along the top. The second line (**LIST.**) of the command file accesses this output. Since the file with cluster analysis is usually fairly short, it is often a good idea to print it out because it makes an excellent reference as you attempt to interpret the clustering patterns. As mentioned in the introduction, we began with real data but have since doctored them (the brand names too) to create a more interpretable cluster pattern.

Following this listing, descriptive statistics for each variable will be printed out (mean, standard deviation, minimum, maximum, and N), followed by a listing of the new variable names after they have been changed to z-scores (e.g., **PRICE** becomes **ZPRICE**; **PICTUR1** becomes **ZPICTUR1**; **PICTUR2**, **ZPICTUR2**; and so forth). Since these data are straightforward, we will save space by not reproducing them.

```
------------------------------------------------------------------------
* * * H I E R A R C H I C A L    C L U S T E R    A N A L Y S I S * * *

   21 unweighted cases accepted.
   0 cases rejected because of missing values
Squared Euclidean measure used.
1 Agglomeration method specified:   Complete Linkage
```

	Clusters Combined			Stage Cluster 1st Appears		
Stage	Cluster 1	Cluster 2	Coefficient	Cluster 1	Cluster 2	Next Stage
1	1	3	.002120	0	0	17
2	13	18	2.707647	0	0	9
3	12	17	4.978950	0	0	14
4	20	21	5.014226	0	0	7
5	11	14	8.508929	0	0	10
6	5	8	11.724795	0	0	8
7	19	20	11.871443	0	4	14
8	2	5	13.173624	0	6	13
9	13	15	14.316567	2	0	12
10	**9**	**11**	**19.832735**	**0**	**5**	**15**
11	6	7	22.900782	0	0	15
12	10	13	23.879719	0	9	16
13	2	4	28.378151	8	0	17
14	**12**	**19**	**31.666840**	**3**	**7**	**16**
15	6	9	40.469818	11	10	18
16	10	12	44.623737	12	14	19
17	1	2	47.720360	1	13	20
18	6	16	49.963055	15	0	19
19	6	10	64.785378	18	16	20
20	1	6	115.780998	17	19	0

The procedure followed by cluster analysis at Stage 1 is to cluster the two cases that have the smallest squared Euclidean distance between them. Then SPSS will recompute the distance measures between all single cases and clusters (there is only one cluster of two cases after the first step). Next, the 2 cases (or clusters) with the smallest distance will be combined, yielding either 2 clusters of 2 cases (with 17 cases unclustered) or one cluster of 3 (with 18 cases unclustered). This process continues until all cases are clustered into a single group. To clarify, we will explain Stages 1, 10, and 14 (shown above).

At **STAGE 1**, Case 1 is clustered with Case 3. The squared Euclidean distance between these two cases is .00212. Neither variable has been previously clustered (the two zeros under Cluster 1 and Cluster 2), and the next stage (when the cluster containing Case 1 combines with another case) is Stage 17. (Note that at Stage 17, Case 2 joins the Case-1 cluster.)

At **STAGE 10**, Case 9 joins the Case-11 cluster (Case 11 was previously clustered with Case 14 back in Stage 5, thus creating a cluster of 3 cases: Cases 9, 11, and 14). The squared Euclidean distance between Case 9 and the Case-11 cluster is 19.832735. Case 9 has not been previously clustered (the zero under Cluster 1), and Case 11 was previously clustered at Stage 5. The next stage (when the cluster containing Case 9 clusters) is Stage 15 (when it combines with the Case-6 cluster).

At **STAGE 14**, the clusters containing Cases 12 and 19 are joined. Case 12 had been previously clustered with Case 17, and Case 19 had been previously clustered with Cases 20 and 21, thus forming a cluster of 5 cases (Cases 12, 17, 19, 20, 21). The squared Euclidean distance between the two joined clusters is 31.666840. Case 12 was previously joined at Stage 3 with Case 17. Case 19 was previously joined at Stage 7 with the Case-20 cluster. The next stage when the Case-12 cluster will combine with another case/cluster is Stage 16 (when it joins with the Case-10 cluster).

The icicle plot (that follows) displays the same information graphically:

```
-------------------------------------------------------------------------------
Vertical Icicle Plot using Complete Linkage

(Down) Number of Clusters        (Across) Case Label and number

          ----------LOW----------   -----MEDIUM-----  ------HIGH------
          R  E  P  M  M  V  R  D  C  A  B  P  P  E  S  S  F  W  A  M  S
          A  G  A  A  A  C  E  U  L  R  U  O  O  X  I  I  R  H  N  I  O
          S     U  G  G  J  C  L  I  C  R  T  T  P  L  N  O  A  G  T  N
          E     L  N  N     A  L  M     S  A  A  E  V  G  M  C  L  T  N
          S     S  E  E     L     A     T  S  S  R  E  B  S  K  E  E  Y
                A  T  S     L     X     I  O  O  T  R  O  H  A  R  N
                N  O  I     A           N  N  N  S  M     E  C     S
                G  X  A     K           G  I  I  E  O     E  H     U
                            I           S  C  C  E  O     B  Y     B
                            N           T  2        N     A

       2  2  1  1  1  1  1  1  1  1  1  1
       1  0  9  7  2  5  8  3  0  6  4  1  9  7  6  4  8  5  2  3  1
   1  |***********************************************************
   2  |*************************************************  ****************
 3->|*************************** ***************** ****************<-
   4  |************************ *  ************* ****************
   5  |************************ *  *************  **********  ****
   6  |*************  **********  *  *************  **********  ****
   7  |*************  *********  *  *******  ****  **********  ****
   8  |*******  ****  **********  *  *******  ****  **********  ****
   9  |*******  ****  **********  *  *******  ****  *  *******  ****
  10  |*******  ****  *******  *  *  *******  ****  *  *******  ****
  11  |*******  ****  *******  *  *  *******  *  *  *  *******  ****
  12  |*******  ****  *******  *  *  ****  *  *  *  *  *******  ****
  13  |*******  ****  *  ****  *  *  ****  *  *  *  *  *******  ****
  14  |*******  ****  *  ****  *  *  ****  *  *  *  *  ****  *  ****
  15  |****  *  ****  *  ****  *  *  ****  *  *  *  *  ****  *  ****
  16  |****  *  ****  *  ****  *  *  ****  *  *  *  *  *  *  ****
  17  |****  *  ****  *  ****  *  *  *  *  *  *  *  *  *  *  ****
  18  |*  *  *  ****  *  ****  *  *  *  *  *  *  *  *  *  *  ****
  19  |*  *  *  *  *  *  ****  *  *  *  *  *  *  *  *  *  *  ****
  20  |*  *  *  *  *  *  *  *  *  *  *  *  *  *  *  *  *  ****
-------------------------------------------------------------------------------
```

This graph displays the same information as the agglomeration schedule table except that the value of the distance measure is not shown. The numbers to the left indicate the number of clusters at each level. For instance, the line opposite the "20" has 20 clusters, 19 individual cases, and brands 1 and 3 joined into a single cluster. Notice the bold face and the arrows to the right of the "3". At this stage there are 3 clusters, and the experimenters determined that 3 clusters was the most meaningful solution. As you may recall from the introduction, the cluster containing Brands 1, 2, 3, 4, 5, and 8 are VCRs characterized by high price, high picture quality, and many features. The second cluster, Brands 6, 7, 9, 11, 14, and 16, are VCRs characterized by medium-range price, lower picture quality, and fewer features. The final cluster, Brands 10, 12, 13, 15, 17, 18, 19, 20, and 21, are budget models with low price, medium picture quality, and few features.

The dendogram, a tree-type display of the clustering process, is the final output display.

```
------------------------------------------------------------------------------
Dendogram using Complete Linkage


                                  Rescaled Distance Cluster Combine

      C A S E         0        5        10        15        20        25
    Label           Seq +---------+---------+---------+---------+---------+
                        |
    SONNY            1  |-+-------------------+
    MITTENSUB        3  |-+                   |
    WHACKACHY        5  |-----+             +-- -----------------------+
    FROMSHEEBA       8  |-----+-------+     |                          |
    ANGLER           2  |-----+       +-------+                        |
    SINGBO           4  |-------------+                                |
    DULL            13  |-+-----+                                      |
    RECALLAKING     18  |-+     +---+                                  |
    VCJ             15  |-------+   +-------+                          |
    CLIMAX          10  |-----------+       +---- --+                  |
    MAGNESIA        12  |---+---------+     |       |                  |
    MAGNETOX        17  |---+         +-----+       |                  |
    EG              20  |---+-+       |            |                  |
    RASES           21  |---+ +-------+             +--------------------+
    PAULSANG        19  |-----+                     |
    POTASONIC2      11  |---+-----+                 |
    BURSTINGSTAR    14  |---+     +-------+         |
    POTASONIC1       9  |---------+       +---+     |
    SILVERMOON       6  |---------+-------+   +-- --+
    EXPERTSEE        7  |---------+           |
    ARC             16  |-------------------+ |
------------------------------------------------------------------------------
```

All three of the visual displays of the clustering procedure (the agglomeration table, the icicle plot, and the dendogram) provide slightly different information about the process. In addition to the branching-type nature of the dendogram, which allows the researcher to trace backward or forward to any individual case or clusters at any level, it adds an additional feature that the icicle plot does not. The 0 to 25 scale along the top of the chart gives an idea of how great the distance was between cases or groups that are clustered at a particular step. The distance measure has been rescaled from 0 to 25, with 0 representing no distance and 25 rating the greatest distance. While it is difficult to interpret distance in the early clustering phases (the extreme left of the graph), as you move to the right relative distances become more apparent.

Note the vertical line (provided by the authors) that designates the three-cluster solution. A similar vertical line placed in different positions on the graph will reveal the number of clusters at any stage by the number of horizontal lines that are crossed. To find the membership of a particular cluster, simply trace backwards down the branches (or is it roots?) to the name and case number.

Chapter 23

The DSCRIMINANT Command:

Discriminant Analysis

Discriminant analysis is used primarily to predict membership in two or more mutually exclusive groups. The procedure for predicting membership is initially to analyze pertinent variables where the group membership is already known. For instance, a top research university wishes to predict whether applicants will complete a Ph.D. program successfully. Such a university will have many years of records of entry characteristics of applicants and additional information about whether they completed the Ph.D. and how long it took them. They thus have sufficient information to use discriminant analysis. They can identify two discrete groups (those who completed the Ph.D. and those who did not) and make use of entry information such as GPAs, GRE scores, letters of recommendation, and additional biographical information. From these variables it is possible to create a formula that maximally differentiates between the two groups. This formula (if it discriminates successfully) could be used to analyze the likelihood of success for future applicants. There are many circumstances where it is desirable to be able to predict with some degree of certainty outcomes based on measurable criteria: Is an applicant for a particular job likely to be successful or not? Can we identify whether mentally ill patients are suffering from schizophrenia, bipolar mood disorder, or psychosis? If a prisoner is paroled, is he or she likely to return to crime or become a productive citizen? What factors might influence whether a person is at risk to suffer a heart attack or not? The elements common to all five of these examples are that (1) group membership is known for many individuals, and (2) large volumes of information are available to create formulas that might predict future outcomes better than current instruments.

By way of comparison, discriminant analysis is similar to cluster analysis (Chapter 22) in that the researcher is attempting to divide individuals or cases (not *variables*) into discrete groups. It differs from cluster analysis in the procedure for creating the groups. Discriminant analysis creates a regression equation (Chapters 19 and 20) that makes use of a dependent (criterion) variable that is discrete rather than continuous. Based on preexisting data in which group membership is already known, a regression equation can be computed that maximally discriminates between the two groups. The regression equation can then be used to help predict group membership in future instances. Discriminant analysis is a complex procedure and the **DSCRIMINANT** command contains many options and features that extend beyond the scope of this book. We will therefore, throughout this chapter, refer you to the *SPSS/PC+ Advanced Statistics 4.0 Manual* for additional options when appropriate.

Like many of the more advanced procedures, **DSCRIMINANT** follows a set sequence of steps to achieve a final solution. Some of these steps are more experimenter-driven, and others are more data-driven. These steps will be presented here in the introduction. To assist in this explanation, we will introduce yet another example. Then material in the Step by Step and Output sections will provide additional detail.

THE EXAMPLE: ADMISSION INTO A GRADUATE PROGRAM

Neither the **GRADES.SYS** nor the **HELPING.SYS** files provide appropriate data sets to demonstrate the discriminant function. While it is possible to use discriminant analysis to predict, for instance, subject's gender or class standing, it is much easier, in the words of psychologist Gordon Allport, to "just ask them." What we have chosen is a topic where discriminant analysis might actually be used: Criteria for acceptance into a graduate program. Every year, selectors misguess and select students who are unsuccessful in their efforts to finish the degree. A wealth of information is collected about each applicant prior to acceptance, and department records indicate whether that student was successful in completing the course. Our example uses the information collected prior to acceptance to predict successful completion of a graduate program. The file is called **GRADUATE.SYS** and consists of 50 students admitted into the program between 7 and 11 years ago. The dependent variable is **CATEGORY** (1 = finished the Ph.D., 2 = did not finish), and 17 predictor variables are utilized to predict category membership in one of these two groups.

> **GENDER:** 1 = female, 2 = male
> **AGE:** age in years at time of application
> **MARITAL:** 1 = married, 2 = single
> **GPA:** overall undergraduate GPA
> **AREAGPA:** GPA in their area of specialty
> **GREAREA:** score on the major-area section of the GRE
> **GREQUANT:** score on the quantitative section of the GRE
> **GREVERBAL:** score on the verbal section of the GRE
> **LETTER1:** first of the three recommendation letters (rated 1 = weak through 9 = strong)
> **LETTER2:** second of the three recommendation letters (same scale)
> **LETTER3:** third of the three recommendation letters
> **MOTIVE:** applicant's level of motivation (1 = low through 9 = high)
> **STABLE:** applicant's emotional stability (same scale for this and all that follow)

RESOURCE: financial resources and support system in place

INTERACT: applicant's ability to interact comfortably with peers and superiors

HOSTILE: applicant's level of inner hostility

IMPRESS: impression of selectors who conducted an interview

The dependent variable is called **CATEGORY** and has two levels: 1 = those who finished the Ph.D., and 2 = those who did not finish the Ph.D. Finally, although the study has excellent face validity, the data are all fictional—created by the authors to demonstrate the discriminant function.

THE STEPS USED IN DISCRIMINANT ANALYSIS

Step 1: Selection of variables. Theoretical or conceptual concerns, prior knowledge of the researcher, and some bivariate analyses are frequently used in the initial stage. With the **GRADUATE.SYS** file, the number of predictor variables is small enough (17) that it would be acceptable to enter all 17 into the regression equation. If, however, you had several hundred variables (e.g., number of questions on many personality tests), this would not be feasible because of the limitations of available memory. A common first step is to compute a correlation matrix of predictor variables or calculate a number of *t*-tests, to gain an understanding of the bivariate nature of your data. Because the goal of analysis is to find the best discriminant function possible, it is quite normal to try several procedures and several different sets of variables to achieve best results. In the present sample, in a series of *t*-tests significant differences were found between the two levels of **CATEGORY** (those who finished the Ph.D. and those who did not) for **GPA, GREQUANT, LETTER1, LETTER2, LETTER3, MOTIVE, AGE, INTERACT** and **HOSTILE**. In the analyses described below, we will demonstrate first a forced-entry procedure that includes all variables that show significant bivariate relationships and then a stepwise procedure that accesses all 17 independent variables.

Step 2: Procedure. Two entry procedures will be presented in this chapter. The default procedure is called **DIRECT** and, in regression vernacular, is a *forced entry* process. The researcher indicates which variables will be entered, and *all* designated variables will be entered simultaneously. A second procedure, called **WILKES**, is a stepwise procedure that is based on minimizing the Wilks' lambda (λ) after each new variable has been entered into the regression equation. As in stepwise multiple regression analysis, there is a criterion for entry into the regression equation ($F \geq 1.00$ is default) and also a criterion for removal from the equation once a variable has been entered if its contribution to the equation drops below a designated level ($F < 1.00$ is default). Wilks' λ is the ratio of within-groups sum of squares to the total sum of squares. It is designed (in this setting) to indicate whether a particular variable contributes significantly to explaining additional variance in the dependent (or criterion) variable. There is an F and p-value associated with Wilks' λ that indicates the level of significance. A more complete description is given in the Output section.

So, which of these two methods usually produces better results? As disturbing as it might seem, the computer (in a stepwise procedure with all variables entered) generally does better than when the researcher preselects variables. However, there are often conceptual or practical reasons for not allowing the computer to make all of the decisions. With the present data set, when all variables were entered using the **WILKES** procedure (stepwise selection of variables), a regression equation was produced that misclassified only 3 of 50 cases. Using the **WILKES** procedure but entering only the variables that showed bivariate differences, 4 of 50 cases were misclassified. Using the **DIRECT** procedure and entering all 17 variables, 4 of 50 were misclassified, and using the **DIRECT** procedure with only the 9 variables that showed significant bivariate differences, 5 of 50 cases were misclassified. There are several other selection procedures offered by SPSS. There is an extensive discussion of these selection methods in the *SPSS/PC+ Advanced Statistics 4.0 Manual*.

Step 3: Interpretation and use. The rationale behind discriminant analysis is to make use of existing data dealing with group membership and relevant predictor variables to create a formula that will accurately predict group membership, using the same variables with a new set of subjects. The formula created by the **DSCRIMINANT** command will generally not be as accurate in predicting new cases as it was on the original data. With the present data set, **DSCRIMINANT** classified 94% of the individuals correctly, using variables describing the 50 subjects that were used to create the regression formula; but it is unlikely to do that well on subjects where membership is unknown. The *SPSS/PC+ Advanced Statistics 4.0 Manual* describes the *jackknife* procedure to identify a more likely percentage of correct classifications in applications when group membership is unknown. Over time, the discriminant formula can be improved and refined as additional data become available.

The best text known by the authors on discriminant analysis is a recent book by Geoffrey McLachlan (1992). Please see the reference section for additional information.

THE LOGICAL PROGRESSION FOR CONDUCTING DISCRIMINANT ANALYSIS

1. Create file of data, or edit (if necessary) an already existing file.
2. Format file by use of **DATA LIST FILE**, **FORMATS**, and **VARIABLE/VALUE LABELS**; then save as a system file.
3. Access file and formats by the **GET FILE** command.
4. Use the **DSCRIMINANT** command to conduct discriminant analysis.
5. Use the **GROUPS** subcommand to identify the categorical dependent variable for classification.
6. Use the **VARIABLES** subcommand to identify variables used in the discriminant equation.

7. Use the ANALYSIS subcommand if you wish to conduct more than one discriminant analysis using different sets of variables for different procedures.
8. Use the METHOD subcommand to identify which method you wish to employ for creation of the discriminant formula.
9. Use the OPTIONS subcommand to repress or select certain types of output.
10. Use the STATISTICS subcommand to request certain statistical information and to access several types of plots to display data visually.
11. View the results and exit the program.
12. Print data, commands, and output.

STEP BY STEP
Discriminant Analysis

---

1) Name and create a data file (Chapter 2), or edit (if necessary) an already existing file (Chapter 3).

---

2) Name variables, locate column positions, format, create VARIABLE/VALUE LABELS, and then save the formatted DATA FILE as a SYSTEM FILE (Chapter 4).

From the DOS prompt, type:

---

3) dos > SPSSPC ⏎   *This step gets you into the SPSS system.*

To clear the menu from the top window prior to analyzing data:

---

4) ALT – M   *Positions cursor to begin to create the command file.*

From the extreme upper left corner of the scratch pad (lower window), type:

---

5) GET FILE = 'GRADUATE.SYS'.   *1*

LINE 1   Accesses the formatted SYSTEM FILE to begin to analyze data. All statistical procedures in this book will begin with the GET FILE step.

For the simplest forced-entry discriminant analysis using all predictor variables, type in the following three lines:

```
6)  GET FILE = 'GRADUATE.SYS'.                                      1
    DSCRIMINANT GROUPS = CATEGORY(1,2)/                             2
    VARIABLES = GENDER TO IMPRESS.                                  3
```

LINE 1 Same as line 1, step 5 above.

LINE 2 This line directs SPSS to conduct discriminant analysis. You will get error messages until you learn to spell the command name (**DSCRIMINANT**) without the **I**. **CATEGORY** identifies the variable that you wish to use for categorizing into groups. More than two levels are possible. If, for instance, there were three levels of **CATEGORY**, then you would designate it **CATEGORY(1,3)**; if there were four levels, **CATEGORY(1,4)**.

LINE 3 This identifies variables to be used in the analysis. This list includes all variables except **CATEGORY**, the dependent variable. If variables are in order in the system file, the **TO** may be used to designate any subset of variables within the data set. If they are not in order, enter the variable names with a single space between each and follow the last variable name with a period. This default procedure uses the **DIRECT** mode of entry (forced entry for all designated variables).

This more extensive command file demonstrates a number of the options that are available for conducting discriminant analysis.

```
6a)  GET FILE = 'GRADUATE.SYS'.                                    1a
     DSCRIMINANT GROUPS = CATEGORY(1,2)/                           2a
     VARIABLES = GENDER TO IMPRESS/                                3a
     ANALYSIS = GENDER TO IMPRESS/                                 4a
     METHOD = WILKES/                                              5a
     OPTIONS = 4 7/                                                6a
     STATISTICS = 7 11 14 15/                                      7a
     ANALYSIS = GPA GREQUANT LETTER1 LETTER2 LETTER3 MOTIVE AGE
     INTERACT HOSTILE/                                             8a
     METHOD = DIRECT/                                              9a
     OPTIONS = 7/                                                  10a
     STATISTICS = 7 11 14 15.                                      11a
```

LINES 1a-3a These three steps are required. Same as lines 1-3 in step 6 above, except that line 3a is followed by a slash instead of a period to indicate that subcommands follow.

LINES 4a and **8a** These steps are optional. The **ANALYSIS** subcommand allows you to conduct up to 10 different analyses using the same variable list. Note that in the first analysis, all predictor variables are used (followed by the **WILKES** stepwise procedure), and in the second analysis only the 9 variables that showed significant bivariate differences for the two levels of **CATEGORY** are included in a **DIRECT** (forced entry) analysis. Each analysis may be tailored in terms of variables or procedures that follow in whatever way the researcher wishes.

LINES 5a and **9a** These lines are optional. However, without these lines, the default procedure (**DIRECT**) would take place for both analyses. A number of different methods are available for creating the discriminant equation. The **WILKES** stepwise procedure and **DIRECT** method (forced entry) are the most frequently used and the only ones presented here. Note that each **ANALYSIS** sequence includes a **METHOD** subcommand. While the second **METHOD** (line 9a) is not technically necessary (**DIRECT** is the default), if you are doing several analyses with the same set of variables, for consistency of format and ease of later reference, it is usually a good idea to include the extra statement. Please see the *SPSS/PC+ Advanced Statistics 4.0 Manual* for additional methods of creating the discriminant equation.

LINE **6a**   This step is optional.   The OPTIONS subcommand allows 11 different variations for the analysis or output.   Option 4 requests that the step-by-step segment of the WILKES procedure be suppressed. This output takes many pages and is generally not of as much interest as step-by-step output of a multiple regression analysis.   Option 7 requests that the structure matrix of the correlations between discriminating variables and the canonical discriminant function be rotated for easier interpretation. Frequently used OPTIONS are listed below: Refer to the manual for a more complete description of these options.

OPTIONS number	Function
1	Include missing values in the analysis
4	Suppress display of step-by-step output
5	Suppress display of the summary table
6	Rotate the pattern matrix
7	Rotate the structure matrix
8	Substitute means for missing values during classification

LINES **7a** and **11a** These steps are optional.   Four different statistics are requested: **7** requests the Box's *M* test, a measure of multivariate normality. **11** requests the unstandardized discriminant function coefficients. This allows you to write down the entire discriminant equation if you wished to do hand calculations for a small number of subjects. **14** requests discriminant scores and classification information. This tells you what percent of your cases were correctly identified by the discriminant formula. It also shows discriminant scores for each case and indicates whether or not that case was correctly classified. **15** requests an all-groups scatter plot or histogram. This allows for a visual display of the grouping of your cases or subjects. Below are listed the statistical options. Once again, please refer to the manual if you wish a more complete description of these functions.

STATISTICS Number	Function
1	Means for each variable in the ANALYSIS subcommand
2	Standard deviations for each variable in the ANALYSIS subcommand
3	Pooled within-groups covariance matrix
5	Matrix of pairwise *F*-ratios (only available with the WILKES method)
6	Univariate *F*-ratios (a one-way ANOVA for equality of group means)
7	Box's *M* test (tests for the equality of group covariance matrices)
8	Group covariance matrices
9	Total covariance matrix
10	Territorial map
11	Unstandardized discriminant functions and coefficients
12	Classification function coefficients
13	Classification results table
15	All-groups scatter plot or histogram
16	Separate-groups scatter plot or histogram

LINE **10a**   This step is optional. The request for OPTION 7 duplicates line 6a, but OPTION 4 would not be appropriate for the DIRECT forced-entry procedure. There are no multiple pages of output.

7) $\boxed{\text{F9}}\ \boxed{\text{W}}\ \boxed{\text{↵}}$ *to save your command file for future access.*

If file is not already named, enter the file name (e.g., **GRADUATE.CTL**) at the prompt between the **W** and the **ENTER**.

To run the program, first position cursor at the beginning of the GET FILE line, then:

8) $\boxed{\text{F10}}\ \boxed{\text{C}}$ *to run your program from the cursor.*

After viewing the results:

9) $\boxed{\text{F10}}\ \boxed{\text{E}}\ \textbf{FINISH}\ \boxed{\text{↵}}$ *to exit to the DOS prompt.*

To print command files and results:

10) *dos >* **PRINT SPSS.LIS** $\boxed{\text{↵}}\ \boxed{\text{↵}}$ *(Sometimes the second RETURN is not necessary.)*

OUTPUT
Discriminant Analysis

The following OUTPUT *is produced by this* COMMAND FILE. INTERPRETATION *follows each section of output.*

```
GET FILE = 'GRADUATE.SYS'.
DSCRIMINANT GROUPS = CATEGORY(1,2)/
VARIABLES = GENDER TO IMPRESS/
METHOD = WILKES/
OPTIONS = 4 7/
STATISTICS = 1 2 6 7 11 13 14 15.
```

- - - - - - D I S C R I M I N A N T   A N A L Y S I S - - - - - -

Number of Cases by Group

CATEGORY	Unweighted	Weighted	Label
1	25	25.0	FINISHED PHD
2	25	25.0	DID NOT FINISH
Total	50	50.0	

Group means, Wilks' Lambda (U-statistic) and univariate F-ratio

Group	CATEGORY 1 MEAN	CATEGORY 2 MEAN	Total	Wilks' Lambda	F	Signif
GENDER	1.240	1.480	1.360	.93750	3.200	.0799
GPA	3.630	3.390	3.510	.79528	12.360	.0010
AREAGPA	3.822	3.734	3.778	.95063	2.943	.1209
GREAREA	655.600	648.800	652.200	.99765	.113	.7382
GREQUANT	724.000	646.800	685.400	.62833	28.390	.0000
GREVERB	643.200	620.000	631.200	.97397	1.283	.2630
LETTER1	7.720	6.160	6.940	.64962	25.890	.0000
LETTER2	7.640	6.360	7.000	.75619	15.480	.0003
LETTER3	7.960	6.160	7.060	.53352	41.970	.0000
MOTIVE	8.360	7.280	7.820	.67871	22.720	.0000
STABLE	6.400	6.360	6.380	.99985	.007	.9338
RESOURCE	5.920	5.640	5.780	.99303	.370	.5643
MARITAL	1.64	1.56	1.600	.99333	.322	.5730
AGE	29.96	25.12	27.540	.76768	14.530	.0004
INTERACT	7.000	6.160	6.580	.90432	5.079	.0288
HOSTILE	2.120	3.080	2.600	.78667	13.020	.0007
IMPRESS	7.280	6.880	7.080	.97210	1.378	.2463

At the top of the output, beneath *Number of Cases by Group*, is information concerning the number of cases (weighted and unweighted) for each level of the dependent variable (**CATEGORY**) and the labels for each level. The table that follows (actually two tables in the SPSS output, which have been combined) identifies basic preliminary *uni*variate information (the means for the two levels and the overall mean for each variable); and Wilks' lambda, *F*, and significance values contribute *bi*variate information about the differences between means for each variable. The *F* and *Signif* values identify for which variables the two groups differ significantly. This is the type of information that the researcher considers before running a discriminant analysis. Definitions of terms across the top of the chart follow:

GROUP: Names of the independent variables.

CATEGORY 1 MEAN: Mean value for each variable for the first level of CATEGORY, those who finished the PhD.

CATEGORY 2 MEAN: Mean value for each variable for the second level of CATEGORY, those who did not finish.

TOTAL: The mean value for each variable for all subjects. Since there are equal numbers of subjects in each level of CATEGORY, this number is simply the average of the other two means.

WILKS' LAMBDA: The ratio of the within-groups sum of squares to the total sum of squares. This is the proportion of the total variance in the discriminant scores *not* explained by differences among groups. A lambda of 1.00 occurs when observed group means are equal (all the variance is explained by factors *other than* difference between these means), while a small lambda occurs when within-groups variability is small compared to the total variability. A small lambda indicates that group means appear to differ. The associated significance values indicate whether the difference is significant.

F: *F*-values are the same as those calculated in a one-way analysis of variance. This is also the square of the *t*-value calculated from an independent samples *t*-test.

SIGNIFICANCE: The *p*-value: Likelihood that the observed *F*-value could occur by chance.

Next is specification information concerning the discriminant procedure about to take place.

```
-----------------------------------------------------------------------
Dependent variable:  CATEGORY   1=COMPLETED PHD   2=DID NOT COMPLETE
PHD

Stepwise variable selection:  Selection rule:  Minimize Wilks' Lambda

        Maximum number of steps................      34
        Minimum Tolerance Level................     .00100
        Minimum F to enter.....................    1.0000
        Maximum F to remove....................    1.0000

Canonical Discriminant Functions

        Maximum number of functions............       1
        Minimum cumulative percent of variance..  100.00
        Maximum significance of Wilks' Lambda...  1.0000

Prior probability for each group is    .50000
-----------------------------------------------------------------------
```

STEPWISE VARIABLE SELECTION: This procedure enters variables into the discriminant equation, one at a time, based on a designated criterion for inclusion ($F \geq 1.00$ is default); but will drop variables from the equation if the inclusion requirement drops below the designated level when other variables have been entered.

SELECTION RULE: The procedure selected here is to minimize Wilks' Lambda at each step.

MAXIMUM NUMBER OF STEPS: 2 times the number of variables designated in the **ANALYSIS** subcommand line (2 × 17 = 34). This number reflects that it is possible to enter a maximum of 17 variables and to remove a maximum of 17 variables.

MINIMUM TOLERANCE LEVEL: The tolerance level is a measure of linear dependency between one variable and the others. If a tolerance is less than .001, this indicated a high level of linear dependency, and SPSS will not enter that variable into the equation.

MAXIMUM F TO ENTER, MINIMUM F TO REMOVE: The default ($F = 1.00$) is the criterion for entering or removing a variable from the discriminant equation.

CANONICAL DISCRIMINANT FUNCTIONS: The linear discriminant equation(s) to be calculated that maximally discriminates between levels of the dependent (or criterion) variable. This is described in more detail later.

MAXIMUM NUMBER OF FUNCTIONS: Since there are 2 levels of the dependent variable, there is 1 discriminant function to discriminate between them. If there were 3 levels, there would be 2 functions, if 4 levels, 3 discriminant functions, and so forth.

MAXIMUM CUMULATIVE PERCENT OF VARIANCE: Can't explain more than 100% of the variance, folks.

MAXIMUM SIGNIFICANCE OF WILKS' LAMBDA: A value of 1.00 indicates identical mean values (no differences).

PRIOR PROBABILITY FOR EACH GROUP: The .5000 value indicates that groups are weighted equally.

What follows is the final page of output that deals with the regression analysis. This output displays the variables that were included in the discriminant equation with associated statistical data; the variables that did not meet the requirements for entry with associated statistical data; and the order in which variables were entered (or removed), along with Wilks' λ, significance, and variable labels.

```
-----------------------------------------------------------------------------
         ---------- Variables in the analysis after step 11 ----------
```

Variable	Tolerance	F to remove	Wilks' Lambda
GENDER	.7356176	5.8159	.32961
GREAREA	.0045719	4.6320	.32106
GREVERB	.0046334	5.0353	.32400
LETTER2	.3579885	1.9550	.30183
LETTER3	.7039126	3.8125	.31520
MOTIVE	.7619956	4.0256	.31673
RESOURCE	.8451267	3.4278	.30524
AGE	.7435004	5.2676	.32567
IMPRESS	.8779555	2.8513	.30828

```
---------- Variables not in the analysis after step 11 ----------
```

Variable	Tolerance	Minimum Tolerance	F to enter	Wilks' Lambda
GPA	.7470517	.0040878	.10398	.28700
AREAGPA	.7468857	.0040955	.026559	.28757
GREQUANT	.5479999	.0044534	.000019	.28777
LETTER!	.6920511	.0036050	.058205	.28734
STABLE	.8165718	.0043977	.088437	.28712
MARITAL	.9139021	.0045661	.045973	.28743
INTERACT	.6935227	.0045289	.74572	.28217
HOSTILE	.7649823	.0045719	.000929	.28776

```
---------- Summary Table ----------
```

Step	ACTION Entered	Removed	Vars In	Wilks' Lambda	Sig.	Label
1	LETTER3		1	.53352	.0000	THIRD LETTER OF REC
2	MOTIVE		2	.45073	.0000	STUDENTS MOTIVATION
3	LETTER1		3	.41514	.0000	FIRST LETTER OF REC
4	AGE		4	.39137	.0000	AGE IN YEARS AT ENTRY
5	GENDER		5	.36331	.0000	1=FEMALE 2=MALE
6	IMPRESS		6	.33203	.0000	RATING OR SELECTORS IMPRES
7	RESOURCE		7	.31868	.0000	FINANCIAL/PERSONAL RESOURC
8	GREVERB		8	.30981	.0000	GRE SCORE ON VERBAL
9	GREAREA		9	.39766	.0000	GRE SCORE ON AREA SECTION
10		LETTER1	8	.30183	.0000	FIRST LETTER OF REC
11	LETTER2		9	.28777	.0000	SECOND LETTER OF REC

These three charts indicate which variables were included in the final discriminant function and which ones were not. By use of the **OPTIONS = 4** subcommand, SPSS produced only the last page rather than a step-by-step output of the entire selection procedure. Notice that all variables in the analyses after 11 steps have higher than the acceptable tolerance level (.001) and have F-values greater than 1.00. Variables not in the equation all have acceptable tolerance levels, but the F-to-enter value is less than 1.00 for each of them. The third table gives a summary of the step-by-step procedure. Notice that in a total of 11 steps 9 variables were entered, but at step 10 one variable (**LETTER1**) was dropped due to an F-value falling below 1.00. Then at step 11 the final variable was added (**LETTER2**).

This result raises an important experimental concern. When the values for the three letters were originally entered, no attention was given to which was stronger than which. Thus there is no particular rationale to drop **LETTER1** in favor of **LETTER2**, as suggested by these results. The appropriate response for the researcher would be to go back into the raw data file and reorder letters from strongest to weakest for each subject (e.g., **LETTER1** is strongest, **LETTER2**, next strongest and **LETTER3** weakest) and update the system file. Then, when a discriminant analysis is conducted, if one of the letters has greater influence than another, it may have meaning. It might indicate, for instance, that **LETTER1** (the strongest letter) has a significant influence but that **LETTER3** (the weakest) does not contribute significantly to the discriminating process. While this is representative of the thinking the researcher might do, remember that these data are fictional and thus do not reflect an objective reality.

Most of the terms used here are defined on the previous pages. Definitions of terms unique to this section follow:

VARS IN: Indicates the numbers of variables in the discriminant equation at each step.

SIG: This is a measure of multivariate significance, not the significance of each new variable's unique contribution to explaining the variance.

Next is the test for multivariate normality of the data.

```
--------------------------------------------------------------------------
    ---- Test of equality of group covariance matrices using Box's M ----

The ranks and natural logarithms of determinants printed are those of
the group covariance matrices.

Group Label                                    Rank      Log Determinant
1     FINISHED PHD                              9             11.340246
2     NOT FINISHED                              9             12.637819
Pooled within-Groups Covariance Matrix         9             13.705305

Box's M        Approximate F   Degrees of Freedom   Significance
82.381            1.4613         45,        7569.1       .0238
--------------------------------------------------------------------------
```

RANK: Rank or size of the covariance matrix. The **9** indicates that this is a 9 × 9 matrix, the number of variables in the discriminant equation.

LOG DETERMINANT: Natural log of the determinant of each of the two (the two levels of the dependent variable, **CATEGORY**) covariance matrices.

POOLED WITHIN-GROUPS COVARIANCE MATRIX: A matrix composed of the means of each corresponding value within the two 9 × 9 matrices of the two levels of **CATEGORY**.

BOX'S M: Based on the similarities of determinants of the covariance matrices for the two groups. It is a measure of multivariate normality.

APPROXIMATE F: A transformation that tests whether the determinants from the two levels of the dependent variable differ significantly from each other. It is conceptually similar to the *F*-ratio in ANOVA, in which the between-groups variability is compared to the within-groups variability.

SIGNIFICANCE: A significance value < .05 should arouse concern. However, it has been found that even when multivariate normality is violated, the discriminant function can still often perform surprisingly well. If this value is low, it would be well to look at the univariate normality of some of the included variables. For instance, we know that the **GENDER** variable is not normally distributed, but inclusion of **GENDER** improves the discriminating ability of the equation.

What follows is information concerning the canonical discriminant function, correlations between each of the discriminating variables and the canonical discriminant function, the unstandardized discriminant function coefficients (these are the coefficients for the discriminant equation), and the group centroids.

```
--------------------------------------------------------------------------
          ---------- Canonical Discriminant Functions ----------

        Eigen-  Pct of   Cum Canonicl|After Wilks'
Fcn     value   Variance Pct   Corr  |Fcn  Lambda   Chisquare  DF  Sig
                                     |  0   .2878    54.183     9  .000
1*      2.4750  100.00  100.00 .8439 |

    * marks the 1 canonical discriminant function remaining in the
        analysis.

            ---------- Structure Matrix ----------

Pooled-within-groups correlations between discriminating variables and
canonical discriminant functions (Variables ordered by size or
correlation)
```

Variable	Corr.
LETTER3	.59437
GREQUANT	.48949
MOTIVE	.43734
LETTER1	.42874
LETTER2	.36093
AGE	.34968
HOSTILE	-.32595
GPA	.26962
AREAGPA	.17158
GENDER	-.16412
IMPRESS	.10769
GREVERB	.10391
INTERACT	.07031
STABLE	.05865
RESOURCE	.05326
GREAREA	.03084
MARITAL	.01318

```
---- Unstandardized Canonical Discriminant ----
            Function Coefficients

    GENDER       -1.037702
    GREAREA      -7.894245
    GREVERB       8.037469
    LETTER2     - .3716190
    LETTER3       .4244069
    MOTIVE        .5124164
    RESOURCE      .1807967
    AGE           .1044078
    IMPRESS       .2707463
    (constant)  -8.106466

----- Canonical Discriminant Functions -----
    evaluated at Group Means (Group Centroids)

    Group        FUNC  1
      1          1.54143
      2         -1.54143
```

UNSTANDARDIZED CANONICAL DISCRIMINANT FUNCTION COEFFICIENTS: This is the list of coefficients (and the constant) of the discriminant equation. Each subject's discriminant score would be computed by entering his or her variable values for each of the 9 variables in the equation. The discriminant equation follows:

$$D = -8.11 + -1.03(\textbf{GENDER}) + -7.89(\textbf{GREAREA}) + 8.04(\textbf{GREVERB}) + -.37(\textbf{LETTER2}) +$$
$$.42(\textbf{LETTER3}) + .51(\textbf{MOTIVE}) + .18(\textbf{RESOURCE}) + .10(\textbf{AGE}) + .27(\textbf{IMPRESS})$$

FCN: Function. The zero (0) designates prior-to-analysis information. The one (1) designates information about the *only* discriminant function created with two levels of the criterion variable. If there were three levels of the criterion variable, there would be information listed about two discriminant functions.

WILKS' LAMBDA: Ratio of the within-groups sum of squares to total sum of squares (more complete definition earlier in this chapter).

CHI-SQUARE: A measure of whether the two levels of the function significantly differ from each other based on the discriminant function. A high chi-square value indicates that the function discriminates well.

DF: Degrees of freedom is equal to the number of variables used in the discriminant function (9).

SIG: *p*-value of the chi-square function.

EIGENVALUE: Between-groups sums of squares divided by within-groups sums of squares. A large eigenvalue is associated with a strong function.

PCT OF VARIANCE, CUM PCT: The function always accounts for 100% of the variance.

CANONICAL CORRELATION: To those who have heard the term for years and never quite known what it was, your moment has come: The canonical correlation is a correlation between the discriminant scores and the levels of the dependent variable. Please refer to the chart on the following page to further clarify. Note the scores in the extreme right column. Those are discriminant scores. They are determined by substituting into the discriminant equation the relevant variable measures for each subject. There are 50 subjects; thus there will be 50 discriminant scores. There are also 50 codings of the dependent variable (**CATEGORY**) that show 25 subjects coded 1 (finished the Ph.D.), and 25 subjects coded 2 (didn't finish). The canonical correlation is the correlation between those two sets of numbers. A high correlation indicates a function that discriminates well.

POOLED-WITHIN-GROUP-CORRELATIONS: "Pooled within group" differs from "values for the entire (total) group" in that the pooled values are the average (mean) of the group correlations. If the *N*s are equal (as they are here), then this would be the same as the value for the entire group. The list of 17 values is the correlations between each variable of interest and the discriminant scores. For instance, the first correlation listed (LETTER3 .59437) is the correlation between the 50 ratings for LETTER3 and the 50 discriminant scores (extreme right column on the chart that follows).

GROUP CENTROIDS: The average discriminant score for subjects in the two groups. More specifically, the discriminant score for each group when the variable means (rather than individual values for each subject) are entered into the discriminant equation. Note that the two scores are equal in absolute value but have opposite signs. The dividing line between group membership is zero (0).

The following chart gives straightforward information about group membership, probability of group membership, and discriminant scores. Only 16 of the 50 cases are shown.

Case Numbr	Mis Val	Sel	Actual Group	Highest Group	Probability P(D/G)	Probability P(G/D)	2nd Group	P(G/D)	Discrim Scores
1			1	1	.9878	.9918	2	.0082	1.5567
2			1	1	.4790	.9990	2	.0010	2.2494
3			1	1	.6217	.9981	2	.0019	2.0348
4			1	1	.7209	.9747	2	.0253	1.1842
5			2 **	1	.6242	.9264	2	.0376	1.0516
6			1	1	.4719	.9991	2	.0009	2.2609
..			.	.	.	.	.	.	.
..			.	.	.	.	.	.	.
37			2	2	.6807	.9702	1	.0298	-1.1299
38			2	2	.7121	.9738	1	.0262	-1.1724
39			1 **	2	.3141	.8287	1	.1613	- .5347
40			2	2	.6393	.9980	1	.0020	-2.0101
..			.	.	.	.	.	.	.
..			.	.	.	.	.	.	.
45			2	2	.4204	.9062	1	.0938	- .7357
46			2	2	.3297	.9996	1	.0004	-2.5162
47			1 **	2	.9757	.9922	1	.0078	-1.5719
48			2	2	.2761	.9997	1	.0003	-2.6305
49			2	2	.8198	.9957	1	.0043	-1.7692
50			2	2	.3528	.9995	1	.0005	-2.4705

Classification Results

Actual Group	No. of Cases	Predicted Group Membership CATEGORY 1	Predicted Group Membership CATEGORY 2
CATEGORY 1---FINISH PHD	25	23 (92%)	2 (08%)
CATEGORY 2---NOT FINISH	25	1 (04%)	24 (96%)

Percent of "grouped" cases correctly classified: 94.00%

MIS VAL: Indicates number of missing values for a particular subject or case.

SEL: Indicates whether a case has been excluded from the analysis by prior designation.

ACTUAL GROUP: Indicates the actual group membership of that subject or case.

HIGHEST GROUP: Indicates the group the discriminant function assigned this subject or case to. Asterisks (**) indicate a misclassification.

P(D/G): Given the discriminant value for that case (*D*), what is the probability of belonging to that group (*G*)?

P(G/D): Given that this case belongs to a given group (*G*), how likely is the observed discriminant score (*D*)?

2ND GROUP: What is the second most likely assignment for a particular case? Since there are only two levels in the present data set, the second most likely group will always be the "other one."

DISCRIM SCORES: Actual discriminant scores for each subject, based on substitution of variable values into the discriminant formula.

CLASSIFICATION RESULTS: Simple summary of number and percent of subjects classified correctly and incorrectly.

The final output shown here is a visual display of where each subject's discriminant scores reside along a continuum of values. Note that the scales to the right and left indicate the number of subjects (also note that there are *two* numbers for each subject). The **2** and the **1** to the right of the word *Centroids* marks the location of the group centroids (± 1.54143). The logistics of fitting numbers onto a sheet of paper limit the accuracy of this display.

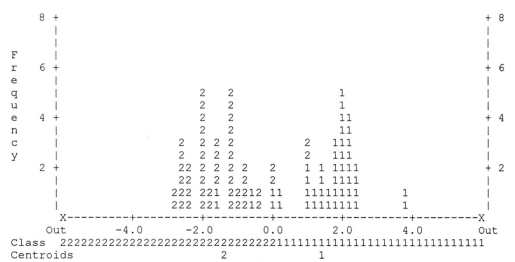

Chapter 24

The RELIABILITY Command:
Coefficient Alpha (α) and Split-Half Reliability

Many constructs are measured in which a subset of relevant items is selected, administered to subjects, and scored—and then inferences are made about the true population values. Examples abound: An introductory psychology course administers a final exam of 100 questions to test students' knowledge. Performance on the final is designed to be representative of knowledge of the entire course content. The quantitative section of the GRE is designed to measure general mathematical ability. The 11 subscales of the Wechsler Intelligence Scale are designed to measure general intellectual aptitude—intelligence. Thirty-three questions on the *Mehrabian-Epstein Scale of Empathic Tendency* are designed to measure the subject's general empathic tendency. And this process continues outside of academia: When Reynaldo Nehemiah, former world record holder in the 110-meter hurdles, expressed interest in playing football with the San Francisco 49ers, they measured his 40-yard speed, his vertical leaping ability, and his strength in a number of lifts as indicators of his ability to play football successfully.

Of the thousands of measurement scales that have been constructed, two critical questions are asked of each: "Is it reliable?" and "Is it valid?" The question of *reliability* (the topic of this chapter) addresses the issue of whether this instrument will produce the same results each time it is administered to the same person in the same setting. Instruments used in the social sciences are generally considered reliable if they produce similar results regardless of who administers them and regardless of which forms are used. The tests given to Nehemiah were certainly reliable: The same tests given many times over several weeks would yield a 40-yard dash of about 4.2 seconds, a vertical leap of about 53 inches, and a bench press of about 355 pounds. But this raised the second question. The cognoscenti of football coined the phrase, "Yeah, but can he take a hit?" They acknowledged Nehemiah's exceptional physical skills, but he hadn't played football since high school. Were these measures of physical skill good predictors of his ability to play in the NFL? They were concerned about the *validity* of the measure used by the 49ers. In a general sense, validity asks the question, "Does it actually measure what it is trying to measure?"

This chapter deals with the issue of *reliability*. We addressed the issue of *validity* briefly because the two words are so often linked together, and many budding researchers get the two mixed up. We do not have a chapter on validity, unfortunately, because validity is frequently determined by nonstatistical means. Construct validity is sometimes assessed with the aid of factor analysis, and discriminant analysis can assist in creating an instrument that measures well what the researcher is attempting to measure; but face validity is established by observational procedures, and construct validity (although factor analysis may be used to assist) is often theory-based.

The two types of *reliability* discussed in this chapter are Chronbach's alpha (also referred to as *coefficient alpha* or α) and split-half reliability. We will first explain the theoretical and statistical procedure on which coefficient alpha is based and then, more briefly, do the same for split-half reliability. There are other measures of reliability (these will be mentioned but not explained in the Step by Step section), but α is the measure that is most widely used. We will then present the example that will be used to demonstrate coefficient alpha and split-half reliability, and conclude this introductory section with the logical progression for computing reliability measures.

COEFFICIENT ALPHA (α)

Chronbach's alpha is designed as a measure of internal consistency; that is, do all items within the instrument measure the same thing? Alpha is measured on the same scale as a Pearson r (correlation coefficient) and typically varies between 0 and 1. Although a negative value is possible, such a value indicates a scale in which some items measure the opposite of what other items measure. The closer the alpha is to 1.00, the greater the internal consistency of items in the instrument being assessed. At a more conceptual level, coefficient alpha may be thought of as the correlation between a test score and all other tests of equal length that are drawn randomly from the same population of interest. For instance, suppose 1,000 questions existed to test students' knowledge of course content. If ten 100-item tests were drawn randomly from this set, coefficient alpha would approximate the average correlation between all pairs of tests. The formula that determines alpha is fairly simple and makes use of the number of items in the scale (k) and the average correlation between pairs of items (r):

$$\alpha = \frac{kr}{1+(k-1)r}$$

As the number of items in the scale (k) increases, the value of α becomes larger. Also, if the intercorrelation between items is large, the corresponding α will also be large.

SPLIT-HALF RELIABILITY

Split-half reliability is most frequently used when the number of items is large and it is possible to create two halves of the test that are designed to measure the same thing. An example for illustration is the *16 Personality Factor Questionnaire* (16PF) of Raymond Cattell. This 187-item test measures 16 different personality traits. There are 10 to 14 questions that measure each trait. If you wished to do a split-half reliability measure with the 16PF, it would be foolish to compare the first half of the test with the second half, because questions in each half are designed to measure many different things. It would be better to compute reliabilities of a single trait. If you wished to check the reliability of AGGRESSION (assessed by 14 questions), the best procedure would be to select 7 questions randomly from the 14 and compare them to the other 7. Once item selection is completed, SPSS conducts split-half reliability by computing correlations between the two parts. The split-half procedure can also be utilized if two different forms of a test are taken, or if the same test is administered more than once.

THE EXAMPLE

We once more use real data from the HELPING2.SYS file ($N = 517$) to demonstrate reliability analysis. One segment of this file contains 14 questions that measure the subjects' empathic tendency. These are questions from the *Mehrabian-Epstein Scale of Empathic Tendency* mentioned earlier. The variables are named EMPATHY1 to EMPATH14, and the content of the questions is included in the Output section.

THE LOGICAL PROGRESSION FOR CONDUCTING RELIABILITY ANALYSIS

1. Create file of data, or edit (if necessary) an already existing file.
2. Format file by use of DATA LIST FILE, FORMATS, and VARIABLE/VALUE LABELS; then save as a system file.
3. Access file and formats by the GET FILE command.
4. Use the RELIABILITY command to conduct reliability analysis.
5. Use the VARIABLES subcommand to identify variables used in the analysis.
6. Use the STATISTICS subcommand to access certain preliminary information.
7. Use the SUMMARY subcommand to include additional output.
8. Use the SCALE subcommand to name your model and specify variables for analysis.
9. Use the MODEL subcommand to identify which type of reliability analysis you wish.
10. View the results and exit the program.
11. Print data, commands, and output.

STEP BY STEP
Reliability Analysis

---

1) *Name and create a data file (Chapter 2), or edit (if necessary) an already existing file (Chapter 3).*

---

2) *Name variables, locate column positions, format, create VARIABLE/VALUE LABELS, and then save the formatted DATA FILE as a SYSTEM FILE (Chapter 4).*

From the DOS prompt, type:

3) dos > **SPSSPC** ⏎   *This step gets you into the SPSS system.*

To clear the menu from the top window prior to analyzing data:

4) ALT ─ M   *Positions cursor to begin to create the command file.*

From the extreme upper left corner of the scratch pad (lower window), type:

5) **GET FILE = 'HELPING2.SYS'.**   *1*

LINE **1** Accesses the formatted **SYSTEM FILE** to begin to analyze data. All statistical procedures in this book will begin with the **GET FILE** step.

The simplest default reliability analysis is accessed by this command file:

6) **GET FILE = 'HELPING2.SYS'.**   *1*
   RELIABILITY VARIABLES = EMPATHY1 TO EMPATH14/   *2*
   SUMMARY = TOTAL/   *3*
   SCALE (ALPHA) = ALL.   *4*

LINE **1** Same as step 5, line 1 above.

LINE **2** This line accesses the **RELIABILITY** procedure and identifies the variables in the system file you wish to utilize. Since **EMPATHY1** to **EMPATH14** are in order in the system file, the **TO** connector may be used to indicate all 14 variables. Any further designation of variables (as is possible in line 4 of this command file) will be based on the order of variables in the *command* file rather than on the order of variables in the *system* file. This line ends with a slash because a subcommand follows.

LINE **3** The request for **TOTAL** output yields important information concerning the combined means, variances, correlations, and alpha value if an item is deleted. Although SPSS can calculate alpha without this information (lines 3 and 4 are actually optional), this output is of considerable value to the researcher and should almost certainly be included.

LINE **4** The **SCALE** subcommand allows you to name your graph (this is the first thing listed at the top of the output) and allows you to specify which variables (of those listed in the **RELIABILITY VARIABLES** = line) you wish to include for this particular analysis—we select **ALL** variables in this analysis. This option of restating which variables you wish has great practical value, because usually a number of different reliability analyses will be conducted from the same data set. How this is accomplished is detailed in the next section.

The extended command file shown below includes a number of options available with the RELIABILITY command. Within this command file we request reliability analyses based on Chronbach's alpha and split-half reliability. There is actually no conceptual rationale for using a split-half reliability here, but it does allow you to see how it is requested.

```
6a)  GET FILE = 'HELPING2.SYS'.                                          1a
     RELIABILITY VARIABLES = EMPATHY1 EMPATHY3 TO EMPATHY7 EMPATHY9
     EMPATH11 TO EMPATH13/                                               2a
     STATISTICS = DESCRIPTIVES CORRELATIONS SCALE/                       3a
     SUMMARY = MEANS VARIANCES CORRELATIONS TOTAL/                       4a
     SCALE (ALPHA) = ALL/                                                5a
     MODEL = ALPHA/                                                      6a
     SCALE (SPLIT) = ALL/                                                7a
     MODEL = SPLIT.                                                      8a
```

LINE **1a** Same as step 6, line 1 above.

LINE **2a** This line is necessary. Notice the substantial difference in look between the variables line in step 6, line 2 and here. A frequent part of the process of creating a scale with maximum internal consistency is to eliminate items that do not contribute (or correlate highly) with the overall scale. Through results provided in the original output, 5 items of the original 14 have been deleted, with a corresponding increase of alpha from .68 to .80. This procedure will be clarified in the Output section.

LINE **3a** This line is optional. The **STATISTICS** subcommand accesses several different descriptive and diagnostic statistics. **DESCRIPTIVES** yields item means and standard deviations; **CORRELATIONS** produces a correlation matrix of all included variables; and **SCALE** provides mean, variance, standard deviation and *N* for the *sum* of the variables for each subject.

LINE **4a** This line is optional. **MEANS, VARIANCES,** and **CORRELATION** give summary data for means, variances, and inter-item correlations. These data include the mean, minimum, maximum, range, max/min, and variance of the mean scores. **CORRELATION** also accesses the squared multiple correlation column on the item-total statistics. **TOTAL** generates the remainder of the chart, which includes the scale mean if the item is deleted, the scale variance if item is deleted, the corrected item-total correlation, and the alpha if the item is deleted. In the Output section, we will reproduce the chart and explain in more detail.

LINES **5a** and **7a** These lines are optional. This is the procedure that SPSS uses to allow the researcher to run a series of reliability checks in the same session and drawing from the same data set. The name in parentheses (**ALPHA** and **SPLIT** respectively) are names that you create (any combination of letters or numbers up to eight characters), and they should relate in some specific way to your analysis. This name will appear at the top of each analysis. Following the equals sign, indicate which variables you wish to include in the analyses. In both cases here we include **ALL** variables listed in the **VARIABLES** line. If you wish a subset of these variables, list each variable, with a space between each. Close these commands with a slash.

LINES **6a** and **8a** These lines are required if you include the SCALE subcommand in the analysis. The MODEL subcommand indicates which type of reliability analysis you wish to conduct. Options include ALPHA (the default), SPLIT, GUTTMAN, PARALLEL, and STRICTPARALLEL. The *SPSS/PC+ Statistics 4.0 Manual* describes these procedures.

---

7) | F9 | W | ↵ | *to save your command file for future access.*

If file is not already named, enter the file name (e.g., **HELPING2.CTL**) at the prompt between the **W** and the **ENTER**.

To run the program, first position cursor at the beginning of the GET FILE line, then:

---

8) | F10 | C | *to run your program from the cursor.*

After viewing the results:

---

9) | F10 | E | FINISH | ↵ | *to exit to the DOS prompt.*

To print command files and results:

---

10) *dos* > PRINT SPSS.LIS | ↵ | ↵ | *(Sometimes the second RETURN is not necessary.)*

OUTPUT
Reliability Analysis

THE SIMPLEST DEFAULT PROCEDURE FOR COMPUTING COEFFICIENT ALPHA

The following OUTPUT is produced by this COMMAND FILE. INTERPRETATION follows.

```
GET FILE = 'HELPING2.SYS'.
RELIABILITY VARIABLES = EMPATHY1 TO EMPATH14/
SUMMARY = TOTAL/
SCALE (ALPHA) = ALL.
```

```
--------------------------------------------------------------------------
- R E L I A B I L I T Y   A N A L Y S I S   -   S C A L E   (A L P H A) -
```

Number	Variable	Label
1.	EMPATHY1	SAD TO SEE LONELY STRANGER
2.	EMPATHY2	ANNOYED AT SORRY-FOR-SELF PEOPLE (*NEG)
3.	EMPATHY3	EMOTIONALLY INVOLVED WITH FRIENDS PROBLEM
4.	EMPATHY4	DISTURBED WHEN BRING BAD NEWS
5.	EMPATHY5	PERSON CRYING UPSETTING
6.	EMPATHY6	REALLY INVOLVED IN A BOOK OR MOVIE
7.	EMPATHY7	ANGRY WHEN SOMEONE ILL TREATED
8.	EMPATHY8	AMUSED AT SNIFFLING AT MOVIES (*NEG)
9.	EMPATHY9	DO NOT FEEL OK WHEN OTHERS DEPRESSED
10.	EMPATH10	HARD TO SEE WHY OTHERS SO UPSET (*NEG)
11.	EMPATH11	UPSET TO SEE ANIMAL IN PAIN
12.	EMPATH12	UPSET TO SEE HELPLESS OLD PEOPLE
13.	EMPATH13	IRRITATION RATHER THAN SYMPATHY AT TEARS (*NEG)
14.	EMPATH14	REMAIN COOL WHEN OTHERS EXCITED (*NEG)

ITEM-TOTAL STATISTICS

Variable	SCALE MEAN IF ITEM DELETED	SCALE VARIANCE IF ITEM DELETED	CORRECTED ITEM-TOTAL CORRELATN	ALPHA IF ITEM DELETED
EMPATHY1	62.2689	81.3132	.4033	.6539
EMPATHY2	63.3694	94.5202	-.0527	.7180
EMPATHY3	62.5706	81.3230	.4565	.6483
EMPATHY4	62.1683	81.7022	.4526	.6492
EMPATHY5	62.3985	79.3215	.4731	.6436
EMPATHY6	62.3056	81.8522	.3847	.6566
EMPATHY7	61.2205	84.7459	.3978	.6586
EMPATHY8	62.1277	84.8945	.2283	.6800
EMPATHY9	62.8279	85.3947	.2706	.6725
EMPATH10	62.7446	91.2864	.0477	.7040
EMPATH11	61.5996	82.2560	.3997	.6552
EMPATH12	61.5126	81.9868	.4357	.6512
EMPATH13	61.4507	84.6279	.3025	.6682
EMPATH14	63.3385	88.4608	.1642	.6864

RELIABILITY COEFFICIENTS

```
N OF CASES = 517      N OF ITEMS = 14      ALPHA = .6848
--------------------------------------------------------------------------
```

The first chart lists the variables for which a reliability check is being conducted. Note that five of the items are marked with a (*NEG). These are questions that have been phrased negatively to control for response bias. The scoring on these items was reversed before beginning calculations. The second chart is designed to designate similarities and differences between each variable and composites of the other variables.

SCALE MEAN IF ITEM DELETED: For each subject ($N = 517$) the 13 variables (excluding the variable to the left) are summed. The values shown are the means for the 13 variables across all 517 subjects.

SCALE VARIANCE IF ITEM DELETED: The variance of summed variables when the variable to the left is deleted

CORRECTED ITEM-TOTAL CORRELATION: Correlation of the designated variable with the sum of the other 13.
ALPHA IF ITEM DELETED: The resulting alpha if the variable to the left is deleted.

Note that for four of the variables, the correlations between each of them and the sum of all other variables is quite low; in the case of EMPATHY2, it is even negative. Correspondingly, the ALPHA value would increase (from the .6848 shown at the bottom of the chart) if these items were deleted from the scale. In the analyses that follow, all items that *reduce* the alpha value have been deleted. After deleting the four indicated here a second analysis was run, and it was found that a fifth variable's deletion would also increase the value of ALPHA. Five variables were eventually dropped from the scale: variables 2, 8, 10, 13, and 14. Please be vividly aware that variables are not *automatically* dropped just because a higher ALPHA results. There are often theoretical or practical reasons for keeping such variables

COEFFICIENT ALPHA AND SPLIT-HALF RELIABILITY

The following OUTPUT *is produced by this* COMMAND FILE. INTERPRETATION *follows each portion of output.*

```
GET FILE = 'HELPING2.SYS'.
RELIABILITY VARIABLES = EMPATHY1 EMPATHY3 TO EMPATHY7 EMPATHY9 EMPATH11
EMPATH12/
STATISTICS = DESCRIPTIVES CORRELATIONS SCALE/
SUMMARY = MEANS VARIANCES CORRELATIONS TOTAL/
SCALE (ALPHA) = ALL/
MODEL = ALPHA/
SCALE (SPLIT) = ALL/
SCALE = SPLIT.
```

Note: Interpretation of the descriptive statistics and correlation matrix are straightforward and are not shown.

```
--------------------------------------------------------------------------
- R E L I A B I L I T Y   A N A L Y S I S   -   S C A L E   (A L P H A) -

# OF CASES = 517
                                    Mean   Variance   Std Dev   # Var
STATISTICS FOR SUMMED VARIABLES:  44.7544  71.1314    8.4339       9

                              Mean    Min    Max   Range  Max/Min  Variance
ITEM MEANS                   4.9727  4.242  5.849  1.6074  1.3789    .2856
ITEM VARIANCES               2.3166  1.632  2.663  1.0308  1.6315    .1101
INTER-ITEM CORRELATIONS       .3026   .120   .521   .4008  4.3426    .0090
--------------------------------------------------------------------------
```

STATISTICS FOR SUMMED VARIABLES: There are a total of nine variables being considered. This line lists descriptive information about the *sum* of the nine variables for the entire sample of 517 subjects.
ITEM MEANS: This is descriptive information about the 517 subjects' means for the nine variables. In other words, the $N = 9$ for this list of descriptive statistics. The "mean of means" = 4.9727. The minimum of the nine means = 4.2418, and so forth.

ITEM VARIANCES: A similar construct as that used in the line above (**ITEM MEANS**). The first number is the mean of the nine variances, the second is the lowest of the nine variances, and so forth.

INTER-ITEM CORRELATIONS: This is descriptive information about the correlation of each variable with the sum of the other eight. There are nine correlations computed: the correlation between the first variable and the sum of the other eight variables, the correlation between the second variable and the sum of the other eight, and so forth. The first number listed is the mean of these nine correlations (.3026), the second is the lowest of the nine (.1199), and so forth. The mean of the inter-item correlations (.3026) is the r in the $\alpha = rk/[1 + (k - 1)r]$ formula.

```
----------------------------------------------------------------------
- R E L I A B I L I T Y    A N A L Y S I S   -   S C A L E   (A L P H A) -

ITEM-TOTAL STATISTICS              # OF CASES = 517
```

	SCALE MEAN IF ITEM DELETED	SCALE VARIANCE IF ITEM DELETED	CORRECTED ITEM- TOTAL CORRELATION	SQUARED MULTIPLE CORRELATION	ALPHA IF ITEM DELETED
EMPATHY1	39.9536	55.8467	.5223	.3158	.7700
EMPATHY3	40.2553	57.4773	.5093	.3370	.7720
EMPATHY4	39.8530	56.1411	.5898	.3996	.7616
EMPATHY5	40.0832	54.6578	.5724	.3680	.7626
EMPATHY6	39.9903	58.6298	.3988	.2207	.7875
EMPATHY7	38.9052	61.1092	.4200	.2085	.7835
EMPATHY9	40.5126	59.0139	.3990	.1852	.7870
EMPATH11	39.2843	58.6302	.4318	.3144	.7823
EMPATH12	39.1973	57.2633	.5267	.4030	.7698

```
RELIABILITY COEFFICIENTS       9 ITEMS

ALPHA   =   .7952          STANDARDIZED ITEM ALPHA   =   .7962
----------------------------------------------------------------------
```

This table is the same as that presented earlier except that values shown relate to 9 rather than 14 variables, and an additional column has been added: **SQUARED MULTIPLE CORRELATION.** Notice further that the **ALPHA** has increased to .7952 (from .6848 with 14 variables). Also notice that the overall alpha value cannot be improved by deleting another variable. Four of the columns have been described on the previous page. Terms new to this chart are described below.

SQUARED MULTIPLE CORRELATION: These values are determined by creating a multiple regression equation to generate the *predicted correlation* based on the correlations for the other eight variables. The numbers listed are these predicted correlations.

ALPHA: Based on the formula: $\alpha = rk/[1 + (k - 1)r]$, where k is the number of variables considered (9 in this case) and r is the mean of the inter-item correlations (.3026, from previous page). The alpha value is inflated by a larger number of variables; so there is no set interpretation as to what is an acceptable alpha value. A rule of thumb that applies to most situations is:

$\alpha > .9$—excellent

$\alpha > .8$—good

$\alpha > .7$—acceptable

$\alpha > .6$—questionable

$\alpha > .5$—poor

$\alpha < .5$—unacceptable

STANDARDIZED ITEM ALPHA: This is the alpha produced if the composite items (in the chart on the previous page, *not* the scores for the 517 subjects) are changed to *z*-scores before computing the **ALPHA**. The almost identical values produced here (.7952 vs. .7962) indicate that the means and variances in the original scales do not differ much, and thus standardization does not make a great difference in the **ALPHA**.

Note: Much information in the **SPLIT-HALF** output is identical to that for the **ALPHA** output. Only output that is different is included here.

```
-------------------------------------------------------------------------------
      - R E L I A B I L I T Y    A N A L Y S I S  -  S C A L E  (S P L I T) -

STATISTICS FOR      MEAN       VARIANCE    STD DEV    # OF VARIABLES
PART 1              23.6364    31.1117     5.5778          5
PART 2              21.1108    17.1081     4.1362          4
SCALE               44.7544    71.1314     8.4339          9

ITEM MEANS    MEAN      MINIMUM    MAXIMUM    RANGE     MAX/MIN    VARIANCE
PART 1        4.7273    4.4990     4.9014     .4023     1.0894     .0321
PART 2        5.2795    4.2418     5.8491     1.6074    1.3789     .5049
SCALE         4.9727    4.2418     5.8491     1.6074    1.3789     .2856
ITEM VARIANCES
PART 1        2.4461    2.1201     2.6630     .5429     1.2561     .0692
PART 2        2.1547    1.6322     2.4744     .8421     1.5159     .1383
SCALE         2.3166    1.6322     2.6630     1.0308    1.6315     .1101
ITEM-TOTAL CORRELATIONS
PART 1        .3892     .2599      .5042      .2444     1.9403     .0054
PART 2        .3315     .2258      .5207      .2949     2.3058     .0101
SCALE         .3026     .1199      .5207      .4008     4.3426     .0090

RELIABILITY COEFFICIENTS      9 ITEMS
CORRELATION BETWEEN FORMS   =      .4965
EQUAL-LENGTH SPEARMAN-BROWN  =     .6636
GUTTMAN SPLIT-HALF   =             .6442
UNEQUAL LENGTH SPEARMAN-BROWN  = .6657

ALPHA FOR PART 1 (5 ITEMS) = .7586  ALPHA FOR PART 2 (4 ITEMS) = .6616
-------------------------------------------------------------------------------
```

The **STATISTICS FOR ITEM MEANS, ITEM VARIANCES,** and **INTER-ITEM CORRELATIONS** sections are identical to those shown on page 225 except that it has similar numbers for the two halves of the scale as well for the entire scale. The third line (**SCALE**) has identical numbers to those on page 225. Please refer there for an explanation.

CORRELATION BETWEEN FORMS: An estimate of the reliability of the measure if it had five items.

EQUAL-LENGTH SPEARMAN-BROWN: The reliability of a 10-item test (.6636) if it was made up of equal parts that each had a five-item reliability of .4965.

GUTTMAN SPLIT-HALF: Another measure of the reliability of the overall test, based on a lower-bounds procedure.

UNEQUAL-LENGTH SPEARMAN-BROWN: The reliability acknowledging that this test has 9 and not 10 items.

Chapter 25

The NLR Command:

Nonlinear Regression

In most of the analysis chapters of this book (Chapters 6-30) you will find somewhere in the introduction a sentence or two with comments such as, "We cannot possibly explain this procedure adequately in only a few pages." In no chapter do the authors feel this sentiment more strongly than in this chapter on nonlinear regression. We have included this chapter only after a stiff reminder that this is *not* a statistics text but a manual describing how to use SPSS procedures. If you wish more information on nonlinear regression, we direct you to two other sources: The *SPSS/PC+ Advanced Statistics 4.0 Manual*, although limited in its presentation, does describe nonlinear regression in greater detail than we do here. The best book we found was *Nonlinear Regression* by Seber and Wild (1989), published by John Wiley & Sons. The problem with nonlinear regression is that there is a wide diversity of different types of equations that may be analyzed, and each equation often provides unique difficulties that extend beyond the scope of this book. What we do here is present a single example that demonstrates how to use SPSS procedures to generate a solution.

The NLR command is designed to compute parameters for already existing equations in order to adapt them to optimally fit a particular data set. For instance, an equation designed to measure population growth is:

$$Y_i = C/(1 + e^{(A+BX_i)})$$

where Y_i is the predicted population in any given year; A, B, and C are parameters of the equation that need to be estimated; and X_i is a variable coded to represent a particular year (because raising e to the 1994th power would overtax the computer's memory capabilities). The reason that A, B, and C have not long ago been determined is that, depending on your data set, those values will be different. The growth rate in Japan would differ from the growth rate in the United States, which would differ from the growth rate in Brazil, and so forth. For each data set, different parameters would need to be estimated. To compute such parameters is the primary purpose of nonlinear regression.

It is important to distinguish between relations that are *curvilinear* and relations that represent nonlinear models—or as the SPSS manual designates it, equations that are *intrinsically nonlinear*. The procedure for testing curvilinear relationships was described in Chapters 19 and 20. Any equation that can be transformed to fit the pattern:

$$F(X) = B_0 + B_1X + B_2X^2 + B_3X^3 + \ldots + B_kX^n$$

would be curvilinear (if any of the exponents are different from 1). In words, if any function of X can be expressed as the sum of a constant and coefficient(s) times variables raised to power(s), this would be a curvilinear equation, but not an intrinsically nonlinear equation. Recall that in Chapter 19, the curvilinear equation tested was:

$$\text{EXAM}_{(\text{predicted})} = 30.377 + 18.926(\text{ANXIETY}) + -1.521(\text{ANXIETY})^2$$

Note that this is the format of the $F(X)$ equation shown above. Most intrinsically nonlinear equations are exponential; that is, they contain an *e*-raised-to-some-power component. Note that the population growth function listed above is an exponential equation. In sum, the **NLR** command is used to calculate parameters for intrinsically nonlinear equations. If you wish to test for a curvilinear relationship, then use the **REGRESSION** command.

STEPS IN CALCULATING PARAMETERS FOR A NONLINEAR EQUATION

To illustrate the steps in nonlinear regression, we will first introduce our example. This real data comes from the U.S. Census Bureau and lists the U.S. population every decade from 1790 to 1990. The parameters for the population growth equation will be based on these data.

The starting point for using nonlinear regression is to select an appropriate equation and acquire a set of data upon which to determine the parameters. The equation selected for this procedure is the population growth function listed above: $Y_i = C/(1 + e^{(A+BX_i)})$. The data set will include U.S. populations by decades from 1790 to 1990.

The second step is to estimate the start values for the parameters of interest: A, B, and C. In this equation, selecting starting values involves a combination of knowledge of the data set, understanding of the formula, selective substitution of values (from the original data), and then solving for other variables. Starting values do not need to be accurate, but they do need to be a reasonable estimation. For instance, C represents the asymptotic population value, or the value that the function is never expected to exceed if time is extended indefinitely. The starting value for C might be chosen as 300 million (designated 300.000). The highest population number in the data set is 249.632 million, and although you would probably anticipate the U.S. population eventually going higher than 300 million, that number is within range of a reasonable value. To determine starting values for A and B, substitute some known or estimated values (e.g., $C =$

300.000, Y_i = 5.267 [population in 1800], and X = 1 [the coded number for 1800]), then solve for A, substitute back into the original equation, and solve for B. It is not possible to solve a single equation with two unknowns; that is why the word *estimate* is made salient. If poor starting values are chosen, it takes up more memory and computer time, and if starting values are *really* poor it is sometimes impossible to converge to a final solution.

After start values have been set, the computer begins to solve the equation with the data (the coding for years and population for each year) and the starting parameter values (for A, B, and C) you have designated. SPSS then goes through an iterative process to eventually converge to a final solution. Iteration operates as follows: The equation of interest is solved using the available data and parameter estimates. For each iteration, the direction and step size are determined by the derivatives associated with each parameter. You may provide the derivatives in the command file for each parameter, if you know them (this will often speed up the procedure and sometimes produce a better final solution), or allow the NLR command to generate them. This solution yields parameter values that are closer to the final values than the original estimates were. In the next step the computer substitutes the new (more accurate) values into the equation (once again using the derivatives to determine the direction and step size) and solves again, yielding a solution in which parameter values are even closer to a final solution. The iterative process continues until the difference between the two most recent values does not change more than a prespecified level. The SPSS default is that when the residual sum of squares does not change more than .00000001 (one hundred-millionth) on consecutive iterations, iteration will cease and final parameter values will be printed.

After iteration is complete, parameter values may be inserted to create the equation that reflects U.S. population growth. The values generated from these data were: A = 3.99198, B = -.227687, and C = 386.4837. Rounding to the nearest hundredth and substituting these values into the original equation yields:

$$Y_i = 386.48/(1 + e^{3.99 + (-.228)X_i})$$

Now to find any predicted population value (Y_i), simply insert the associated coded value (X_i) and solve.

It is of interest that the SPSS manual used the same equation we have employed here to represent U.S. population growth, but they had data only through 1960. To demonstrate the influence that the additional three decades of data have on the equation and its predictive ability, we will use both equations (the SPSS manual equation and ours) to estimate U.S. population for the year 2000. Substituting first into the SPSS equation (left) and then into the equation that includes years through 1990 (right):

$$Y_i = 243.99/(1 + e^{3.89 + (-.279)X_i})$$
$$Y_{21} = 243.99/(1 + e^{3.89 + (-.279)21})$$
$$Y_{21} = 243.99/(1 + .6387)$$
$$Y_{21} = 214.023 \text{ million}$$

$$Y_i = 386.48/(1 + e^{3.99 + (-.228)X_i})$$
$$Y_{21} = 386.48/(1 + e^{3.99 + (-.228)21})$$
$$Y_{21} = 386.48/(1 + .4502)$$
$$Y_{21} = 266.499 \text{ million}$$

Note how much difference the two sets of data make to the predictive ability of the two equations. With data through 1960 only, the *asymptotic* value of 243.99 million (theoretically the highest possible value with time extended indefinitely) is lower than *actual* population in 1990. With the three additional decades added, the estimated population for the year 2000 (266.499 million) at least seems reasonable. This illustrates why parameters need to be updated whenever significant new data are acquired.

A final word on the data set we will use for this chapter: The system file is called **GROWTH.SYS** and consists of three variables: **POP**, the U.S. population in millions by decades from 1790 to 1990; **YEAR**, the years 1790 to 1990 by decades; and *X*, the coded number for each decade—that is, 1790 = 0, 1800 = 1, . . . 1990 = 20. *A*, *B*, and *C* are the three equation parameters that we are estimating.

THE LOGICAL PROGRESSION FOR CONDUCTING NONLINEAR REGRESSION

1. Create file of data, or edit (if necessary) an already existing file.
2. Format file by use of **DATA LIST FILE**, **FORMATS**, and **VARIABLE/VALUE LABELS**; then save as a system file.
3. Access file and formats with the **GET FILE** command.
4. Use the **LIST** command (if the file is short) to have handy access to your data.
5. Use the **PLOT** command to create a visual display of your data.
6. Use the **MODEL PROGRAM** command to enter starting values for the parameters of interest.
7. Use the **COMPUTE** command to create a new variable called **PRED** (predicted values) that is calculated from the equation for which parameters are being computed.
8. Use the **NLR** command to designate the variables (from the data file) that will be used to compute the parameter values.
9. Use the **SAVE** subcommand to save predicted values and residuals.
10. View the results and exit the program.
11. Print data, commands, and output.

STEP BY STEP
Nonlinear Regression

> *1) Name and create a data file (Chapter 2), or edit (if necessary) an already existing file (Chapter 3).*

> *2) Name variables, locate column positions, format, create VARIABLE/VALUE LABELS, and then save the formatted DATA FILE as a SYSTEM FILE (Chapter 4).*

From the DOS prompt, type:

> 3) dos> **SPSSPC** ↵   *This step gets you into the SPSS system.*

To clear the menu from the top window prior to analyzing data:

> 4) ALT ⌐M   *Positions cursor to begin to create the command file.*

From the extreme upper left corner of the scratch pad (lower window), type:

> 5) **GET FILE = 'GROWTH.SYS'.**   *1*

LINE 1 Accesses the formatted **SYSTEM FILE** to begin to analyze data. All statistical procedures in this book will begin with the **GET FILE** step.

Only one command file is used to demonstrate nonlinear regression. For additional procedures or options, consult the manual.

> 6) **GET FILE = 'GROWTH.SYS'.**   1
>   **LIST.**   2
>   **PLOT PLOT = POP WITH YEAR.**   3
>   **MODEL PROGRAM A = 3.9 B = −.3 C = 300.**   4
>   **COMPUTE PRED = C/(1 + EXP(A + B*X)).**   5
>   **NLR POP WITH X/**   6
>   **SAVE PRED RESID (RESID).**   7

LINE 1 Same as step 5, line 1 above.
LINE 2 This line is optional. The files used with nonlinear regression are usually not large, and it is often helpful to have a listing of the data to supplement your interpretation of output.
LINE 3 This line is optional. This line requests a plot of population with year. Once again, it is often helpful to have the data graphed for visual reference.
LINE 4 This step is required. This line identifies starting values for the three parameters of interest in the equation that follows.
LINE 5 This step is required. Here a new variable is computed, called **PRED**, that is the predicted value for the population-growth equation that follows. Note that two lines later, the **PRED** values are saved and may be printed out or graphed for a visual display. Note that the equation that follows adheres strictly to the coding for division, exponentials, and multiplication presented in Chapter 5.
LINE 6 This step is required. The **NLR** command begins the iterative procedure that eventually converges to yield the final parameter values. Note that the Y_i (population) and the X_i (coding of year) are designated as the variables upon which the regression procedure is based.
LINE 7 This line is optional. The **SAVE** subcommand saves the predicted values and the residuals for future use.

> 7) F9 W ↵   *to save your command file for future access.*

If file is not already named, enter the file name (e.g., **GROWTH.CTL**) at the prompt between the **W** and the **ENTER**.

To run the program, first position cursor at the beginning of the GET FILE line, then:

8) `F10` `C`   *to run your program from the cursor.*

After viewing the results:

9) `F10` `E` FINISH `↵`   *to exit to the DOS prompt.*

To print command files and results:

10) *dos >* PRINT SPSS.LIS `↵` `↵`   *(Sometimes the second RETURN is not necessary.)*

OUTPUT
Nonlinear Regression

The following OUTPUT is produced by this COMMAND FILE. INTERPRETATION follows.

```
GET FILE = 'GROWTH.SYS'.
LIST.
PLOT PLOT = POP WITH YEAR.
MODEL PROGRAM A=3.9 B=-.3 C=300.
COMPUTE PRED = C/(1+EXP(A+B*X)).
NLR POP WITH X.
```

- - - - - - N O N L I N E A R   R E G R E S S I O N - - - - - -

POP	YEAR	X		POP	YEAR	X
3.895	1790	0		75.734	1900	11
5.267	1800	1		91.812	1910	12
7.182	1810	2		109.806	1920	13
9.566	1820	3		122.775	1930	14
12.834	1830	4		131.669	1940	15
16.985	1840	5		150.697	1950	16
23.069	1850	6		178.464	1960	17
31.278	1860	7		203.302	1970	18
38.416	1870	8		226.505	1980	19
49.924	1880	9		249.632	1990	20
62.692	1890	10				

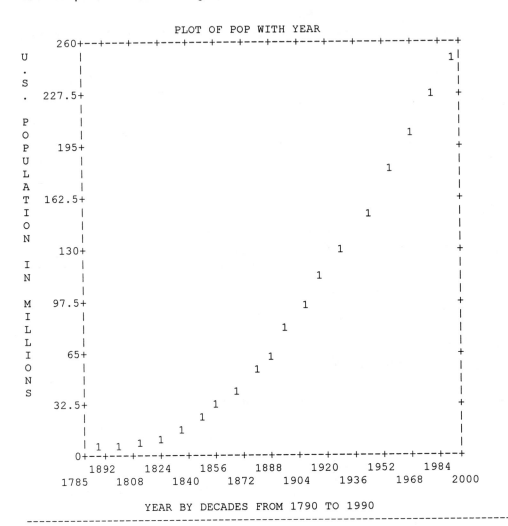

```
                        PLOT OF POP WITH YEAR
       260+--+---+---+---+---+---+---+---+---+---+---+---+--+
   U      |                                              1 |
   .      |                                                |
   S      |                                                |
   .  227.5+                                         1    +
          |                                                |
   P      |                                                |
   O      |                                       1        |
   P  195+                                                +
   U      |                                                |
   L      |                                   1            |
   A      |                                                |
   T 162.5+                                               +
   I      |                               1                |
   O      |                                                |
   N      |                                                |
      130+                           1                    +
   I      |                                                |
   N      |                       1                        |
          |                                                |
   M   97.5+                   1                          +
   I      |                                                |
   L      |                 1                              |
   L      |                                                |
   I   65+              1                                 +
   O      |            1                                   |
   N      |                                                |
   S      |         1                                      |
      32.5+      1                                        +
          |    1                                           |
          |  1                                             |
          | 1  1  1   1                                    |
        0+--+---+---+---+---+---+---+---+---+---+---+---+--+
         1892    1824    1856    1888    1920    1952    1984
      1785    1808    1840    1872    1904    1936    1968    2000

               YEAR BY DECADES FROM 1790 TO 1990
```

There are 18 cases. There is enough memory for them all.

Iteration	Residual SS	A	B	C
1	21390.24318	3.90000000	−.30000000	300.000000
1.1	1830.804289	3.72172806	−.23277648	307.230580
2	1830.804289	3.72172806	−.23277648	307.230580
2.1	650.9916124	3.98867828	−.22861913	371.686280
3	650.9916124	3.98867828	−.22861913	371.686280
3.1	415.7569668	3.99159211	−.22768574	386.273193
4	415.7569668	3.99159211	−.22768574	386.273193
4.1	415.7569558	3.99159211	−.22768574	386.469981
5	415.7215845	3.99199496	−.22769191	386.469981
5.1	415.7215802	3.99198357	−.22768696	386.483858
6	415.7215802	3.99198257	−.22768696	386.482858
6.1	415.7215802	3.99198623	−.22768717	386.483715

Run stopped after 12 model evaluations and 6 derivative evaluations.
Iterations have been stopped because the relative reduction between
successive residual sum of squares is at most SSCON = 1.000E-08 (e.g.,
.00000001)

Nonlinear Regression Summary Statistics   Dependent Variable POP

Source	DF	Sum of Squares	Mean Square
Regression	3	277776.66042	92592.22014
Residual	18	415.72158	23.09564
Uncorrected Total	21	278192.38200	
(Corrected Total)	20	123648.73142	

R Squared = (1 - Residual SS) / (Corrected SS) = .99664

		Asymptotic	Asymptotic 95% Confidence Interval	
Parameter	Estimate	Std. Error	Lower	Upper
A	3.991986231	.076533593	3.831195	4.152777
B	-.227687171	.011745936	-.252365	-.203010
C	386.483715120	32.487942210	318.229381	454.738349

Asymptotic Correlation Matrix of the Parameter Estimates

		A	'B	C
A		1.0000	-.5596	-.1872
B		-.5596	1.0000	.9139
C		-.1872	.9139	1.0000

First things first. The reason we went through the process is to acquire the parameter estimates. These are shown just above the Asymptotic Correlation Matrix. Note that the procedure converged in only six iterations (indicating a combination of pretty good start values and an equation that fit the data fairly well). Note also the astonishingly high R square value (.99650). This value means that 99.65% of the variance in the data are accounted for by the formula that we used. This is underlined by a regression sum of squares of 277,776 (with 3 degrees of freedom) and a residual sum of squares of only 416 (with 18 degrees of freedom).

The first page recreates the command file, lists the data file (including the POPulation, the YEAR, and the X coding for each year). Also on the first page of output, a scatter plot of the data is shown. The asymptotic nature of the relationship is evident from the shape of the curve. Note, however, that in the real world, population growth is not asymptotic. There is no (reasonable) set number which a population cannot grow beyond. Because of this, each decade (when new figures become available) the researcher would reestimate parameters to create a formula that reflects a more complete set of data.

ITERATION: The process of solving an equation based on predetermined values, then replacing the original values with the computer values, and solving the equation again. This process continues until some criterion (in terms of amount of change from one iteration to the next) is achieved.

SSCON = **1.000E–08**: This is the default value at which iteration ceases. **1.000E–08** is the computer's version of 1.000×10^{-8}, scientific notation for .00000001 (one hundred-millionth). This criterion utilizes the residual sum of squares as the value to determine when iteration ceases. Note (in the iteration table) that there is no change in the seventh decimal position between the fifth and sixth iterations.

REGRESSION: The explained variance. 3 DF (degrees of freedom) is equal to the number of parameters to be estimated, SUM OF SQUARES is the total variation accounted for by the equation, and the MEAN SQUARE is the sum of squares divided by the degrees of freedom.

RESIDUAL: The unexplained variance. 18 degrees of freedom is the number of data points (21) minus the number of parameters (3). Sum of squares is the amount of total variation *not* accounted for by the equation.

MEAN SQUARE: The sum of squares divided by the degrees of freedom.

UNCORRECTED TOTAL: The sum of the previous two lines—the sum of squared values of the dependent variable.

CORRECTED TOTAL: The sum of squared deviations about the mean.

R SQUARED: The proportion of variation accounted for by the equation.

PARAMETER: *A*, *B*, and *C*, to be estimated.

ESTIMATE: The final iterated value for each parameter.

ASYMPTOTIC STD. ERROR: Standard errors and confidence intervals cannot be calculated exactly, and for both values we depend on estimates based on large (asymptotic) values. The asymptotic standard error is a standard error based on asymptotic values.

ASYMPTOTIC 95% CONFIDENCE INTERVALS: Confidence intervals based on asymptotic values.

ASYMPTOTIC CORRELATION MATRIX OF PARAMETER ESTIMATES: The specific correlations have individual meaning only if the researcher has a clear idea of how each parameter affects the equation. Without such knowledge, many large values may indicate that the equation is overparameterized (e.g., that fewer parameters might do as good a job). This is not, however, automatically true. Conceptual and research concerns will determine this.

Chapter 26

The LOGISTIC REGRESSION Command:

Logistic Regression Analysis

Logistic regression is an extension of multiple regression (Chapter 20) in which the dependent variable is not a continuous variable. In logistic regression, the dependent variable may have only two values. Usually these values refer to membership-nonmembership or yes-no.

Since logistic regression is an extension of multiple regression, we will assume that you are familiar with the fundamentals of multiple regression analysis: namely, that several variables are regressed onto another variable, using forward, backward, or other selection processes and criteria. These basic concepts are the same for logistic regression as for multiple regression. The meaning of the regression equation is somewhat different in logistic regression, however. In a standard regression equation, a number of weights are used with the predictor variables to predict a value of the criterion or dependent variable. In logistic regression, however, the value that is being predicted represents a probability, and it varies between 0 and 1. In addition to this, it is possible to use a categorical predictor variable, using an indicator-variable coding scheme. This is described in the Step by Step and Output sections in more detail, but it essentially breaks up a single categorical predictor variable into a series of variables, each coded as 0 or 1 indicating whether or not the subjects are in a particular category.

At this point, the basic mathematics of logistic regression will be summarized, using the example that will be applied in this chapter. The example utilizes the third (and final) helping file named **HELPING3.SYS**. This is a file of real data ($N = 537$) that deals with issues similar to the **HELPING1.SYS** and **HELPING2.SYS** files presented in earlier chapters, but variable names are different in several instances. It is described in greater detail in the *Data Disk* section of the Appendix. This file is similar to that used in Chapter 20, in which the amount of help given to a friend was predicted by feelings of: (a) sympathy aroused in the helper in response to the friend's need (**SYMPATHY**); (b) feelings of anger or irritation aroused in the helper by the friend's need (**ANGER**); and (c) self-efficacy of the helper in relation to the friend's need (**EFFICACY**). In this case, however, instead of predicting the *amount* of help given to a friend, our model will predict a different dependent variable: Whether or not the friend thought that the help given was useful or not. This is coded as a yes-or-no (dichotomous) variable. It should be noted that, although the rest of the data in the **HELPING3.SYS** file are real data, this categorical dependent variable is fictional, created for this example.

MATHEMATICS OF LOGISTIC REGRESSION

To understand logistic regression; probabilities, odds, and logarithm of the odds must be understood. Probabilities are simply the likelihood that something will happen; a probability of .20 of rain means that there is a 20% chance of rain. In the technical sense used here, odds are the ratio of the probability that an event will occur divided by the probability that an event will not occur. If there is a 20% chance of rain, then there is an 80% chance of no rain; the odds, then, are:

$$\text{Odds} = \frac{\text{prob(rain)}}{\text{prob(no rain)}} = \frac{.20}{.80} = \frac{1}{4} = .25$$

Although probabilities always vary between 0 and 1, odds may be greater than 1: If there were an 80% chance of rain, for example, the odds would be 4.0. A 50% chance of rain has odds of 1.

A key concept in logistic regression analysis is a construct known as a *logit*. A logit is the natural logarithm (*ln*) of the odds. If there is a 20% chance of rain, then there is a logit of

$$ln(.25) = -1.386 \ldots$$

In the example used in Chapter 20, the regression equation looked something like this:

$$\text{HELP} = B_0 + B_1 \times \text{SYMPATHY} + B_2 \times \text{ANGER} + B_3 \times \text{EFFICACY}$$

where the amount of helping was a function of a constant, plus coefficients times the amount of sympathy, anger, and efficacy. In the example used in this chapter, in which we examine whether or not the subjects' help was useful instead of how much they helped, the regression equation might look something like this. Please note that we have now switched to the variable names used in the **HELPING3.SYS** file: Sympathy (**SYMPATHT**), anger (**ANGERT**), and efficacy (**EFFICT**).

$$ln\left[\frac{\text{prob(helping)}}{\text{prob(not helping)}}\right] = B_0 + B_1(\text{SYMPATHT}) + B_2(\text{ANGERT}) + B_3(\text{EFFICT})$$

In this equation, the log of the odds of helping is a function of a constant, plus a series of weighted averages of sympathy, anger, and efficacy. If you wish to work in terms of the odds-of-helping or the probability-of-helping instead of the log-odds-of-helping, this equation may be converted to the following:

$$\frac{\text{prob(helping)}}{\text{prob(not helping)}} = e^{B_0} \times e^{B_1(\text{SYMPATHT})} \times e^{B_2(\text{ANGERT})} \times e^{B_3(\text{EFFICT})}$$

or

$$\text{prob(helping)} = \frac{1}{1 + e^{-B_0} \times e^{-B_1(\text{SYMPATHT})} \times e^{-B_2(\text{ANGERT})} \times e^{-B_3(\text{EFFICT})}}$$

This equation is probably not very intuitive to most people (several of my students would certainly agree with this!); it takes a lot of experience before interpreting logistic regression equations becomes intuitive. Because of this as well as other problems in selecting an appropriate model (since model selection involves both mathematical and theoretical considerations), you should use extreme caution in interpreting logistic regression models. Due to this complexity we refer you to three sources if you wish to gain a greater understanding of logistic regression: The *SPSS/PC+ Advanced Statistics 4.0 Manual* covers logistic regression in much greater detail than we do here, and then there are textbooks by McLachlan (1992) and Wickens (1989), both of which are quite good. Please see the reference section for complete information on these sources.

THE LOGICAL PROGRESSION FOR CONDUCTING LOGISTIC REGRESSION ANALYSIS

1. Create file of data, or edit (if necessary) an already existing file.
2. Format file by use of **DATA LIST FILE**, **FORMATS**, and **VARIABLE/VALUE LABELS**; then save as a system file.
3. Access file and formats by the **GET FILE** command.
4. Use the **LOGISTIC REGRESSION** command to access logistic regression analysis.
5. Use the **VARIABLES** subcommand to identify which variables will be used.
6. Use the **CONTRAST** subcommand to specify categorical predictor variables, if desired.
7. Use the **CRITERIA** subcommand to enter significance values other than the defaults for variables to be entered or removed.
8. Use the **METHOD** subcommand to identify whether you wish forced entry; forced removal; or forward, backward, or stepwise procedure(s).
9. Use the **PRINT** subcommand to obtain correlations among the variables in the model, if desired.
10. Use the **CLASSPLOT** subcommand to obtain classification plots, if desired.
11. View the results and exit the program.
12. Print data, commands, and output.

STEP BY STEP
Logistic Regression Analysis

> 1) *Name and create a data file (Chapter 2), or edit (if necessary) an already existing file (Chapter 3).*

> 2) *Name variables, locate column positions, format, create VARIABLE/VALUE LABELS, and then save the formatted DATA FILE as a SYSTEM FILE (Chapter 4).*

From the DOS prompt, type:

> 3) *dos >* **SPSSPC** ⏎   *This step gets you into the SPSS system.*

To clear the menu from the top window prior to analyzing data:

> 4) ALT ─ M   *Positions cursor to begin to create the command file.*

From the extreme upper left corner of the scratch pad (lower window), type:

> 5) GET FILE = 'HELPING3.**SYS**'.   1

LINE **1** Accesses the formatted **SYSTEM FILE** to begin to analyze data. All statistical procedures in this book will begin with the **GET FILE** step.

The following file instructs SPSS to perform a logistic regression on CATHELP (whether or not the help was rated as useful or not), as predicted by sympathy (SYMPATHT), anger (ANGERT), self-efficacy (EFFICT), and ethnicity (ETHNIC).

> 6) GET FILE = 'HELPING3.**SYS**'.   1
> LOGISTIC REGRESSION VARIABLES CATHELP WITH SYMPATHT ANGERT
> EFFICT ETHNIC/   2
> CONTRAST (ETHNIC)/   3
> CRITERIA PIN(.10) POUT (.10)/   4
> METHOD FSTEP(LR)/   5
> PRINT DEFAULT CORR/   6
> CLASSPLOT.   7

LINE **1** The same as step 5, line 1 above.

LINE **2** **LOGISTIC REGRESSION** is the command that SPSS uses to compute logistic regression analysis. The first subcommand should be **VARIABLES**, followed by the categorical variable that you wish to predict based on your other variables. In this case, **CATHELP** equals 0 if help was *not* rated as useful and 1 if it *was* rated useful. Note that these are computer generated numbers. The original coding for CATHELP was 1 = not helpful, 2 = helpful. The word WITH separates the predicted variable from the predictor variables.

LINE 3 CONTRAST is used when a categorical predictor variable is included; in this case, individuals may be Caucasian, Black, Hispanic, Asian, or other. Because there is no particular order to these ethnicities, the CONTRAST command is used to convert this single categorical variable into a series of variables (each of them a contrast between one of the first four variables and the final, fifth variable) that may be entered into the logistic regression equation. If you have more than one categorical variable that you wish to code like this, include additional CONTRAST subcommands.

LINE 4 PIN specifies the probability value used to add a variable to the regression equation; POUT specifies the values used to drop a variable from the regression equation. This line is optional; by default, SPSS uses PIN = .05 and POUT = .10.

LINE 5 The METHOD subcommand specifies the way that SPSS will build the regression equation. FSTEP(LR), shown here, tells SPSS to build the equation by entering variables one at a time, using likelihood ratio estimates to determine which variable will add the most to the regression equation. You may also specify BSTEP(LR), in which SPSS builds the equation starting with all variables and then removes them one by one if they do not contribute enough to the regression equation. If you already know what variables you want entered into the equation, you may type the word ENTER, followed by the names of all variables that you want entered within the logistic regression equation. For example: **METHOD ENTER SYMPATHT ANGERT EFFICT ETHNIC/**

LINE 6 This line is optional. If you want correlations between all variables that have been entered into the regression equation, then select this option.

LINE 7 This optional line produces a plot of probabilities for all cases, providing a graphical representation of how well the regression equation is working.

---

7) | F9 | W | ↵ | *to save your command file for future access.*

If file is not already named, enter the file name (e.g., **HELPING3.CTL**) at the prompt between the W and the ENTER.

To run the program, first position cursor at the beginning of the GET FILE line, then:

---

8) | F10 | C | *to run your program from the cursor.*

After viewing the results:

---

9) | F10 | E | FINISH | ↵ | *to exit to the DOS prompt.*

To print command files and results:

---

10) dos> PRINT SPSS.LIS | ↵ | ↵ | *(Sometimes the second RETURN is not necessary.)*

OUTPUT
Logistic Regression Analysis

The following OUTPUT *is produced by this* COMMAND FILE. INTERPRETATION *follows each section of output.*

```
GET FILE = 'HELPING3.SYS'.
LOGISTIC REGRESSION VARIABLES CATHELP WITH SYMPATHT ANGERT EFFICT
ETHNIC/
CONTRAST (ETHNIC)/
CRITERIA PIN(.10) POUT(.10)/
METHOD FSTEP(LR)/
PRINT DEFAULT CORR/
CLASSPLOT.
```

Note: Since forward- and backward-stepping analyses involve reanalyzing the regression several times (adding or deleting variables from the equation each time), they may produce several sets of output, as illustrated here. The final set of output shows the final regression equation, but output is produced for each step in the development of the equation to see how the regression equation was formed. Only the final set of output is shown here.

- - - - - L O G I S T I C   R E G R E S S I O N - - - - - -

                            Parameter

		Value	Freq		Coding		
				(1)	(2)	(3)	(4)
ETHNIC							
	CAUCASIAN	1	293	1.000	.000	.000	.000
	BLACK	2	50	.000	1.000	.000	.000
	HISPANIC	3	80	.000	.000	1.000	.000
	ASIAN	4	70	.000	.000	.000	1.000
	OTHER/	5	44	-1.000	-1.000	-1.000	-1.000

Note: This coding results in deviation coefficients.

PARAMETERS: If **CONTRAST**s are used in the analysis, a table will be produced at the beginning of the output that shows how the computer has converted from the various values of your variable (the rows in the table) to coding values of several different variables within the computer (the columns). In this case, **ETHNIC** had five levels in the original data and has been broken down into four new variables, labeled **ETHNIC(1)** through **ETHNIC(4)**. These variables are a series of contrasts between the various ethnicities.

Variable(s) Entered on Step Number

2..   SYMPATHT MEAN RATING OF FOUR SYMPATHY QUESTIONS

```
Estimation terminated at iteration number 4 because
Log Likelihood decreased by less than .01 percent.
```

	Chi-Square	df	Significance
-2 Log Likelihood	599.713	534	.0254
Model Chi-Square	144.635	2	.0000
Improvement	29.792	1	.0000
Goodness of Fit	531.159	534	.5266

VARIABLE(S) ENTERED ON STEP NUMBER 2: In step 1 of this analysis, **SYMPATHT** was entered into the regression equation; here, **EFFICT** was entered. Note that although **ETHNIC** is composed of four variables now (because of the **CONTRAST** subcommand), if **ETHNIC** is entered into the regression equation all four of the computer variables based on **ETHNIC** would be entered simultaneously.

−2 LOG LIKELIHOOD: This and the following measures are used to indicate how well the model fits the data. Smaller −2 log likelihood values mean that the model fits the data better; a perfect model has a −2 log likelihood value of zero. In this case, the χ^2 value (distributed with the number of subjects minus the number of parameters degrees of freedom) has a nonsignificant value ($p > .10$), so the model *does* fit the data well. Significant χ^2 values indicate that the model differs significantly from the theoretically "perfect" model.

MODEL χ^2: This value tests whether or not all of the variables entered in the equation have a significant effect; in this case, a high χ^2 value indicates that the variables in the equation significantly impact the dependent variable. This test is functionally equivalent to the overall F-test in multiple regression.

IMPROVEMENT: This value examines change in −2 log likelihood of the model based on the current step in building the model (by adding **SYMPATHT** here). In this case, the improvement of the model was slight ($p = .066$). More significant values indicate that the variable(s) added at the last step are contributing more to the model.

GOODNESS OF FIT: This statistic compares the observed values for the subjects in the sample with the predicted values that the subjects should have, based on the model. As in the −2 log likelihood values, the *non*significance ($p = .499$) indicates that the model *does* fit the data well.

```
          Classification Table for CATHELP
          Predicted     NOT HELPFUL     HELPFUL
                          0.00            1.00
          Observed          1               2        Percent Correct
NOT HELPFUL 0.00      1      181             84           68.30%
    HELPFUL 1.00      2       76            197           72.43%
                                         Overall          70.39%
```

CLASSIFICATION TABLE: The classification table compares the predicted values for the dependent variable, based on the regression model, with the actual observed values in the data. When computing predicted values, SPSS simply computes the probability for a particular case (based on the current regression equation) and classifies it into the two categories possible for the dependent variable based on that probability. If the probability is less than .50, then SPSS classifies it as the first value for the dependent variable (0.00, meaning *not helpful* in this example); and if the probability is greater than .50, then SPSS classifies that case as the second value for the dependent variable (1.00 meaning *helpful* in this example). This table compares these predicted values with the values observed in the data. In this case, the model including **SYMPATHT** and **EFFICT** can predict which value of **CATHELP** is observed in the data 70% of the time.

```
-------------------------------------------------------------------------
            ------- Variables in the Equation -------
Variable         B        S.E.      Wald     df      Sig        R     Exp(B)
SYMPATHT       .4673      .0892    27.4590     1     .0000     .1849   1.5957
EFFECT        1.1138      .1276    76.1967     1     .0000     .3157   3.0458
Constant     -7.4709      .7747    93.0062     1     .0000
-------------------------------------------------------------------------
```

VARIABLES IN THE EQUATION: After each step in building the equation, SPSS displays a summary of the effects of the variables that are currently in the regression equation. The **CONSTANT** variable indicates the constant B_0 term in the equation.

B: The weighting value of B used in the equation; the magnitude of B, along with the scale of the variable that B is used to weight, indicates the effect of the predictor variable on the predicted variable. In this case, for example, sympathy and efficacy both have a positive effect on helping.

S.E.: Standard error; a measure of the dispersion of B.

WALD: A measure of the significance of B for the given variable; higher values, in combination with the degrees of freedom, indicate significance.

SIG: The significance of the **WALD** test. In this case, some of the **ETHNIC** contrasts are significant, and some of them are not; they are all included, however, because they are all derived from the same **ETHNIC** variable.

R: The correlation of the predictor variable with the predicted variable; this is a partial correlation, indicating the correlation *independent* from other variables in the equation.

EXP(B): e^B, used to help in interpreting the meaning of the regression coefficients (as you may remember from the introduction to this chapter, the regression equation may be interpreted in terms of B or e^B).

```
-------------------------------------------------------------------------
         Correlation Matrix:
                  Constant   SYMPATHT    EFFECT
        Constant   1.00000    -.61929    -.82457
        SYMPATHT   -.61929    1.00000     .08509
        EFFECT     -.82457     .08509    1.00000
-------------------------------------------------------------------------
```

CORRELATION MATRIX: This is the correlation matrix for all variables in the regression equation, and it is only printed if you request **PRINT DEFAULT CORR**. It is useful because if some variables are highly correlated, then the regression may have multicollinearity and be unstable.

```
-------------------------------------------------------------------------
            ------- Variables not in the Equation -------
Residual Chi Square      5.404 with       5 df     Sig =  .3686

Variable            Score     df      Sig        R
ANGER               .6403      1     .4236     .0000
ETHNIC             4.8920      4     .2986     .0000
    ETHNIC(1)       .6500      1     .4201     .0000
    ETHNIC(2)       .3356      1     .5624     .0000
    ETHNIC(3)       .0017      1     .9670     .0000
    ETHNIC(4)      2.1597      1     .1417     .0146
-------------------------------------------------------------------------
```

VARIABLES NOT IN THE EQUATION: All variables that are not entered into the equation that could possibly be entered are listed here. The **RESIDUAL CHI-SQUARE** value tests whether the variables not in the equation are significantly different from zero. Since the significance here is large, the variables not in the equation have an effect not significantly different from zero, and none are likely to be worth entering into the equation in the future. The **SIG** indicates for each variable whether it has a significant impact on the predicted variable, independently from the other predictor variables. Here, **ANGERT** does not have an impact on **CATHELP**. Note here that **ETHNIC** is divided into four variables, indicating the four different contrasts that SPSS is performing.

```
--------------------------------------------------------------------
              Observed Groups and Predicted Probabilities
        20 |                                                        |
           |                                                        |
           |                     2  2           2 2  2              |
    F      |                     2  2           2 2 22              |
    R   15 |              2      2  2    22      2 2 22              |
    E      |              2      2  2    22 2    2 2 22          2   |
    Q      |          2   1      2  2    22 22   2 2 22 2        2   |
    U      |          2   1 2    1  2    222222 2 2 22 2    22   2   |
    E   10 |      2   12 2122 22 1 22    2222222 2 22 2 2 22   2 2   |
    N      |      212  12 2121 22 1222 2 2222222 2 12 2 2 22   2 2   |
    C      |     1111   11 2111211211222221221222122212 222 22 2222  2  |
    Y      |     1111 1 11 1111111211212121221222122212 222 22 2222 222 |
         5 |     1111 11 11 1111111211112121111211122212 122 2222222 222 |
           | 1 1111 11 11 1111111111112111111111211112122 2222222 222 |
           | 1 11111111111111111111111111111111111121111211221212222222 |
           |11111111111111111111111111111111111111111111121111212111211122 |
Predicted  --------------------------------------------------------------------
  Prob:    0          .25          .5          .75              1
  Group:   1111111111111111111111111111111112222222222222222222222222222222
           Predicted Probability is of Membership for 1.00
           Symbols: 1 - 0.00
                    2 - 1.00          Each Symbol Represents 1.25 Case.
--------------------------------------------------------------------
```

OBSERVED GROUP AND PREDICTED PROBABILITIES: This graph is produced if you request **CLASSPLOT**. Each case is plotted as a 1 or a 2, depending on what its classification is in the original data. It is plotted along the *x*-axis based on its predicted probability from the regression equation. If the logistic regression equation were perfect, all of the 1's would be to the left of all of the 2's.

```
--------------------------------------------------------------------
              ------- Model if Term Removed -------
Term       Log                           Significance
Removed    Likelihood    -2 Log LR   df   of Log LR
SYMPATHT    -314.753      29.792      1      .0000
EFFICT      -350.086     100.458      1      .0000
     No variables can be removed.
     No variables can be added.
--------------------------------------------------------------------
```

MODEL IF TERM REMOVED: All variables in the model are tested here to see if they should be removed from the model. If the **SIGNIFICANCE OF LOG LR** values for a variable are larger than **POUT** (the criteria for removing a variable from the equation), then that variable will be dropped. In this example, since all of the −2 Log LR values are less than **POUT**, no variables can be removed. Because no variables can be removed and no variables can be added, the logistic regression equation is complete.

Chapter 27

The HILOGLINEAR Command:

Hierarchical Log-Linear Models

Both this chapter and the chapter that follows focus on log-linear models: The present chapter on *hierarchical* models, and the next (Chapter 28) on *non*hierarchical models. The first part of this introduction will discuss log-linear models in general and is applicable (and, indeed, necessary) for both this chapter and the next.

LOG-LINEAR MODELS

Log-linear models allow the analysis of chi-square-type data using regression-like models, and in many ways they appear to be similar to ANOVA. As in chi-square analysis, log-linear models deal with frequency tables in which several categorical variables categorize the data. If only two categorical variables are in the data for analysis, then chi-square analyses are indeed the simplest analysis available. For example, in Chapter 8, on chi-square analysis, the relationship between gender and ethnicity was examined in the **GRADES.SYS** file. If, however, you wish to analyze several different categorical variables together, then it quickly becomes difficult or impossible to interpret chi-square tables visually: A chi-square table and analysis of **GENDER** by **ETHNICIT** by **YEAR** in school by whether or not the student attended the **REVIEW** session is virtually impossible to interpret. It is for this purpose that log-linear models were developed.

In this chapter, the example will be drawn from the same **HELPING3.SYS** file ($N = 537$) used in the previous chapter. In particular, hierarchical log-linear models will be tested for **GENDER** $\times$ **ETHNIC** $\times$ **INCOME** level $\times$ **CATHELP** (whether or not the person receiving help thought the help was useful or not). Note that in this example, **INCOME** is a categorical variable, indicating whether subjects earned less than $15,000/year, less than $25,000/year (meaning between 15 and 25,000), less than $50,000/year (meaning between 25 and 50,000), or greater than $50,000/year.

Log-linear models are essentially multiple linear regression models in which the classification variables (and their interaction terms) are the independent (predictor) variables, and the dependent variable is the natural logarithm of the frequencies of cases in a cell of the frequency table. Using the natural log (*ln*) of the frequencies produces a linear model. A log-linear model for the effects of gender, ethnicity, income level, and their interactions on a particular cell in the crosstabulation table, might be represented by the following equation:

$$ln(\text{FREQUENCY}) = \mu + \lambda^{G} + \lambda^{E} + \lambda^{I} + \lambda^{G \times E} + \lambda^{G \times I} + \lambda^{E \times I} + \lambda^{G \times E \times I}$$

There will be different values for each of these variables for each of the cells in the model. In this equation, *Frequency* represents the frequency present within a particular cell of the data. μ represents the overall grand mean of the effect; it is equivalent to the constant in multiple regression analysis. Each of the λ's represents the effect of one or more independent variables on *F*. λ^{G} represents the main effect (here's where log-linear models start sounding similar to ANOVA) of **GENDER**, λ^{E} represents the main effect (also known as first-order effect) of **ETHNIC**, and λ^{I} represents the main effect of **INCOME** level on the frequency. λ values with multiple superscripts are interaction terms; for example, $\lambda^{G \times E}$ represents the two-way (second-order) interactive effect of **GENDER** and **ETHNIC** on frequency; and $\lambda^{G \times E \times I}$ represents the three-way (third-order) interactive effect of **GENDER, ETHNIC,** and **INCOME** on the frequency. The model presented here is a saturated model because it contains *all* possible main effect and interaction terms. Because it is a saturated model, it can perfectly reproduce the data; however, it is not parsimonious and usually not the most desirable model.

The purpose of SPSS's **HILOGLINEAR** and **LOGLINEAR** procedures is to assist you in choosing an unsaturated log-linear model that will fit your data, as well as to calculate parameters of the log-linear model (the μ's and λ's).

THE HILOGLINEAR PROCEDURE

Although any of the terms may be deleted from the saturated model in order to produce a simpler, more parsimonious model, many researchers explore *hierarchical* log-linear models. In hierarchical models, in order for an effect of a certain order to be present, all effects of a lower order must be present. In other words, in a hierarchical model, in order for a two-way interaction (second-order effect) of **GENDER** and **ETHNIC** to be present, there must also be main effects (first-order effects) of both **GENDER** and **ETHNIC**. Likewise, in order for a third-order interactive effect of **GENDER, ETHNIC,** and **INCOME** level to be present, second-order interactive effects of **GENDER** by **ETHNIC**, **GENDER** by **INCOME** level, and **ETHNIC** by **INCOME** level must be present.

There are three primary techniques that SPSS provides in assisting with model selection. All three techniques are useful and will usually yield similar or identical results. Ultimately, however, the choice of which model or models you will use has to rely on both the results provided by SPSS *and* your understanding of the data and what the data mean. The three techniques are summarized here, with a more detailed example provided in the Output section.

Examine Parameter Estimates

One technique used in developing a model is to calculate parameter estimates for the saturated model. SPSS provides, along with these parameter estimates, *standardized* parameter estimates. If these standardized parameter estimates are small, then they probably do not contribute very much to the model and might be considered for removal.

Partitioning the Chi-Square Statistic

SPSS can, in addition to providing parameter estimates for the model, calculate a chi-square value that indicates how well the model fits the data. This chi-square value may also be subdivided and may be useful in selecting a model. SPSS can test whether all one-way and higher effects are nonsignificant; whether all two-way and higher effects are nonsignificant; whether all three-way and higher effects are nonsignificant; and so on. The HILOGLINEAR program can also test that all one-way effects are zero, all two-way effects are zero, and so on. These tests examine a combination of all first-order effects, second-order effects, and so forth. However, just because the second-order effects *overall* may not be significant doesn't mean that *none* of the second-order effects are significant. Similarly, just because the second-order effects are significant overall doesn't mean that *all* of the second-order effects are significant. Because of this, SPSS can also examine partial chi-square values for individual main effects and interactive effects. This procedure usually takes quite a while for the computer to calculate, but it is often useful in helping with model selection.

Backward Elimination

Another way to select a model is to use backward elimination; this is very similar to stepwise backwards elimination in multiple regression analysis. In backward elimination, SPSS starts with a saturated model and removes effects that are not contributing to the model significantly. This model-building technique is subject to the constraints of hierarchical log-linear modeling; third-order effects are not examined as candidates for exclusion if fourth-order effects are present, since if they were removed the assumptions of hierarchical models would be violated. The model is considered to fit best when all remaining effects contribute significantly to the model's fit.

We acknowledge that hierarchical log-linear models are complex and direct you to three other sources for a more complete picture than has been presented here: The *SPSS/PC+ Advanced Statistics 4.0 Manual* does a fairly thorough job of description and has the advantage of explaining the procedure in the context of SPSS documentation. Two other textbooks are quite good: Agresti (1990) and Wickens (1989); please see the reference section for a more complete description of these sources.

LOGICAL PROGRESSION FOR CREATING HIERARCHICAL LOG-LINEAR MODELS

1. Create file of data, or edit (if necessary) an already existing file.
2. Format file by use of DATA LIST FILE, FORMATS, and VARIABLE/VALUE LABELS; then save as a system file.
3. Access file and formats by the GET FILE command.
4. Use the HILOGLINEAR command to access hierarchical log-linear analysis.
5. Identify which variables will be used.
6. Use PRINT ASSOCIATION if you wish to partition the chi-square value into its component main and interactive effects. Note: You may not use this step at the same time that you are using logical progression steps 7 through 9.
7. Use METHOD = BACKWARD if you wish to perform backward elimination.
8. Use the MAXORDER subcommand if you wish to limit the analysis to a lower order than is possible with the number of variables present. (This is useful if you don't want to try to interpret higher-order interaction effects.)
9. Use the CRITERIA subcommand if you wish to specify the number of iterations allowed, the maximum number of eliminations allowed, or the *p*-value to use in deciding whether or not to eliminate an effect from the model.
10. Run the program and view the results.
11. Repeat logical progression steps 4 through 9 if you wish to perform additional analysis (either to partition the chi-square value or else to perform backward elimination). Use the DESIGN subcommand if you wish to analyze a particular model.
12. Run the program, view the results, and exit the program.
13. Print data, commands, and output.

Note: Due to the structure of the HILOGLINEAR command, it is not possible to partition the chi-square value at the same time that you are performing backward elimination. For this reason, you should *not* use both step 6 (above) and steps 7 through 9 (above) in the same HILOGLINEAR command.

STEP BY STEP
Hierarchical Log-Linear Models

> *1) Name and create a data file (Chapter 2), or edit (if necessary) an already existing file (Chapter 3).*

> *2) Name variables, locate column positions, format, create VARIABLE/VALUE LABELS, and then save the formatted DATA FILE as a SYSTEM FILE (Chapter 4).*

From the DOS prompt, type:

> 3) dos > **SPSSPC** $\boxed{\leftarrow}$ *This step gets you into the SPSS system.*

To clear the menu from the top window prior to analyzing data:

> 4) $\boxed{\text{ALT}}\!\!-\!\!\boxed{\text{M}}$ *Positions cursor to begin to create the command file.*

From the extreme upper left corner of the scratch pad (lower window), type:

> 5) **GET FILE** = 'HELPING3.**SYS**'.   1

LINE 1 Accesses the formatted **SYSTEM FILE** to begin to analyze data. All statistical procedures in this book will begin with the **GET FILE** step.

The following command instructs SPSS to perform a hierarchical log-linear analysis of GENDER, ETHNIC, INCOME, and CATHELP (whether or not the individuals helped felt that they had benefited). The saturated model is tested, and parameter estimates will be produced, along with partitioning of the chi-square into individual effects.

> 6) **GET FILE** = 'HELPING3.**SYS**'.   1
>   **HILOGLINEAR** GENDER (1,2) ETHNIC (1,5) INCOME (1,4) CATHELP (1,2)/   2
>   **PRINT** = DEFAULT ASSOCIATION.   3

LINE 1 The same as step 5, line 1, above.

LINE 2 The **HILOGLINEAR** command instructs SPSS to perform hierarchical log-linear analysis. Follow the command with a list of all independent variables that you wish to use and put the range of values that the independent variables may have in parentheses after each variable. For example, values for **GENDER** may be 1 or 2, and values for **INCOME** may be 1 through 4.

LINE 3 This line is optional. Use it if you wish to get partial chi-square values for each of the main and interactive effects. If this line is deleted, then parameter estimates and other information for the saturated model will still be produced.

The following command instructs SPSS to perform a hierarchical log-linear analysis beginning with the saturated model of GENDER by ETHNIC by INCOME by CATHELP, and to build a model using backward elimination.

> 6a) **GET FILE** = 'HELPING3.**SYS**'.   1a
>   **HILOGLINEAR** GENDER (1,2) ETHNIC (1,5) INCOME (1,4) CATHELP (1,2)/   2a
>   **PRINT** = DEFAULT ASSOCIATION.   3a
>   **HILOGLINEAR** GENDER (1,2) ETHNIC (1,5) INCOME (1,4) CATHELP (1,2)/   4a
>   **METHOD** = BACKWARD/   5a
>   **MAXORDER** = 3/   6a
>   **CRITERIA** = ITERATE(50) P(.05) MAXSTEPS(25).   7a

LINES **1a-3a** The same as in step 6, above. Note that lines 2a and 3a are optional; if you do not want parameter estimates and partial chi-squares you may omit line 2a, and if you do not want partial chi-squares you may omit line 3a.

LINE **4a** This is the same as line 2a. We recommend repeating this line because SPSS can't calculate partial chi-squares at the same time that it is building a model using backward elimination.

LINE **5a** The METHOD = BACKWARD subcommand instructs SPSS to start with a saturated model and remove terms that do not significantly contribute to the model, through a process of backward elimination.

LINE **6a** It is sometimes desirable to avoid analyzing higher-order interactions. For example, this example allows for up to fourth-order interactions (GENDER × ETHNIC × INCOME × CATHELP). In order to avoid analyzing higher-order interactions, the MAXORDER = subcommand can restrict analysis to lower-order interactions. In this example, we have restricted the analysis to first-, second-, and third-order interactions. If you want to analyze all possible effects, do not include this subcommand.

LINE **7a** CRITERIA allows you to specify several details of the way SPSS performs the backwards elimination. ITERATE specifies the number of iterations that SPSS will take to calculate each chi-square change if a particular effect is dropped from the model. The default number of iterations is 20 and need not be specified unless a different value is desired. **P** provides a p-value that SPSS will use as a criterion for dropping effects from the model; SPSS drops effects that are not significant at the level of the p-value. Because the default is $p = .05$, it was not necessary to specify the p-value here. Each time that SPSS removes an effect from the model, this is a *step*. MAXSTEPS = allows you to set the maximum number of steps that SPSS will perform, to something other than the default of 10.

Note: If your model contains structural zeros, you must specify them using the CWEIGHT subcommand. Since the use of this command is beyond the scope of this book, please see the *SPSS/PC+ Advanced Statistics 4.0 Manual* for details.

Note: If your data file does not contain a separate case for each subject or data point, then you may choose to enter the entire crosstabulation table as part of the command file. For an illustration of how to do this, see Chapter 8, step 6e.

It should also be noted that it is not necessary to work with a saturated model. If you wish, you may specify any particular design for the model that you wish, by placing as the last line (after line 7a) the subcommand DESIGN = followed by a list of all desired effects in the model. For example, if a model included a main effect of GENDER and an interactive effect of ETHNIC by INCOME, then the last line of the HILOGLINEAR command would be DESIGN = GENDER, ETHNIC*INCOME.

---

7) [F9] [W] [↵]   *to save your command file for future access.*

If file is not already named, enter the file name (e.g., **HELPING3.CTL**) at the prompt between the **W** and the **ENTER**.

To run the program, first position cursor at the beginning of the GET FILE line, then:

---

8) [F10] [C]   *to run your program from the cursor.*

After viewing the results:

> 9) ⌊F10⌋ ⌊E⌋ FINISH ⌊←⌋   to exit to the DOS prompt.

To print command files and results:

> 10) *dos* > PRINT SPSS.LIS ⌊←⌋ ⌊←⌋   *(Sometimes the second RETURN is not necessary.)*

OUTPUT
Hierarchical Log-Linear Models

The following OUTPUT is produced by this COMMAND FILE. INTERPRETATION follows each section of output.

```
GET FILE = 'HELPING3.SYS'.
HILOGLINEAR GENDER(1,2) ETHNIC(1,5) INCOME(1,4) CATHELP(1,2)/
PRINT = DEFAULT ASSOCIATION.
HILOGLINEAR GENDER(1,2) ETHNIC(1,5) INCOME(1,4) CATHELP(1,2)/
METHOD = BACKWARD/
MAXORDER = 3/
CRITERIA = ITERATE(50) P(.05) MAXSTEPS(25).
```

Tests that K-way and higher order effects are zero.

K	DF	L.R. Chisq	Prob	Pearson Chisq	Prob	Iteration
4	12	13.408	.3401	12.330	.4195	4
3	43	62.361	.0283	59.044	.0524	3
2	70	112.633	.0009	102.374	.0070	2
1	79	428.287	.0000	618.095	.0000	0

These tests examine whether all effects at a certain order and above are zero. For example, the first line in this table tests whether all fourth-order effects are equal to zero. As indicated by the small chi-square values and the large p-values, there is no fourth-order effect. The second line ($K = 3$) indicates that the third- and fourth-order effects are not different from zero, and the third line ($K = 2$) indicates that the second-, third-, and fourth-order effects *are* different from zero (note $p = .007$). The last line ($K = 1$) suggests that, in the first- through fourth-order effects, there are some effects that are not equal to zero (note $p = .0000$).

K: The order of effects for each row of the table (4 = fourth-order and higher effects, 3 = third-order and higher effects, etc.).
DF: The degrees of freedom for Kth and higher-order effects.
L.R. CHISQ: The likelihood-ratio chi-square value testing that Kth and higher-order effects are zero.
PEARSON CHISQ: The Pearson chi-square value testing that Kth and higher-order effects are zero.

PROB: The probability that K-order and higher effects are equal to zero; small p-values suggest that one or more of the effects of order K and higher are not equal to zero.

ITER: The number of iterations that SPSS took to estimate the chi-square values.

```
-------------------------------------------------------------------------------
Tests that K-way effects are zero.
    K      DF    L.R. Chisq     Prob    Pearson Chisq     Prob    Iteration
    1       9       315.653    .0000          515.721    .0000            0
    2      27        50.272    .0042           43.331    .0242            0
    3      31        48.953    .0213           46.714    .0348            0
    4      12        13.408    .3401           12.330    .4195            0
-------------------------------------------------------------------------------
```

Here SPSS examines whether or not effects of each *particular* order in the design are equal to zero. Significant p-values suggest that the effects of a particular level are not equal to zero; in this case, the one-, two-, and three-way effects are not equal to zero.

K: The order of effects for each row of the table (1 = first-order effects, 2 = second-order effects, etc.).

DF: The degrees of freedom for Kth-order effects.

L.R. CHISQ: The likelihood-ratio chi-square value testing that Kth-order effects are zero.

PEARSON CHISQ: The Pearson chi-square value testing that Kth-order effects are zero.

PROB: The probability that K-order effects are equal to zero; small p-values suggest that one or more of the effects of order K are not equal to zero.

ITER: The number of iterations that SPSS took to estimate the chi-square values. For this table, this column will always be zero.

```
-------------------------------------------------------------------------------
Tests of PARTIAL associations.
Effect Name                      DF    Partial Chisq     Prob    Iter
GENDER*ETHNIC*INCOME             12           17.673    .1260       4
GENDER*ETHNIC*CATHELP             4            7.939    .0938       3
GENDER*INCOME*CATHELP             3           12.470    .0059       4
ETHNIC*INCOME*CATHELP            12           14.680    .2594       4
GENDER*ETHNIC                     4            3.214    .5227       3
GENDER*INCOME                     3            1.605    .6583       3
ETHNIC*INCOME                    12           32.394    .0012       3
GENDER*CATHELP                    1            4.169    .0412       3
ETHNIC*CATHELP                    4            5.399    .2488       3
INCOME*CATHELP                    3            4.918    .1779       3
GENDER                            1           10.248    .0014       2
ETHNIC                            4          236.046    .0000       2
INCOME                            3           66.886    .0000       2
CATHELP                           1            2.473    .1158       2
-------------------------------------------------------------------------------
```

This table examines partial chi-square values for each effect in the saturated model. Each partial chi-square examines the unique contribution of that effect to the model; those with low p-values contribute to the model significantly. In this case, there are main effects of **GENDER**, **ETHNIC**, and **INCOME**; two-way interactions between **GENDER** by **CATHELP** and **ETHNIC** by **INCOME**; as well as a three-way interaction of **GENDER** by **INCOME** by **CATHELP**. Because these partial chi-squares are not necessarily independent, their partial associations (displayed here) as a portion of the total chi-square for the saturated model may not be equivalent to the chi-square in nonsaturated models.

DF: These degrees of freedom refer to the particular effects listed in each line.

PARTIAL CHI-SQUARE: The partial chi-square for each effect.

PROB: The probability that the effect is equal to zero; small probabilities indicate that the given effect has a large contribution to the model.

ITER: The number of iterations that the computer took to calculate the partial association for each effect. This procedure takes quite a while; the number of iterations is there to remind you how long it took to compute each partial association.

Estimates for Parameters.

.
.

ETHNIC*INCOME

Parameter	Coeff.	Std. Err.	Z-Value	Lower 95 CI	Upper 95 CI
1	-.1094269287	.19057	-.57421	-.48294	.26409
2	-.1701748589	.22173	-.76749	-.60476	.26441
3	-.1126158596	.15926	-.70710	-.42478	.19954
4	-.6824807624	.36984	-1.84535	-1.40736	.04240
5	.7257495472	.26866	2.70140	.19918	1.25232
6	-.0233976743	.25276	-.09257	-.51881	.47201
7	-.0966040450	.24469	-.39480	-.57619	.38299
8	.2256749092	.24800	.90998	-.26040	.71175
9	.1096424852	.20073	.54621	-.28379	.50308
10	.7330105611	.23621	3.10327	.27005	1.19597
11	-.4831889921	.37115	-1.30189	-1.21063	.24426
12	-.4276172574	.26355	-1.62252	-.94418	.08894

.
.

INCOME

Parameter	Coeff.	Std. Err.	Z-Value	Lower 95 CI	Upper 95 CI
1	-.1832940387	.14238	-1.28734	-.46236	.09577
2	-.4908628679	.15797	-3.10726	-.80049	-.18124
3	.2435742286	.11668	2.08756	.01488	.47226

Parameter estimates are provided for each main effect and interaction. These are the λ's from the log-linear equation presented in the introduction of this chapter. In this example, only one interaction (**ETHNIC × INCOME**) and one main effect (**INCOME**) are presented. Because the parameters are constrained to sum to zero, only some of the parameters appear here. In this example, the **ETHNIC × INCOME** parameters may be interpreted as shown in the following table, where parameters in **bold** print are calculated by SPSS and those in *italics* are calculated by summing each row and column in the table to zero.

INCOME	ETHNICITY Caucasian	Black	Hispanic	Asian	Other	SUM
<15,000	**-.109**	**-.682**	**-.097**	**.733**	*.155*	0
<25,000	**-.170**	**.726**	**.226**	**-.483**	*-.299*	0
<50,000	**-.112**	**-.023**	**.110**	**-.428**	*.453*	0
>50,000	*.391*	*-.021*	*-.239*	*.178*	*-.309*	0
SUM	0	0	0	0	0	0

These parameters suggest that Caucasians with higher incomes are far more frequent in this sample than those with lower incomes, and that Afro-Americans (coded **BLACKS** in the **HELPING3.SYS** file), Hispanics, and Asians are more common with lower incomes. The parameters for **INCOME** may be interpreted in the same way as the **ETHNIC** × **INCOME** interaction:

		INCOME		
<15,000	<25,000	<50,000	>50,000	SUM
−.183	−.491	.244	.430	0

These parameters suggest that there are few individuals with less than $25,000/year income, and more with greater than $50,000/year income. In this case, the fact that the z-values for most of these parameters are large (greater than 1.96 or less than −1.96) imply that the parameters are significant (at $p < .05$) and support this interpretation of the data.

PARAMETER: The number of the parameter. Parameters go from low codes to high codes of the independent variables. See the above **GENDER** × **ETHNIC** table for an example of the way interactions are coded.

COEFFICIENT: The λ value in the log-linear model equation.

STANDARD ERROR: A measure of the dispersion of the coefficient.

Z-VALUE: A standardized measure of the parameter coefficient; large z-values (those whose absolute value is greater than 1.96) are significant (α = .05).

LOWER AND UPPER 95% CONFIDENCE INTERVAL: There is a 95% chance that the actual (rather than estimated) coefficient is between the lower and upper confidence interval.

```
---------------------------------------------------------------------
Backward Elimination for DESIGN 1 with generating class
   GENDER*ETHNIC*INCOME
   GENDER*ETHNIC*CATHELP
   GENDER*INCOME*CATHELP
   ETHNIC*INCOME*CATHELP

 Likelihood ratio chi square =    13.40805    DF = 12   P =  .340
```

If Deleted Simple Effect is	DF	L.R. Chisq Change	Prob	Iter
GENDER*ETHNIC*INCOME	12	17.673	.1260	4
GENDER*ETHNIC*CATHELP	4	7.939	.0938	3
GENDER*INCOME*CATHELP	3	12.470	.0059	4
ETHNIC*INCOME*CATHELP	12	14.680	.2594	4

```
Step 1
The best model has generating class
      GENDER*ETHNIC*INCOME
      GENDER*ETHNIC*CATHELP
      GENDER*INCOME*CATHELP

 Likelihood ratio chi square =    28.08846    DF = 24   P =  .256
```

If Deleted Simple Effect is	DF	L.R. Chisq Change	Prob	Iter
GENDER*ETHNIC*INCOME	12	16.925	.1525	4
GENDER*ETHNIC*CATHELP	4	6.731	.1508	3
GENDER*INCOME*CATHELP	3	14.917	.0019	3

```
The final model has generating class
      GENDER*INCOME*CATHELP
      ETHNIC*INCOME
---------------------------------------------------------------------
```

The chi-square values, probability values, and iterations involved in backward elimination were already explained and are not different here from the previous printouts in which the chi-square values were partitioned. Backward elimination begins with, in this case, examining all three-way interactive effects. It begins with this model, rather than the saturated model, because of the **MAXORDER = 3** subcommand included in step 6a. SPSS calculates a likelihood ratio chi-square for the model including all third-order effects, and the chi-square change is computed examining how much the chi-square value will increase if each effect is removed from the model. In our example, because the **ETHNIC*INCOME*CATHELP** interaction contributes least to the model (and not significantly), it is removed in step 1. A likelihood ratio chi-square is again calculated, this time including only the three remaining third-order effects (no second-order effects are listed because they must be included in the model in order for the model to be hierarchical).

In step 2, SPSS will remove the **GENDER*ETHNIC*CATHELP** effect because it contributes the least amount to the model. This process continues (through six steps in this example); lower-order effects are evaluated and considered for elimination only if they may be removed from the model without violating the hierarchical assumptions. In this case, the final model is composed of **GENDER*INCOME*CATHELP** and **ETHNIC*INCOME** interactions.

```
-------------------------------------------------------------------------------
Observed, Expected Frequencies and Residuals.
      Factor              Code        OBS count   EXP count   Residual   Std Resid
GENDER           FEMALE
   ETHNIC           CAUCASIAN
      INCOME           <15,000
         CATHELP          NOT HELPFUL      4.0         5.8       -1.75      -.73
         CATHELP          HELPFUL         14.0        13.9         .10       .03
      INCOME           <25,000
         CATHELP          NOT HELPFUL      7.0         5.4        1.61       .69
         CATHELP          HELPFUL          9.0         7.8        1.16       .41
      INCOME           <50,000
         CATHELP          NOT HELPFUL     11.0        13.7       -2.68      -.72
         CATHELP          HELPFUL         16.0        17.9       -1.92      -.45
      INCOME           >50,000
         CATHELP          NOT HELPFUL     20.0        26.7       -6.68     -1.29
         CATHELP          HELPFUL         34.0        31.1        2.87       .52
   ETHNIC           BLACK
      INCOME           <15,000
         CATHELP          NOT HELPFUL      1.0          .5         .51       .72
         CATHELP          HELPFUL          2.0         1.2         .81       .74
                     .
                     .
                     .
Goodness-of-fit test statistics:
   Likelihood ratio chi square =         59.37980       DF = 0   P = .126
                Pearson chi square =     54.59835       DF = 0   P = .238
-------------------------------------------------------------------------------
```

Observed and expected frequencies are presented for each cell in the design. Note that in order to avoid cells with zero frequencies, SPSS adds .5 to each cell frequency when saturated models are examined. Here, expected frequencies for the final model are chosen through backward elimination. Large residuals indicate possible problems with the model. Because the chi-square values are not large and the p-values are not small, the model does seem to fit the data well.

OBSERVED COUNT: The observed cell count derives from the data and indicates the number of cases in each cell.

EXPECTED COUNT: The expected cell counts indicate the expected frequencies for the cells, based on the model being tested.

RESIDUAL AND STANDARDIZED RESIDUAL: OBSERVED-EXPECTED. Cells with high values here are those that are not well predicted by the model.

GOODNESS-OF-FIT TEST STATISTICS: The likelihood ratio chi-square and the Pearson chi-square statistics examine the fit of the model. Large chi-square values and small p-values indicate that the model does not fit the data well; in this case, since $p > .05$, the data do fit the model adequately.

Chapter 28

The LOGLINEAR Command:

Nonhierarchical Log-Linear Models

Log-linear modeling, using the SPSS **LOGLINEAR** command, is a very flexible procedure. Because of its great flexibility, it is difficult to provide a simple step-by-step approach to these operations. Using the **LOGLINEAR** process often involves executing the command multiple times, testing various models in an attempt to discover the best fit. Because of these subtleties in using log-linear models, this chapter will attempt to (a) provide a general introduction to log-linear modeling for those who need a review of the basic ideas involved and (b) provide step-by-step computer instructions for running several common types of models. For more complex models, beyond the scope of this book, we refer you to the *SPSS/PC+ Advanced Statistics 4.0 Manual* for the details.

If you are not familiar with the basic concepts of log-linear models, and if you have not read Chapter 27, then be sure to read the first portion of that chapter before continuing with this chapter. The general introduction applies to creating both hierarchical log-linear models (Chapter 27) and nonhierarchical log-linear models (this chapter).

NONHIERARCHICAL VERSUS HIERARCHICAL LOG-LINEAR MODELS

In hierarchical log-linear models (using the **HILOGLINEAR** procedure of Chapter 27), if an effect of a given order is present, then all effects of lesser order must also be present. This constraint is unique to *hierarchical* log-linear models. In the **LOGLINEAR** procedure of SPSS, this is not a necessary constraint: You may include any main or interactive effect, or omit an effect if you don't want the effect included. Furthermore, whereas the **HILOGLINEAR** procedure can calculate only parameter estimates for saturated models, the **LOGLINEAR** procedure can calculate parameter estimates whether or not the model is saturated.

As in the previous two chapters, we use the **HELPING3.SYS** file ($N = 537$) in this chapter. A model is tested including the main effects of **GENDER**, **ETHNIC**, and **CATHELP** (whether or not the help given was useful or not), along with the two-way interactive effects of **GENDER** by **ETHNIC** and **GENDER** by **CATHELP**. One thing to remember:

Testing a single model, as is done in the examples in this chapter, is usually only one step among many in the quest for the best possible model.

USING COVARIATES WITH LOG-LINEAR MODELS

It is possible to use one or more variables as covariates in the model. Because these covariates are not categorical variables, it is possible to use covariates to test for particular types of trends within categorical variables. For example, in the **HELPING3.SYS** file, **INCOME** seems to be related to the number of people in each income category: There are 73 people with less than $15,000/year income, 51 people with less than $25,000/year (meaning between 15 and 25,000), 106 people with less than $50,000 per year (meaning between 25 and 50,000), and 159 people with greater than $50,000 per year. In our example, we test a model that examines **INCOME** and **INCOME**^{3} (**INCOME** cubed) to see if a model that includes these two factors predicts well the number of subjects from each income group, or, produces a model that fits the data well.

LOGIT MODELS

The **LOGLINEAR** command also has the ability to work with logit models. Logit models are similar to log-linear models, with several exceptions. First of all, logit models allow a dichotomous variable to be treated as a dependent variable and one or more categorical variables to be treated as independent variables. Second, instead of predicting the frequency within a particular cell, a dichotomous dependent variable is designated and membership into one of two distinct categories (the logit—see Chapter 26 for a description) is predicted for each cell. Finally, *two times* the parameter estimates provided by SPSS predict the logit. In the example presented in this chapter, we test a model in which **GENDER** and a **GENDER** by **ETHNIC** interaction (the two categorical independent variables) predict **CATHELP** (the dichotomous dependent variable).

A FEW WORDS ABOUT MODEL SELECTION

The procedures described in this chapter assume that you know what model you want to test. In practice, this is not an easy task. Model selection usually depends on a tight interplay of theory and testing of multiple models. If the different models tested have different degrees of freedom, then they may be compared using chi-square differences in order to determine whether or not one model is significantly better than another. The goal of model selection is to find a model with the best fit possible, that is as parsimonious as possible. Obviously, this process is too complex and involves too much artistry to fully describe in a step-by-step format. However, the model selection process is likely to *use* (if not consist of) the procedures described in the Step by Step section.

SOME TYPES OF MODELS BEYOND THE SCOPE OF THIS CHAPTER

In addition to the complexities of model selection, this chapter does not describe several types of models and procedures used with the **LOGLINEAR** command because these procedures are complex enough that they are difficult to describe in any fewer words than are used by the SPSS manual. Some of these procedures and techniques not described here are listed in the following table, along with the page numbers to which you may refer in the *SPSS/PC+ Advanced Statistics 4.0 Manual* for further information. If you have another SPSS manual, of course, the page numbers will be different, but each model type should be listed. For additional information about log-linear models that extends beyond the SPSS manuals, we refer you to Agresti (1990) and Wickens (1989). Additional information about these sources is in the reference section.

Technique, Analysis, or Procedure	Page Numbers
Equiprobability models	B161-162, 164
Linear-by-linear association models	B173-174
Row- and column-effects models	B174-175
Accessing the design matrix	B183-184
Specifying cell weights for the model	B186-187, C31
Incomplete tables (tables with structural and random zeros)	B175-180
Using linear combinations of cells	B187-188, C32
Using difference, Hilmert, simple, repeated, polynomial, or user-defined contrasts	B189, C33-34

THE LOGICAL PROGRESSION FOR CREATING LOG-LINEAR MODELS

1. Create file of data, or edit (if necessary) an already existing file.
2. Format file by use of **DATA LIST FILE**, **FORMATS**, and **VARIABLE/VALUE LABELS**; then save as a system file.
3. Access file and formats by the **GET FILE** command.
4. Use the **LOGLINEAR** command to access log-linear analysis.
5. Identify which variables will be used.
6. Use the **WITH** subcommand to specify covariates, if desired.
7. Use the **BY** subcommand to specify which variables are dependent and which are independent in a logit model, if desired.
8. Use the **PRINT** subcommand to specify what output you wish (frequencies, residuals, and parameter estimates may be specified).
9. If desired, use the **CRITERIA** subcommand to change the default criteria used in determining a model solution.
10. Specify one or more **DESIGN**s that you wish the **LOGLINEAR** procedure to test.
11. View the results and exit the program.
12. Print data, commands, and output.

STEP BY STEP
Log-Linear Models

> *1)* *Name and create a data file (Chapter 2), or edit (if necessary) an already existing file (Chapter 3).*

> *2)* *Name variables, locate column positions, format, create VARIABLE/VALUE LABELS, and then save the formatted DATA FILE as a SYSTEM FILE (Chapter 4).*

From the DOS prompt, type:

> *3)* *dos > SPSSPC* ⏎   *This step gets you into the SPSS system.*

To clear the menu from the top window prior to analyzing data:

> *4)* ⎡ALT⎤—⎡M⎤   *Positions cursor to begin to create the command file.*

From the extreme upper left corner of the scratch pad (lower window), type:

> *5)* **GET FILE** = '<u>HELPING3</u>.**SYS**'.   *1*

LINE 1 Accesses the formatted **SYSTEM FILE** to begin to analyze data. All statistical procedures in this book will begin with the **GET FILE** step.

The following command instructs SPSS to test a log-linear model including the main effects of GENDER, ETHNIC, and CATHELP, as well as interactive effects of GENDER by ETHNIC and GENDER by CATHELP.

> *6)* **GET FILE** = '<u>HELPING3</u>.**SYS**'.   *1*
> **LOGLINEAR** <u>GENDER(1,2)</u> <u>ETHNIC(1,5)</u> <u>CATHELP(1,2)</u>/   *2*
> **PRINT** = **FREQ RESID ESTIM**/   *3*
> **CRITERIA** = **CONVERGE**(<u>.005</u>) **ITERATE**(<u>30</u>)/   *4*
> **DESIGN** = <u>GENDER, ETHNIC, CATHELP, GENDER</u> **BY** <u>ETHNIC, GENDER</u> **BY**
> <u>CATHELP</u>.   *5*

LINE 1 The same as step 5, line 1 above.

LINE 2 The **LOGLINEAR** command instructs SPSS to perform a log-linear analysis. Listed after the command are all variables to be included in the model; the variables must be categorical, and after each variable you should include the range of variables (for example, in this case **GENDER** may range from 1 to 2 and **ETHNIC** from 1 to 5). You may include a smaller range in parentheses after the variable name, and **ETHNIC(1,4)** might make more sense in this case because the fifth level of **ETHNIC** is *other or decline to state*.

LINE 3 The **PRINT** subcommand identifies for SPSS what output you desire for the analysis. You do not have to include **FREQ**, **RESID**, or **ESTIM** but should include any that you want computed. **FREQ** outputs tables of observed and estimated frequencies for all cells in the model. **RESID** outputs actual and standardized residuals for these cells, and **ESTIM** produces parameter estimates for the model. If you do not enter this line at all, SPSS will produce frequencies and residuals by default.

LINE **4** Use **CRITERIA** only when the default criteria used for fitting the model are not appropriate; they usually do not need to be changed. **CONVERGE** specifies the accuracy that must be attained in order to accept convergence of the model's equations. In this example, we have specified that the values calculated must change less than .005 in order for convergence to be attained; the default value is .001. The maximum number of iterations allowed by default is 20, but 30 iterations have been specified as the maximum here through the use of the word **ITERATE**.

LINE **5** You must specify the **DESIGN** of the model that you want SPSS to test here. In this example, we have specified a model containing main effects of **GENDER**, **ETHNIC**, and **CATHELP**, as well as interactive effects of **GENDER** by **ETHNIC** and **GENDER** by **CATHELP**. Specify interactions through the use of the word **BY**. If you want **LOGLINEAR** to calculate more than one design, then you may add additional **DESIGN** lines at the end of the **LOGLINEAR** command (after line 5). Notice that commas separate the effects in the **DESIGN** section of your command file.

The following command instructs SPSS to test a log-linear model examining the effects of INCOME1 (which tests for a linear effect of INCOME) and INCOME3 (which tests for a third-power effect of INCOME). The COMPUTE commands may vary here or be absent entirely, depending on what effect you wish to examine.

```
6a)  GET FILE = 'HELPING3.SYS'.                                1a
     COMPUTE INCOME1 = INCOME.                                 2a
     COMPUTE INCOME3 = INCOME**3.                              3a
     LOGLINEAR INCOME(1,4) WITH INCOME1 INCOME3/               4a
     PRINT = FREQ RESID ESTIM/                                 5a
     CRITERIA = CONVERGE(.005) ITERATE(30)/                    6a
     DESIGN = INCOME1 INCOME3.                                 7a
```

LINE **1a** The same as step 6, line 1 above.

LINES **2a-3a** These **COMPUTE** commands calculate **INCOME1** as the linear effect of **INCOME**, and **INCOME3** as the third-power effect of **INCOME**. These lines could be different or absent, depending on your particular analysis.

LINE **4a** The **LOGLINEAR** command instructs SPSS to perform a log-linear analysis. Listed after the command are all variables to be included in the model. The variables must be categorical, and after each variable you should include the range of levels. After the categorical variables, the keyword **WITH** should be followed by the names of any covariates that you wish to use in the analysis.

LINE **5a** The **PRINT** subcommand instructs SPSS what output you desire for the analysis. You do not have to include **FREQ**uencies, **RESID**uals, or **ESTIM**ates of parameters but should include any that you want printed. If you do not enter this line at all, SPSS will produce frequencies and residuals.

LINE **6a** **CRITERIA** is used only when the default criteria used for fitting the model are not adequate. They usually do not need to be changed. **CONVERGE** specifies the accuracy that must be attained in order to accept convergence of the model's equations, and **ITERATE** controls the maximum number of iterations allowed.

LINE **7a** Here, you should specify the **DESIGN** of the model that you want SPSS to test. This example examines the effects of **INCOME1** and **INCOME3**. Specify interactions through the use of the word **BY**. If you want **LOGLINEAR** to calculate more than one design, then you may add additional **DESIGN** lines at the end of the **LOGLINEAR** command (after line 7a).

The following command performs a logit analysis, using CATHELP as the dependent (dichotomous) variable and GENDER and ETHNIC as the independent variables. The effect of CATHELP and the effect of GENDER by CATHELP on the logit are examined, as is the interactive effect of GENDER by ETHNIC by CATHELP.

```
6b)  GET FILE = 'HELPING3.SYS'.                                        1b
     LOGLINEAR CATHELP(1,2) BY GENDER(1,2) ETHNIC(1,5)/               2b
     PRINT = FREQ RESID ESTIM/                                        3b
     CRITERIA = CONVERGE(.005) ITERATE(30)/                          4b
     DESIGN = CATHELP, CATHELP BY GENDER, CATHELP BY GENDER BY ETHNIC. 5b
```

LINE **1b** The same as above.

LINE **2b** The LOGLINEAR command instructs SPSS to perform a log-linear analysis. Listed after the command are the dependent variables to be included in the model; the variables must be dichotomous, and after each variable you should include the possible range of values—which should always be **(1,2)**. The names of the dependent variable(s) should be followed by the word BY, and the BY followed by the independent variable(s). The independent variables must also have their ranges specified in parentheses. Note: A smaller range may be specified if desired.

LINE **3b** The PRINT subcommand instructs SPSS what output you desire for the analysis. You do not have to include FREQuencies, RESIDuals, or ESTIMates of parameters but should include any that you want printed. If you do not enter this line at all, SPSS will produce frequencies and residuals.

LINE **4b** CRITERIA is used only when the default criteria used for fitting the model are not adequate. They usually do not need to be changed. CONVERGE specifies the accuracy that must be attained in order to accept convergence of the model's equations, and ITERATE controls the maximum number of iterations allowed.

LINE **5b** Here you should specify the DESIGN of the model that you want SPSS to test. If you want LOGLINEAR to calculate more than one design, then you may add additional DESIGN lines at the end of the LOGLINEAR command (after line 5b).

Note: If your data file does not contain a separate case for each subject or data point, then you may choose to enter the entire crosstabulation table as part of the command file. For an illustration of how to do this, see Chapter 8, step 6e.

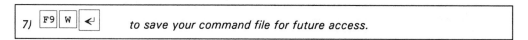

7) F9 W ↵   *to save your command file for future access.*

If file is not already named, enter the file name (e.g., **HELPING3.CTL**) at the prompt between the **W** and the **ENTER**.

To run the program, first position cursor at the beginning of the GET FILE line, then:

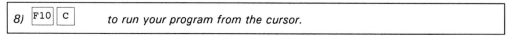

8) F10 C   *to run your program from the cursor.*

After viewing the results:

9) F10 E FINISH ↵   *to exit to the DOS prompt.*

To print command files and results:

```
10) dos> PRINT SPSS.LIS  ↵  ↵        (Sometimes the second RETURN is not necessary.)
```

OUTPUT
Log-Linear Models

The following OUTPUT is produced by this COMMAND FILE. INTERPRETATION follows.

```
GET FILE = 'HELPING3.SYS'.
LOGLINEAR GENDER(1,2) ETHNIC(1,5) CATHELP(1,2)/
PRINT = FREQ RESID ESTIM/
CRITERIA = CONVERGE(.005) ITERATE(30)/
DESIGN = GENDER, ETHNIC, CATHELP, GENDER BY ETHNIC, GENDER BY CATHELP.
```

Note: Because the interpretation of log-linear models with covariates (or designs that are logit models) is virtually identical to log-linear models without covariates (or that are not logit models), we include only one sample output. Logit models also produce an *analysis of dispersion* and *measures of association*. These measures indicate the dependent variable's dispersion, and how much of the total dispersion of the dependent variable comes from the model. These measures are difficult to interpret without considerable experience and so are not discussed here.

```
-------------------------------------------------------------------------
                   Observed, Expected Frequencies and Residuals
          Factor           Code      OBS count  EXP count  Residual Adj Resid
GENDER            FEMALE
  ETHNIC            CAUCASIAN
    CATHELP           NOT HELPFUL    70.00       74.12     -4.123      -.920
    CATHELP           HELPFUL        95.00       90.88      4.123       .920
  ETHNIC            BLACK
    CATHELP           NOT HELPFUL    13.00       15.27     -2.274      -.829
    CATHELP           HELPFUL        21.00       18.73      2.274       .829
  ETHNIC            HISPANIC
    CATHELP           NOT HELPFUL    22.00       22.46      -.462      -.143
    CATHELP           HELPFUL        28.00       27.54       .462       .143
  ETHNIC            ASIAN
    CATHELP           NOT HELPFUL    28.00       20.22      7.785      2.513
    CATHELP           HELPFUL        17.00       24.78     -7.785     -2.513
GENDER            MALE
  ETHNIC            CAUCASIAN
    CATHELP           NOT HELPFUL    75.00       71.85      3.151       .892
    CATHELP           HELPFUL        53.00       56.15     -3.151      -.892


  Goodness-of-Fit test statistics
       Likelihood Ratio Chi Square =      8.28127    DF = 8   P =  .406
                   Pearson Chi Square =   8.29786    DF = 8   P =  .405
-------------------------------------------------------------------------
```

OBSERVED COUNT: The observed cell count derives from the data and indicates the number of cases in each cell.

EXPECTED COUNT: The expected cell counts indicate the expected frequencies for the cells, based on the model being tested.

RESIDUAL AND STANDARDIZED RESIDUAL: The residuals are the observed counts minus the expected counts. High residuals indicate that the model is not adequate. SPSS calculates the adjusted residuals using an estimate of the standard error. The distribution of adjusted residuals is a standard normal distribution, and numbers greater than 1.96 or less than –1.96 are *not* likely to have occurred by chance ($\alpha = .05$).

GOODNESS-OF-FIT TEST STATISTICS: The likelihood-ratio chi-square and the Pearson chi-square statistics examine the fit of the model. Large chi-square values and small *p*-values indicate that the model does *not* fit the data well. Be aware that this is the opposite of thinking in interpretation of most types of analyses. Usually one looks for a large test statistic and a small *p*-value to indicate a significant effect. In this case, a large chi-square and a small *p*-value would indicate that your data differs significantly (or does not fit well) the model you have created. The degrees of freedom is the number of non-zero cells in the model, minus the number of parameters in the model.

Estimates for Parameters

GENDER

Parameter		Coeff.	Std. Err.	Z-Value	Lower 95 CI	Upper 95 CI
GENDER	1	.2987315069	.05772	5.17581	.18561	.41186
ETHNIC	2	1.3195255857	.07339	17.97949	1.17568	1.46337
	3	-.5099875778	.13074	-3.90089	-.76623	-.25374
	4	-.0028520686	.10633	-.02682	-.21125	.20555
	5	-.1466928027	.11242	-1.30485	-.36704	.07365
CATHELP	6	.0106862039	.04444	.24049	-.07641	.09778
GENDER BY	ETHNIC					
	7	-.1705759974	.07339	-2.32422	-.31442	-.02673
	8	.0793522385	.13074	.60696	-.17689	.33560
	9	-.0421207781	.10633	-.39615	-.25052	.16628
	10	-.0036399499	.11242	-.03238	-.22399	.21671
GENDER BY	CATHELP					
	11	-.1125757960	.04444	-2.53348	-.19967	-.02548

Parameter estimates are provided for each effect. Because the parameters are constrained to sum to zero, only some of the parameters appear here; the method for interpreting and calculating other parameters is described in Chapter 27.

PARAMETER: The number of the parameter. Parameters go from low codes to high codes of the independent variables. With interaction terms, the codes for the independent variables that are listed later in the command file, change more quickly than the independent variables listed earlier in the file. Compare the output (above) with the command file on the previous page, and this should become clear.

COEFFICIENT: The λ value in the log-linear model equation.

STANDARD ERROR: A measure of the dispersion of the coefficient.

Z-VALUE: A standardized measure of the parameter coefficient: Large *z*-values (those whose absolute value is greater than 1.96) are significant ($\alpha = .05$).

LOWER AND UPPER 95% CONFIDENCE INTERVAL: There is a 95% chance that the coefficient is between the lower and upper confidence interval.

Chapter 29

The PROBIT Command:

Probit and Logit Analysis

There are many times when a therapist, a salesperson, an educator, a CEO, a researcher, or someone else, wishes to know how much of a particular "dose" of something is necessary to achieve a particular outcome. Examples include: How much money invested in an advertising campaign will produce a 20% increase in sales? How many hours per week spent studying for the GRE are required to achieve a score of 1200? How many miles run per week will result in a 3-hour marathon? What concentration of a particular insecticide is required to kill 90% of pests? How many weeks of therapy are necessary for a person to no longer be categorized as clinically depressed? Common to all these examples are two variables: (a) an influencing variable that is measured on a continuous scale (e.g., money spent, hours studied, miles run, level of concentration, number of weeks) and (b) an outcome variable that is categorical and measures either success or nonsuccess (there was or was not a 20% increase of sales, a score of 1200 achieved, a 3-hour marathon run, 90% of insects killed, or a reclassification as nondepressive). Probit and logit analyses are designed to answer the type of questions posed above.

The first questions that come to mind are "What is a *probit,* and what is a *logit*?" Neither word appears frequently in the pages of *National Inquirer* or *Cosmopolitan*, and even many people knowledgeable about research statistics have never encountered them. Both probit and logit are transformation procedures used as techniques for standardizing raw data. Both transformations vary in value between approximately 8.0 and 2.0 and operate in a manner similar to a z-score; in fact, a probit transformation *is* simply a z-score with a 5.0 added to avoid negative numbers. The logit transformation produces somewhat similar scores to probit, but is determined by the formula:

$$\frac{\ln(P/(1-P))}{2} + 5$$

where ln is the natural logarithm, and P is the proportion of successful outcomes. An example illustrates both. (Please note that the term *logit* has a slightly different meaning and application in the chapters on logistic regression and log-linear models—Chapters 26-28.)

If 150 subjects spent 30 hours per week studying for the GRE, and 111 of them were successful in scoring more than 1200 points, the decimal that represents the proportion of successful outcomes is $111/150 = .74$.

Probit: The z-score associated with .74 or 74% successful outcomes is .64 (as acquired from any table of z-scores). The probit is the z-score plus 5, so the probit associated with 74% successful outcomes is 5.64.

Logit: The logit for the same outcome is determined by substituting the .74 (and $1-.74$, or .26) into the equation presented earlier:

$$\frac{\ln(.74/.26)}{2} + 5 \;\rightarrow\; \frac{\ln(2.84615)}{2} + 5 \;\rightarrow\; \frac{1.045969}{2} + 5 \;\rightarrow\; .523 + 5 = 5.52$$

Note that both techniques produce similar numbers. When there are 50% successful outcomes, then the probit and the logit are equal. The z-score for 50% (the mean) is 0, and the natural logarithm of $(.50/.50) = 1$ is also 0. Therefore with the 5 added, the probit and the logit for 50% successful outcomes is 5.0. The default SPSS procedure is to use the probit values, but via a **MODEL** subcommand you may request the logit instead. Neither has an inherent advantage over the other; which one you use depends on your application.

THE EXAMPLE USED TO DEMONSTRATE THE PROBIT PROCEDURE

We have created a fictional data set to demonstrate probit analysis. The example has good face validity for an organization devoted to helping students achieve a higher GRE score. Let us suppose that a firm wishes to identify which of three different techniques of studying for the GRE is superior. Suppose further that they wish to test the influence of the number of hours per week spent studying on GRE performance. To accomplish this they choose 18 evenly matched groups of 150 students each. (This is reasonable since about 15,000 students per year take their course—our imaginary firm is doing very well.) The 2,700 subjects are pretested and then divided into 18 groups in such a way that the mean score on the Quantitative section of the GRE (coded *GRE-Quant*) for each group is between 520 and 530.

Subjects in the first 6 groups are assigned to Treatment A: Over 10 weeks, they attend two 3-hour sessions each week and take (and score) a total of four practice exams. The next 6 groups are assigned to Treatment B, in which there is no formal instruction but all subjects are given a computer program to guide them in their study. They also take and score four practice exams during the 10 weeks. The final 6 groups are assigned to Treatment C, in which there is no formal instruction but subjects are given a book produced by the company to guide their study for the GRE-Quant. These groups also take four practice exams during the 10 weeks.

The second variable of interest to the company (and the variable that probit analysis is designed specifically to measure) is the influence on the exam scores of the number of study hours per week *outside of class instruction or exam taking*. The 6 hours per week in Treatment A are included as part of the study time (e.g., 44 hours outside of class for Treatment A are equal to 50 hours for Treatments B and C). There are six different conditions for each of the six groups: Study 50 hours per week, 40 hours per week, 30 hours per week, 20 hours per week, 10 hours per week, or a control of 0 hours per week (they take the four practice exams but do not attend classes or use the books or the computer program). The goal is to score 650 or higher on the GRE-Quant. If this seems a little confusing, the chart that follows will clarify.

Below is the data file used for the probit analysis. The file is called **GRE.SYS** and contains 7 variables: **COURSE** is the coding for treatment: $A = 1$, $B = 2$, and $C = 3$. **HRSPENT** indicates whether that group spent 50, 40, 30, 20, 10, or 0 hours per week of study. **NUMBER** indicates the number of subjects in each group (150). **SUCCEED** identifies the number of subjects in the group who scored 650 or higher on the GRE-Quant after the course. **DECIMAL** is the proportion of subjects who were successful (number successful divided by number in group). Finally **XPROBIT** and **XLOGIT** show the *hand-calculated* probit and logit scores associated with each proportion. You do not need to include these in the data file because SPSS will calculate them for you. They are included here just to allow you to see how these constructs vary. The four variables that are used in the analysis are: **COURSE, HRSPENT, SUCCEED,** and **NUMBER**. Note that even the **DECIMAL** variable is not needed because this value is also computer calculated.

COURSE	HRSPENT	NUMBER	SUCCEED	DECIMAL	XPROBIT	XLOGIT
1	50	150	138	.92	6.41	6.22
1	40	150	126	.84	5.99	5.83
1	30	150	111	.74	5.64	5.53
1	20	150	93	.62	5.31	5.25
1	10	150	66	.44	4.85	4.88
1	0	150	42	.28	4.42	4.53
2	50	150	132	.88	6.17	6.01
2	40	150	117	.78	5.77	5.63
2	30	150	103	.68	5.47	5.37
2	20	150	81	.54	5.10	5.08
2	10	150	54	.36	4.64	4.71
2	0	150	21	.14	3.92	4.08
3	50	150	120	.80	5.84	5.68
3	40	150	111	.74	5.64	5.53
3	30	150	90	.60	5.25	5.21
3	20	150	75	.50	5.00	5.00
3	10	150	51	.34	4.59	4.67
3	0	150	24	.16	4.01	4.17

Probit analysis is designed to (a) calculate the line of best fit (note that this relationship is *linear*), (b) calculate a Pearson goodness-of-fit chi-square value to indicate how well your data fits the regression equation, and (c) calculate predicted values for the discrete dependent variable (proportion of subjects who are expected to score 650 or higher) for varying levels of the dosage (hours spent studying in this case). To identify the necessary dosage, a range of 35 probability values are printed that vary from .01 (1% successful) to .99 (99% successful). There is additional information calculated that will be described in the Output section.

If you wish a more complete explanation, two texts that we have found to be especially good in their descriptions and applications of probit and logit analyses are Agresti (1990) and Wickens (1989). The *SPSS/PC+ Advanced Statistics 4.0 Manual* also provides a fairly detailed explanation and integrates it with SPSS documentation. Please see the reference section for additional information about these sources.

THE LOGICAL PROGRESSION FOR CONDUCTING PROBIT ANALYSIS

1. Create file of data, or edit (if necessary) an already existing file.
2. Format file by use of **DATA LIST FILE**, **FORMATS**, and **VARIABLE/VALUE LABELS**; then save as a system file.
3. Access file and formats by the **GET FILE** command.
4. Use the **PROBIT** command to specify the number of successes, the number in the sample, the dosage variable of interest, and to conduct probit analysis.
5. Use the **BY** connector to include a coded variable to indicate two or more levels of the independent variable.
6. Use the **NATRES** subcommand to enter baseline information about the number of occurrences that will take place without any dosage.
7. View the results and exit the program.
8. Print data, commands, and output.

STEP BY STEP
Probit Analysis

> 1) *Name and create a data file (Chapter 2), or edit (if necessary) an already existing file (Chapter 3).*

> 2) *Name variables, locate column positions, format, create VARIABLE/VALUE LABELS, and then save the formatted DATA FILE as a SYSTEM FILE (Chapter 4).*

From the DOS prompt, type:

---

3) *dos> **SPSSPC** $\boxed{\leftarrow}$*   *This step gets you into the SPSS system.*

To clear the menu from the top window prior to analyzing data:

---

4) $\boxed{\text{ALT}}\text{—}\boxed{\text{M}}$ *Positions cursor to begin to create the command file.*

From the extreme upper left corner of the scratch pad (lower window), type:

---

5) **GET FILE = 'GRE.SYS'.**   *1*

LINE 1 Accesses the formatted **SYSTEM FILE** to begin to analyze data. All statistical procedures in this book will begin with the **GET FILE** step.

The simplest default probit analysis can be accomplished with a single line in the command file:

---

6) **GET FILE = 'GRE.SYS'.**   *1*
    PROCESS IF (COURSE = 1).   *2*
    PROBIT SUCCEED OF NUMBER WITH HRSPENT.   *3*

LINE 1 Same as line 1 from step 5 above.

LINE 2 The **PROCESS IF** statement is necessary in this case because of the structure of our data file. We are selecting only subjects who are in the Treatment A (coded **1**) condition for this analysis.

LINE 3 The **PROBIT** line always follows the same order: The word **PROBIT** followed by the number of successes variable, then the **OF** connector, the number of subjects in each group variable, then the **WITH** connector, and finally the dosage variable—hours spent studying, in this case.

To compare the three different treatment conditions (COURSE = 1, 2, or 3), omit the PROCESS IF command used in the previous step and include COURSE(1,3) following a BY connector.

6a) **GET FILE = 'GRE.SYS'.**   *1a*
     PROBIT SUCCEED OF NUMBER WITH HRSPENT BY COURSE(1,3).   *2a*

LINE 1a Same as line 1 from step 6 above.

LINE 2a This line is identical to line 3 above except for the inclusion of **BY COURSE(1,3)**. **BY** is the standard connector, while **COURSE** is the name of our treatment variable. Make sure that *in your original data file* this variable is coded in a manner similar to that shown in the introductory section of this chapter. It is always necessary to indicate which levels of the treatment variable you wish by including the range in parentheses after the treatment variable. You may select a subset of levels of the treatment variable by selecting the first and second numbers to indicate the range of values you wish.

Often there is a certain baseline rate of incidence of the desired phenomenon (scoring 650 on the GRE-Quant in this case) without any of the treatment administered. Such a baseline was included in the present data set by those who scored 650 or more without any study.

6b) **GET FILE** = 'GRE.SYS'.   1b
    PROBIT <u>SUCCEED</u> **OF** <u>NUMBER</u> **WITH** <u>HRSPENT</u> **BY** <u>COURSE</u>(1,3)/   2b
    NATRES.   3b

LINE 1b Same as above.

LINE 2b This line is identical to line 2a above except that it ends with a slash instead of a period.

LINE 3b The **NATRES** subcommand allows the **PROBIT** procedure to include a baseline rate into its calculations in a manner similar to a covariate. This baseline is accessed in two different ways: Either have a control group with 0 of the dosage variable included in the data file (as we do here), or indicate in parentheses the percentage of baseline occurrences following the **NATRES** subcommand. For instance, if there was a 20% natural occurrence, you would replace line 3b with **NATRES(.2).**

---

7) F9 W ↵   *to save your command file for future access.*

If file is not already named, enter the file name (e.g., **GRE.CTL**) at the prompt between the **W** and the **ENTER**.

To run the program, first position cursor at the beginning of the GET FILE line, then:

---

8) F10 C   *to run your program from the cursor.*

After viewing the results:

---

9) F10 E **FINISH** ↵   *to exit to the DOS prompt.*

To print command files and results:

---

10) dos > **PRINT SPSS.LIS** ↵ ↵   *(Sometimes the second RETURN is not necessary.)*

OUTPUT
Probit Analysis

The following OUTPUT is produced by this COMMAND FILE. INTERPRETATION follows each section of output.

```
GET FILE = 'GRE.SYS'.
PROBIT SUCCEED OF NUMBER WITH HRSPENT BY COURSE(1,3)/
NATRES.
```

```
--------------------------------------------------------------------
      * * * * * * * P R O B I T   A N A L Y S I S * * * * * * *

DATA information:

      15 unweighted cases accepted.
       0 cases rejected because of out-of-range group values.
       0 cases rejected because of missing data.

Group Information

      COURSE       Level    N of Cases    Label
                     1            5        CLASSROOM
                     2            5        COMPUTER PROGRAM
                     3            5        BOOK

Natural Response rate to be estimated
      The number of  subjects in the CONTROL group   450.0
      The number of responses in the CONTROL group    87.0
```

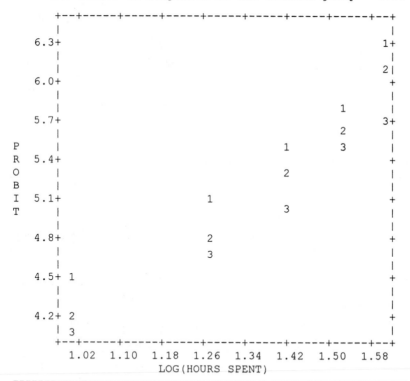

```
ML converged at iteration 4.  The converge criterion = .00007

Parameter estimates, PROBIT model:  [PROBIT(p) + 5] = Intercept + BX]

             Regression Coeff.    Standard Error     Coeff/S.E.
HRSPENT           2.47814              .17552         14.11871
```

Intercept	Standard Error	Intercept/S.E.	COURSE
1.90503	.26480	7.19418	CLASSROOM
1.66840	.27118	6.15228	COMPUTER PROG
1.45917	.27698	5.26807	BOOK

Pearson Goodness-of-Fit   Chi Square =   5.959   DF = 11   P = .876

Since Goodness-of-Fit Chi Square is NOT significant, no heterogeneity factor is used in the calculation of confidence limits.

Observed and Expected Frequencies

COURSE	HRSPENT	Number of Subjects	Observed Responses	Expected Responses	Residual	Prob
1	1.70	150.0	138.0	130.147	7.853	.86764
1	1.60	150.0	126.0	121.389	4.611	.80926
1	1.48	150.0	111.0	107.122	3.878	.71415
1	1.30	150.0	93.0	82.708	10.292	.55139
1	1.00	150.0	66.0	40.301	25.699	.26867
2	1.70	150.0	132.0	121.532	10.468	.81021
2	1.60	150.0	117.0	110.765	6.235	.73844
2	1.48	150.0	103.0	94.344	8.666	.62889
2	1.30	150.0	81.0	68.582	12.418	.45721
2	1.00	150.0	54.0	29.505	24.495	.19670
3	1.70	150.0	120.0	112.260	7.740	.74840
3	1.60	150.0	111.0	99.923	11.077	.66615
3	1.48	150.0	90.0	82.145	7.855	.54764
3	1.30	150.0	75.0	56.361	18.639	.37574
3	1.00	150.0	51.0	21.594	29.406	.14396

DATA INFORMATION: 15 cases were accepted for analysis. The three groups that reported 0 hours studying are considered a control group.

GROUP INFORMATION: Identifies the three groups with the number that codes them (classroom = 1, computer program = 2, book = 3). It also identifies 5 cases at each level of the independent variable, **COURSE**.

NATURAL RESPONSE RATE TO BE ESTIMATED: When there are groups that have a zero dose of the independent variable (0 study hours in this example), the probit procedure treats such cases as a natural response rate and notes that 87 of 450 subjects were successful without any study.

THE PLOT: Shows the relatively linear relation of all three treatment conditions. It also shows that Treatment 1 worked better than Treatment 2, which was better than Treatment 3. The visual display (showing the relatively linear relationship) suggests that probit analysis should work well with this data set.

ML CONVERGED: It took four iterations to converge to regression coefficients and intercept values based upon a convergence criteria of .00007.

REGRESSION COEFFICIENT: The pooled slope for all three lines. Analysis revealed that the three slopes did not differ significantly from each other; so a single slope has been computed for all three distributions.

INTERCEPT: Although the same regression coefficient (slope) is used for the three distributions, they all have different intercepts, indicating again that results for **GROUP 1** > **GROUP 2** > **GROUP 3**.

STANDARD ERROR: A measure of the stability or sampling error of the regression coefficients and intercepts.

COEFF/SE.: The regression coefficient divided by the standard error.

INTERCEPT/SE: The intercepts divided by the standard error.

PEARSON GOODNESS-OF-FIT: The χ^2 value of 5.959, 11 degrees of freedom (number of groups – numbers of levels of the IV – 1), and $p = .876$ indicate that values produced by the regression equation do not deviate significantly from the actual data. In other words, the regression equations describe the data well.

OBSERVED AND EXPECTED FREQUENCIES: The COURSE identifies which of the three groups is coded, the HRSPENT is the base-10 logarithm of the number of hours spent per week (e.g., LOG_{10} of 50 = 1.70), the NUMBER OF SUBJECTS is the same for each group (150), the OBSERVED RESPONSES is the number of students scoring higher than 650 on the GRE-Quant in each group, the EXPECTED RESPONSE is the value obtained from the regression equation constructed from the previous table, the RESIDUAL is the observed responses minus the expected responses, and the PROBABILITY indicates whether the observed response differs significantly from the expected response. These results demonstrate that for none of the 15 groups do observed values differ significantly from expected values (Note: $.144 < p < .868$).

```
-------------------------------------------------------------------------------
        Confidence limits for Effective HRSPENT
        COURSE:  1 = CLASSROOM
                                   95% Confidence Limits
        Prob       HRSPENT       Lower            Upper
        .01        2.04249       1.30136          2.88482
        .02        2.63125       1.74322          3.60985
        .03        3.08997       2.09806          4.16246
        .04        3.48703       2.41156          4.63380
        .05        3.84735       2.70058          5.05673
        .06        4.18323       2.97350          5.44737
        .07        4.50177       3.23522          5.81497
        .08        4.80752       3.48886          6.16544
        .09        5.10358       3.73659          6.50277
        .10        5.39218       3.97998          6.82987
        .15        6.77137       5.16569          8.37293
        .20        8.11501       6.35060          9.85155
        .25        9.47832       7.57629         11.33438
        .30       10.89674       8.87105         12.86441
        .35       12.39993      10.25972         14.47706
        .40       14.01762      11.76785         16.20772
        .45       15.78334      13.42437         18.09671
        .50       17.73809      15.26427         20.19418
        .55       19.93493      17.33189         22.56653
        .60       22.44603      19.68601         25.30624
        .65       25.37432      22.40832         28.54821
        .70       28.87468      25.61929         32.49917
        .75       33.19574      29.50991         37.49575
        .80       38.77258      34.41265         44.13335
        .85       46.46616      40.98330         53.60335
        .90       58.35108      50.78996         68.82284
        .91       61.65086      53.45389         73.15609
        .92       65.44645      56.49232         78.19295
        .93       69.89240      60.01669         84.15521
        .94       75.21452      64.19425         91.38036
        .95       81.78083      69.29155        100.41462
        .96       90.23144      75.76980        112.22051
        .97      101.82629      84.52834        128.71629
        .98      119.57826      97.69210        154.56244
        .99      154.04712     122.57901        206.47771
```

```
Estimates of Relative Median Potency

                              95% Confidence Limits
       COURSE     Estimate      Lower         Upper
       1 VS. 2      .8026       .67783        .93896
       1 VS. 3      .6608       .54671        .78077
       2 VS. 3      .8233       .69637        .96311
```

The confidence limits for effective hours spent are displayed from probabilities of .01 to .10 consecutively, from .10 to .90 by intervals of .05, and from .90 to .99 consecutively. SPSS prints out three charts, one for each level of the independent variable (class, computer program, and book). The column titled **HRSPENT** is the variable of critical concern in a probit analysis. This indicates, for instance, that for Group 1 (those who took the class) if we wish an 80% success rate, it is necessary for students to study an average of 38.77 hours per week. A 99% success rate is not realistic, however, because 154 hours per week of study leaves fewer than two hours per day to pursue such peripheral activities as eating or sleeping. The 95% confidence limits indicate that 95% of the time, the true mean will fall within the limits listed.

The final table, *Estimates of Relative Median Potency*, is derived by identifying the potency necessary for a 50% (the median) success rate. For the classroom, the value is 17.74 hours; for the computer program, the value is 22.10; and for the book group, the number of hours necessary for 50% success rate is 26.84. The comparison of Course 1 versus Course 2 is 17.47/22.10 = .8026. This indicates that (at the median level) the computer program process was only 79.2% as effective as the classroom technique. Similar computations are carried out for a Course 1 versus Course 3 comparison and for a Course 2 versus Course 3 comparison. The 95% confidence limits are derived from similar comparisons from corresponding numbers from the associated charts.

Chapter 30

The NPAR Command:

Nonparametric Tests

This final chapter deals with (as the title suggests) nonparametric tests. Before we become involved in *non*parametric tests, it might be well to consider first, what is a *parametric* test? A parametric test is one that is based on certain parameters. The critical parameter that most of the procedures described in this book are based on is that samples (and the populations from which they are drawn) are normally distributed. Although certain procedures depend on other assumptions or parameters, the **NPAR** command considers primarily populations that are *not* normally distributed and how to conduct statistical tests if the assumption of normality is violated.

When normality of the distribution is not present, the nonparametric tests use other techniques (that do not require a normal distribution) to test hypotheses. These techniques may include, among others, analyses based on:

- ranked values
- summation of how many values in one distribution are larger (or smaller) than values in another distribution
- use of weighted comparisons
- tests to determine whether a distribution of values deviates from randomness or is binomially distributed
- single-group tests of deviation from normality
- comparisons of frequencies
- calculation of the frequency of values above or below a grand median to compare groups

In addition, nonparametric tests may calculate statistics about one sample or make comparisons between two or more samples. Despite this seeming complexity, most nonparametric tests are easy to understand and even easier to conduct. We will not attempt further explanation here because it is more profitable to explain the tests one at a time.

To demonstrate nonparametric tests, we will make use, once more, of the original data file first presented in Chapters 1 and 2: the **GRADES.SYS** file. This is an excellent file to demonstrate nonparametric tests because the contents of the file are so easily understood. Tests will be conducted on the following variables within the file: **GENDER**, the five 10-point quizzes (**QUIZ1** to **QUIZ5**), **FINAL** (the score on a 75-point final exam), **ETHNICIT** (the ethnic makeup of the sample), and **SECTION** (membership of subjects in the three sections of the class). The *N* for this sample is 105.

This will be the first and only chapter of the analysis chapters (Chapters 6-30) that deviates substantially from the normal format. In this chapter, the Step by Step and the Output sections will be combined into one. We begin this section with the (by now) familiar first five steps and end the section with the equally familiar final four steps. However, each of the nine procedures here will be treated independently. Each section will have its own introduction, followed by step 6 (or 6a, 6b, etc.), followed by the output, an interpretation of the output, and definitions of terms. The order follows.

1. **MANN-WHITNEY AND WILCOXON RANK-SUM TEST**: A test of whether two groups differ from each other based on ranked scores.
2. **THE SIGN TEST**: Tests whether two distributions differ based on a comparison of paired scores. That is, for how many of the paired scores is the value for group A larger than the value for group B (positive sign), or is the group B score larger than the group A score (negative sign)?
3. **THE WILCOXON MATCHED-PAIRS SIGNED-RANKS TEST**: The same as the sign test except the positive and negative signs are weighted by the mean rank of positive versus negative comparisons.
4. **RUNS TEST**: Tests whether the elements of a single dichotomous group differ from a random distribution.
5. **THE BINOMIAL TEST**: Tests whether the elements of a single dichotomous group differ from a binomial distribution (each outcome equally likely).
6. **THE KOLMOGOROV-SMIRNOV ONE-SAMPLE TEST**: Tests whether the distribution of the members of a single group differ significantly from a **NORMAL** (or **UNIFORM**, or **POISSON**) distribution.
7. **THE ONE-SAMPLE CHI-SQUARE TEST**: Tests whether observed scores differ significantly from expected scores for levels of a single variable.
8. **THE FRIDMAN 2-WAY ANOVA**: Tests whether three or more groups differ significantly from each other, based on average rank of groups rather than the distribution of values.
9. **THE K-SAMPLE MEDIAN TEST**: Tests whether two or more groups differ on the number of instances (within each group) greater than the median value or less than the median value.

For additional information, the most comprehensive book on nonparametric statistics discovered by the authors is a text by Siegel and Castellan (1988). Please see the reference section for additional detail.

STEP BY STEP
Nonparametric Tests

---

1) *Name and create a data file (Chapter 2), or edit (if necessary) an already existing file (Chapter 3).*

---

2) *Name variables, locate column positions, format, create VARIABLE/VALUE LABELS, and then save the formatted DATA FILE as a SYSTEM FILE (Chapter 4).*

From the DOS prompt, type:

3) *dos > SPSSPC* ⏎   *This step gets you into the SPSS system.*

To clear the menu from the top window prior to analyzing data:

4) ALT ─ M   *Positions cursor to begin to create the command file.*

From the extreme upper left corner of the scratch pad (lower window), type:

5) **GET FILE** = 'GRADES.SYS'.   1

LINE 1 Accesses the formatted **SYSTEM FILE** to begin to analyze data. All statistical procedures in this book will begin with the **GET FILE** step.

MANN-WHITNEY AND WILCOXON RANK-SUM TEST

Description, Command File, Output, Interpretation

The Mann-Whitney U and Wilcoxon rank-sum W test accomplish essentially what a t-test does when the distributions of the two samples deviate significantly from normal. If the distributions do *not* differ significantly from normal, the t-test should be used because it has greater power. In our example we consider whether females and males (the **GENDER** variable) differ significantly on their scores on the **FINAL** exam. The Mann-Whitney and Wilcoxon procedure rank orders all 105 scores, determines the rank of each subject, and then computes the average rank for the two groups. Clearly the group with the higher average rank scored higher on the test. The U and the W tests determine whether that difference is significant.

This command file conducts the test described above.

```
6)  GET FILE = 'GRADES.SYS'.                              1
    NPAR TESTS M-W = FINAL BY GENDER(1,2).                2
```

LINE 1 Same as step 5, line 1 above.

LINE 2 This line identifies **FINAL** as the continuous variable and **GENDER** as the grouping variable. Even though gender has only two levels, it is necessary to include the coding in parentheses following the variable name.

```
------------------------------------------------------------------------
        - - - Mann-Whitney U - Wilcoxon Rank-Sum W Test - - -

        FINAL
by      GENDER

Mean Rank      Cases     Label
    55.81         64     GENDER = 1    FEMALE
    48.61         41     GENDER = 2    MALE
                 ___
                 105     Total


      U           W          Z        2-tailed P    (corrected for ties)
   1132.0      1993.0    -1.1836        .2366
------------------------------------------------------------------------
```

Note that the mean rank for females is higher (55.81) than the mean rank for males, (48.61), indicating that females scored higher than males. The U statistic is the number of times members of the lower-ranked group (males) precede members of the higher-ranked group (females). W is the sum of the ranks for the group with the smaller number of observations (males). Significance levels for either U or W are identical. The Z is the standardized score associated with the significance value ($p = .2366$). Since the p-value is large, we conclude that the rank order of scores on the final does not differ significantly for males and females.

THE SIGN TEST

Description, Command File, Output, Interpretation

The sign test utilizes pairwise comparisons of two different distributions to identify which is larger than which, and then from this information it determines if the two distributions differ significantly from each other. To demonstrate, we compare the scores on QUIZ1 with the scores on QUIZ2. By default, the sign test compares the second distribution with the first distribution. For the first subject, QUIZ1 was 9 and QUIZ2 was 7. This would rate as a negative (–) difference. For the second subject, QUIZ1 was 6, QUIZ2 was 7. This would rate as a positive (+) difference. The signs test sums all the positives, negatives, and ties and then computes a z-score and a p-value associated with the frequency of the positives and negatives.

This command file conducts the test described above.

```
6a) GET FILE = 'GRADES.SYS'.                              1a
    NPAR TESTS SIGN = QUIZ1 WITH QUIZ2.                   2a
```

LINE 1a Same as step 5, line 1 above.
LINE 2a This line compares QUIZ1 with QUIZ2 via the sign procedure.

```
-----------------------------------------------------------------------
        QUIZ1
with    QUIZ2

        Cases
          34  -  Diffs (QUIZ2 < QUIZ1)              Z = 1.6366
          50  +  Diffs (QUIZ2 > QUIZ1)
          21     Ties                       2-tailed P =   .1017
         105     Total
-----------------------------------------------------------------------
```

Note that in 34 instances QUIZ2 was less than QUIZ1, in 50 instances QUIZ2 was greater than QUIZ1, and in 21 instances both quizzes had the same score. The z-score associated with these values is 1.16366, and the p-value associated with that z-score is .1017. The relatively high significance indicates that the quizzes do not significantly differ from each other. It should be noted that, since the distributions of both quizzes *are* normal, a t-test would be appropriate here. If a t-test is conducted on these data, QUIZ2 *is* significantly greater than QUIZ1 ($p <$ .005). The t-test is significant, whereas the sign test is not because the t-test has greater statistical power.

WILCOXON MATCHED-PAIRS SIGNED-RANKS TEST
Description, Command File, Output, Interpretation

The difficulty with the sign test is that a difference between paired quizzes of 10 (10 on one, 0 on the other) and a difference of 1 (e.g., 6 on one, 5 on the other) will be coded identically (as a negative). The Wilcoxon matched-pairs signed-ranks test incorporates information about the magnitude of the differences between paired values. To compute this value, first the magnitude of the differences (ignoring the signs) are ranked from high to low. Then the ranks for the negative signs (when QUIZ2 < QUIZ1) are summed and averaged, and the ranks for the positive signs (when QUIZ2 > QUIZ1) are summed and averaged. Finally, significance values are calculated based on z-scores.

This command file conducts the test described above.

```
6b) GET FILE = 'GRADES.SYS'.                                    1b
    NPAR TESTS WILCOXON = QUIZ1 WITH QUIZ2.                     2b
```

LINE 1b Same as step 5, line 1 above.
LINE 2b This line compares QUIZ1 with QUIZ2 via the signed-ranks procedure.

```
- - - - - Wilcoxon Matched-pairs Signed-ranks Test - - - - -
      QUIZ1
with  QUIZ2

      Mean Rank    Cases    Label
        35.62        34     Ranks (QUIZ2 < QUIZ1)
        47.18        50     Ranks (QUIZ2 > QUIZ1)
                     21     ties
                    ----
                    105

     Z = -2.5599        2-tailed P = .0105
```

Note the similarities to the sign test (previous page). The frequency of negative ranks, positive ranks, and ties are the same. Additional information includes the mean rank of each group based on the overall magnitude of differences. While visual inspection of output from the sign test shows that QUIZ2 scores are higher than QUIZ1 scores, the additional information of the magnitude of the differences now produces a much larger z-score (–2.56) and a much smaller p-value (.0105). While the sign test did not reveal a significant difference between the two groups, the Wilcoxon test was able to reveal significant differences between the scores on the two quizzes. The test, while much improved over the sign test, is still not as powerful as the t-test, which yields a p-value of .005. If the distributions are normally distributed, use t-tests rather than nonparametric tests.

THE WALD-WOLFOWITZ RUNS TEST

Description, Command File, Output, Interpretation

Aside from the inelegant jokes that might be made about this test's name, the runs test is useful to see if the elements of a particular data set are randomly distributed. For instance, if flipping a coin yielded a sequence of HHTHTTHTTHTHTTTTHTH, does this sequence differ significantly from randomness? In other words, are we flipping a biased coin? Unfortunately this procedure works only with dichotomous data (exactly two possible outcomes). It is not possible to test, for instance, if we are rolling a loaded die. Sticking fiercely by our determination to use the **GRADES.SYS** file to demonstrate all procedures in this chapter, we will test whether the males and females in our file are distributed randomly throughout our data set.

This command file conducts the test described above.

```
6c)  GET FILE = 'GRADES.SYS'.                                    1c
     NPAR TESTS RUNS(2) = GENDER.                                 2c
```

LINE **1c** Same as step 5, line 1 above.

LINE **2c** Note that a discriminating number following the word **RUNS** is required. This procedure will separate the data file into two groups: Items coded less than the designated number and items coded greater or equal to the designated number. **GENDER** represents the distribution for which we are running this test. Since gender is coded 1 = female and 2 = male, this test discriminates between the 1's and the 2's.

```
-------------------------------------------------------------------------
                - - - - - - - Runs Test - - - - - - - -
GENDER

    Runs:       47              Test Value = 2

    Cases:      64    < 2                       Z = -.8205
                41    > 2             2-tailed P =   .4119
               ----
               105   Total
-------------------------------------------------------------------------
```

This output indicates that there were 47 runs. This measures the number of times in the data set when there was a switch from one code to the other code. Thus a single value (that switches at the next case or subject) is considered a run of 1. Longer runs are of course also included in the 47 shown in the output. Test value is the number that discriminates between the two groups. The output identifies 64 females (< 2) and 41 males ($\geq$ 2). The *z*- and *p*-values are dependent on the total number of runs. This test converts the runs number into a *z* statistic on which the probability is determined. The *p*-value indicated here (*p* = .4199) suggests that the order of males and females on the roster does not deviate significantly from randomness.

THE BINOMIAL TEST
Description, Command File, Output, Interpretation

The binomial test measures whether a distribution of values is binomially distributed. Binomial distribution assumes that any outcome is equally likely ($p = .5$). If you tossed an unbiased coin 100 times you would expect approximately 50 heads and 50 tails. We will apply the binomial test to the distribution of males and females in our data set. We already know there are 41 males and 64 females, so the use of the binomial test is only to demonstrate how the procedure works. It is of legitimate interest, however, to see if this distribution differs significantly from 52.5 males and 52.5 females.

This command file conducts the test described above.

```
6d)  GET FILE = 'GRADES.SYS'.                                      1d
     NPAR TESTS BINOMIAL = GENDER(1,2).                            2d
```

LINE 1d Same as step 5, line 1 above.
LINE 2d Note that the two levels of gender are coded differently than for the runs test (previous page). This line will produce output that indicates if the distribution of men and women is binomial.

```
-------------------------------------------------------------------------
        - - - - - - - - Binomial Test - - - - - - - - -

    GENDER

    Cases
                                   Test proportion = .5000
        64  = 1  (FEMALE)      Observed proportion = .6095
        41  = 2  (MALE)
        ---                        Z Approximation
       105  Total                     2-tailed P = .0318
-------------------------------------------------------------------------
```

The test proportion of .5000 is the expected proportion for a binomial distribution. The observed proportion is the larger of the two numbers (64 females) divided by the total number of observations (105). The *p*-value associated with this comparison is .0318, indicating that the number of males and females do differ significantly from the binomial assumption of equal probability of either.

THE KOLMOGOROV-SMIRNOV ONE-SAMPLE TEST
Description, Command File, Output, Interpretation

This test is designed to measure whether a particular distribution differs significantly from a normal distribution (skewness and kurtosis of the distribution = 0), a uniform distribution (values are distributed evenly, such as the numbers 1-100 consecutively), or a Poisson distribution (the value λ equals the mean and the variance of the distribution; as λ becomes large, the distribution approximates normality). This procedure is based on a comparison of the sample cumulative distribution to the hypothesized (normal, uniform, or Poisson) cumulative distribution. To demonstrate this process we will see if the distribution of **FINAL** exam scores from the **GRADES.SYS** file is normally distributed.

This command file conducts the test described above.

```
6e) GET FILE = 'GRADES.SYS'.                                    1e
     NPAR TESTS K-S (NORMAL) = FINAL.                           2e
```

LINE 1e Same as step 5, line 1 above.

LINE 2e The **K-S** accesses the Kolmogorov-Smirnov procedure, and the name within the parentheses (**NORMAL**) identifies which type of distribution you wish to compare your data with. If you don't wish to use a **NORMAL** distribution as the reference, enter **UNIFORM** or **POISSON**.

```
-------------------------------------------------------------------
    - - - - - Kolmogorov - Smirnov Goodness of Fit Test - - - - - -

FINAL     Test distribution: Normal           Mean =  61.48
                                    Standard Deviation =   7.94
                                               Cases =    105
          Most Extreme Differences
      Absolute      Positive      Negative      K-S Z      2-tailed P
       .06438        .04751       -.06438        .660          .777
-------------------------------------------------------------------
```

The mean, standard deviation, and *N* of the sample are first identified. The most extreme differences identify the greatest positive difference and negative difference between the sample and the hypothesized distributions (in *z*-scores). The Kolmogorov-Smirnov *z* indicates a probability of .777. The large significance value indicates that the distribution of **FINAL** scores does not differ significantly from normal.

THE ONE-SAMPLE CHI-SQUARE TEST
Description, Command File, Output, Interpretation

This procedure conducts a one-sample chi-square test rather than the more traditional chi-square test of crosstabulated data. The expected values are simply the total number of cases divided by the number of levels of a variable. To demonstrate the procedure, we will conduct a chi-square analysis on the **ETHNICIT** variable from the **GRADES.SYS** file. With five levels of **ETHNICIT** and an $N = 105$, the expected value for each cell will be $105/5 = 21$. For a more complete description of the chi-square procedure, refer to Chapter 8.

This command file conducts the test described above.

6f) **GET FILE = 'GRADES.SYS'.**		*1f*
NPAR TESTS CHI-SQUARE = ETHNICIT.		*2f*

LINE 1f Same as step 5, line 1 above.
LINE 2f The **CHI-SQUARE** designates the type of procedure we wish to perform. The variable following the equals sign identifies the variable to analyze. Be sure the variable is categorical rather than continuous.

```
-------------------------------------------------------------------
          - - - - - - - - Chi-square Test - - - - - - - -

   ETHNICIT                        Cases
                   Category   Observed   Expected    Residual
   AMERICAN INDIAN      1           5      21.00      -16.00
   ASIAN                2          20      21.00      - 1.00
   AFRO-AMERICAN        3          24      21.00        3.00
   CAUCASIAN            4          45      21.00       24.00
   HISPANIC             5          11      21.00      -10.00
                   Total         105

   Chi-Square = 44.857     D.F. = 4      Significance = .000
-------------------------------------------------------------------
```

Visual inspection of the differences between observed and expected values reveals wide discrepancies. The residuals are each of the observed values minus the corresponding expected values. Computation of the chi-square statistic is described in Chapter 8. The degrees of freedom (D.F.) is the number of levels minus 1. The very small significance level demonstrates that the ethnic breakdown of the class deviates substantially from the expected values (equal frequency of each ethnic group).

THE FRIDMAN TWO-WAY ANOVA
Description, Command File, Output, Interpretation

The Fridman two-way ANOVA is similar to the analysis of variance procedure, with two notable exceptions: (a) Comparisons in the Fridman procedure are based on mean rank of variables rather than on means and standard deviations of raw scores, and (b) rather than calculating an *F*-value, Fridman compares ranked values with expected values in a chi-square analysis. The power of the Fridman procedure is not as great as is that of normal analysis of variance, but if your distributions deviate significantly from normality, the Fridman two-way ANOVA would be appropriate. This is a simple procedure that does not allow for post hoc tests such as Scheffé or Tukey, nor does it allow for planned contrasts. To demonstrate the procedure, we will see whether scores on the five quizzes (**QUIZ1** to **QUIZ5**) from the **GRADES.SYS** file differ significantly from each other.

This command file conducts the test described above.

```
6g)  GET FILE = 'GRADES.SYS'.                          1g
     NPAR TESTS FRIDMAN = QUIZ1 TO QUIZ5.              2g
```

LINE **1g** Same as step 5, line 1 above.

LINE **2g** The **FRIDMAN** designates the type of procedure we wish to perform. The variables following the equals sign identify the variables to be included in the analysis. Since the five quiz scores are in order in the system file, it is acceptable to use the **TO** connector to designate them.

- - - - - - - Fridman Two-way ANOVA - - - - - - -

Mean Rank	Variable
2.68	QUIZ1
3.07	QUIZ2
3.34	QUIZ3
3.04	QUIZ4
2.88	QUIZ5

Cases = 105   Chi-Square = 10.1238   D.F. = 4   Significance = .0384

The Mean Rank values are determined as follows: All 525 quiz scores (105 × 5) are ranked from high to low and numbered from 1 (for the lowest score) to 11 (for the highest). There are 11 possible scores (0 to 10), and there will be, of course, many frequencies for each level. The ranks for each of the five quizzes are summed and then divided by 105. The significance value associated with the chi-square analysis ($p = .0384$) indicates that there is a significant difference between the five quizzes. This difference could be anywhere within the possible pairwise comparisons. Visual inspection would indicate that **QUIZ1** probably differs significantly from **QUIZ3**.

THE K-SAMPLE MEDIAN TEST
Description, Command File, Output, Interpretation

The final procedure in this chapter involves computing the median of two or more distributions and then comparing whether the number of values *below* the grand median (median for all groups) differs from the number of values *above* the grand median for each group compared. A chi-square analysis is used to calculate significance levels. To demonstrate we will compare FINAL scores in each of the three SECTIONS. The procedure is to rank order all scores from all three sections combined to determine the grand median. Then for each section the number of scores above this median and the number of scores below this median are calculated. If any section deviates from approximately equal number of scores above and below the grand median, this would indicate that some biasing factor may be present for that section.

This command file conducts the test described above.

```
6h)  GET FILE = 'GRADES.SYS'.                                    1h
     NPAR TESTS MEDIAN = FINAL BY SECTION(1,3).                  2h
```

LINE **1h** Same as step 5, line 1 above.

LINE **2h** The MEDIAN designates the type of procedure we wish to perform. The first variable (FINAL) designates the continuous variable that we use to compare scores in different sections. The second variable (SECTION) is the grouping variable. Indicate in parentheses the levels you wish to compare. This procedure will compare as many levels of a variable as have been coded in the system file and requested in the command file.

```
-----------------------------------------------------------------------
               - - - - - - Median Test - - - - - -
        FINAL
       by SECTION
                                  SECTION
                           1           2           3
                       |---------|-----------|---------|
            GT Median  |    17   |     16    |    15   |
       FINAL           |---------|-----------|---------|
            LT Median  |    16   |     23    |    18   |
                       |---------|-----------|---------|

            Cases      Median    Chi-Square    D.F.   Significance
             105         62        .7938         2       .6724
-----------------------------------------------------------------------
```

The tables portion of the chart is straightforward, indicating the number of scores in each section greater than the median and the number of scores in each section less than the median. Below the chart the overall median value (62) is indicated, along with the chi-square value determined by comparing the observed values with the expected values. Degrees of freedom are the levels of the one variable minus one (3 − 1) times the levels of the other variable minus one

(2 − 1). The significance value indicates that the distribution of scores in each section does not differ significantly from predicted values.

After completion of any of these procedures proceed to the final four steps:

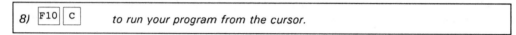

7) F9 W ↵   *to save your command file for future access.*

If file is not already named, enter the file name (e.g., **GRADES.CTL**) at the prompt between the **W** and the **ENTER**.

To run the program, first position cursor at the beginning of the GET FILE line, then:

8) F10 C   *to run your program from the cursor.*

After viewing the results:

9) F10 E FINISH ↵   *to exit to the DOS prompt.*

To print command files and results:

10) *dos* > **PRINT SPSS.LIS** ↵ ↵   *(Sometimes the second RETURN is not necessary.)*

DATA DISK

The enclosed data disk includes nine different data files and nine different system files that have been used to demonstrate procedures in this book. The **GRADES.DAT** and **GRADES.SYS** files are the most thoroughly documented and demonstrate procedures in 19 of the 30 chapters. This file is described in detail in Chapters 1 and 2. For analyses described in the other 11 chapters, it was necessary to employ different types of data to illustrate. On the enclosed disk, *all* files utilized in this book are included with the identical file names. What follows are brief narrative introductions to each file, and when appropriate, critical variables are listed and described. Before presenting this, we comment briefly on how to read a system file from a disk (as opposed to reading it from the hard drive of your computer—as is illustrated in all chapters of this book).

In every one of Chapters 5 through 30, there is a sequence step 5 that reads:

GET FILE = 'FILENAME.SYS'.

When reading from a disk, this line should be replaced by:

GET FILE = 'B:\FILENAME.SYS'.

If, however, you are reading from disk drive A, replace the B with an A.

GRADES.DAT: The data file is described in detail on pages 11-13. This is a fictional file ($N = 105$) created by the authors to demonstrate a number of statistical procedures.

GRADES.SYS: The formatted file that is used to demonstrate procedures in **Chapters 2-18** and in **Chapter 30**. All file names and descriptions are found on page 11. Be aware that in addition to the variable names listed there, four additional variables are included in both the data file *and* system file:

- **TOTAL**   Sum of the five quizzes and the final
- **PERCENT**   The percent of possible points in the class
- **GRADE**   The grade received in the class (A, B, C, D, or F)
- **PASSFAIL**   Whether or not the student passed the course (P or F)

ANXIETY.DAT: A fictional data file ($N = 73$) that lists values to show the relationship between pre-exam anxiety and exam performance.

ANXIETY.SYS: The formatted file that is used to demonstrate simple linear and curvilinear regression (**Chapter 19**). It contains two variables:

- **EXAM**   The score on a 100-point exam
- **ANXIETY**   A measure of pre-exam anxiety measured on a *low*(1) the *high*(10) scale

HELPING1.DAT: A file of real data ($N = 81$) created to demonstrate the relationship between several variables and the amount of time spent helping a friend in need.

HELPING1.SYS: The formatted file that is used to demonstrate multiple regression analysis (**Chapter 20**). Although there are other variables in the file, the ones used to demonstrate regression procedures include:

- **ZHELP**   Z-scores of the amount of time spent helping a friend on a –3 to +3 scale
- **SYMPATHY** Sympathy felt by helper in response to friend's need on a *little*(1) to *much*(7) scale
- **ANGER**   Anger felt by helper in response to friend's need; same 7-point scale
- **EFFICACY** Self-efficacy of helper in relation to friend's need; same scale
- **SEVERITY** Helper's rating of the severity of the friend's problem; same scale
- **EMPATEND** Empathic tendency of the helper as measured by a personality test

HELPING2.DAT: A file of real data ($N = 517$) dealing with issues similar to those in the **HELPING1.DAT** file. Although the file is large (both in number of subjects and number of variables), only the 15 measures of self-efficacy and the 14 empathic tendency questions are used to demonstrate procedures.

HELPING2.SYS: The formatted file that is used to demonstrate factor analysis (**Chapter 21**), cluster analysis (**Chapter 22**), and reliability analysis (**Chapter 24**). Variable names included in analyses include:

- **EFFIC1**   The 15 self-efficacy questions used to demonstrate factor analysis and cluster
  to   analysis. See Chapter 21 for a more complete description of these variables.
  EFFIC15

- **EMPATHY1**   The 14 empathic tendency questions used to demonstrate reliability analysis.
  to   Note that when the number of the question moves from one digit to two
  EMPATH14   digits, the **Y** of **EMPATHY** drops off. Chapter 24 describes these variables in
                    more detail.

HELPING3.DAT: A file of real data ($N = 537$) dealing with issues similar to the previous two files. This is the same file as **HELPING2.DAT** except it has been expanded by 20 subjects and all missing values in the former file have been replaced by predicted values. (See Chapter 5 on missing values to see how this is accomplished.) This file represents over 1000 subjects because both the helper and the recipient of the help responded to a number of questions, so each "subject" actually represents two. Although these data are used only to demonstrate logistic regression and log-linear models, we describe it here in greater detail because a number of categorical variables have been included that make it particularly appropriate to demonstrate cross tabulation and chi-square analyses (Chapter 8). All data are real except for the variable **CATHELP**, which was manufactured to create a discrete measure of help. This variable was produced by classifying all subjects who scored lower than the mean on the help measure as *not-helpful*, and those who scored higher than the mean were classified as *helpful*. See Chapter 26 for greater detail.

HELPING3.SYS: The formatted file used to demonstrate logistic regression (**Chapter 26**) and hierarchical and nonhierarchical log-linear models (**Chapters 27** and **28**). We first list variables used in these three chapters and then include other variables that may prove to be of interest for other types of analyses:

- **CATHELP**   Coded 1 = not helpful, 2 = helpful

- **SYMPATHT** Composite of four sympathy questions on a *low*(1) to *high*(7) scale
- **ANGERT** Composite of four anger-toward-friend questions; same scale
- **EFFICT** Composite of 15 helpers' self-efficacy questions; same scale
- **ETHNIC** Variable name for five levels of ethnicity, see coding that follows

Other variables

- **GENDER** 1 = female; 2 = male
- **OCCUPAT** 1 = professional; 2 = service/support; 3 = blue collar; 4 = unemployed or retired; 5 = student; 6 = decline to state
- **MARITAL** 1 = married; 2 = single; 3 = decline to state
- **SCHOOL** 1 = 1-8 years; 2 = 9-11 years; 3 = 12 years; 4 = 13-14 years; 5 = 15-16 years; 6 = 17-18 years; 7 = 19 or more years
- **ETHNIC** 1 = Caucasian; 2 = Black; 3 = Hispanic; 4 = Asian; 5 = other or decline to state
- **INCOME** 1 = < 15,000; 2 = between 15 and 25,000; 3 = between 25 and 50,000; 4 = > 50,000; 5 = decline to state
- **PROBLEM** 1 = goal disruptive; 2 = relational; 3 = illness; 4 = catastrophic
- **RELATION** 1 = friend; 2 = relative
- **AGE** Age in years, ranges from 17 to 89
- **TOTHELP** The overall help measure: an equal weighting of helpers' rating of time spent helping and quality of help given; and recipients' rating of time spent helping and quality of help, measured on a *z*-score scale, −3 to +3
- **HSEVERET** Helpers' rating of problem severity on a *low*(1) to *high*(7) scale
- **HCONTROT** Helpers' rating of the controllability of the cause of the problem; same scale
- **WORRY** Amount of worry experienced by the helper; same scale
- **OBLIGAT** Feelings of obligation felt by helper toward the recipient; same scale
- **HCOPET** Helper's rating of how well the recipient was coping; same scale

VCR.DAT: A fictitious data file that compares 21 different brands of VCRs on 21 different classifying variables. The distorted brand names and all variables are described on pages 191 and 198 of the cluster analysis chapter.

VCR.SYS: The formatted file that is used to demonstrate cluster analysis (**Chapter 22**). All variable names and descriptions are listed in the chapter.

GRADUATE.DAT: A fictitious data file ($N = 50$) that attempts to predict success in graduate school based on 17 classifying variables.

GRADUATE.SYS: The formatted file that is used to demonstrate discriminant analysis (**Chapter 23**). All variables and associated codings are listed on pages 203 and 204 in the cluster analysis chapter.

GROWTH.DAT: Real data provided by the U.S. Census Bureau of U.S. population by decades from 1790 to 1990.

GROWTH.SYS: This formatted file is used to demonstrate nonlinear regression (**Chapter 25**). There are three variables in the file:

- **POP** U.S. population in millions for the 21 decades
- **YEAR** The year associated with that population
- **X** The coding (0 to 20) for each of the decades

GRE.DAT: This fictitious data file ($N = 18$) describes techniques used by an educational firm to determine the best way of studying for the Graduate Record Exam (GRE).

GRE.SYS: The formatted file that is used to demonstrate probit analysis (**Chapter 29**). There are seven variables in the file; all are listed and described clearly on page 268.

GLOSSARY

ADJUSTED R SQUARE: In multiple regression analysis, R^2 is an accurate value for the sample drawn but is considered an optimistic estimate for the *population* value. The Adjusted R^2 is considered a better population estimate and is useful when comparing the R^2 values between models with different numbers of independent variables.

AGGLOMERATIVE HIERARCHICAL CLUSTERING: A procedure used in cluster analysis by which cases are clustered one at a time until all cases are clustered into one large cluster. See Chapter 22 for a more complete description.

ALPHA: Also, *coefficient alpha* or α; is a measure of internal consistency based on the formula $\alpha = rk/[1 + (k - 1)r]$, where k is the number of variables in the analysis and r is the mean of the inter-item correlations. The alpha value is inflated by a larger number of variables, so there is no set interpretation as to what is an *acceptable* alpha value. A rule of thumb that applies to most situations is: $\alpha > .9$—excellent, $\alpha > .8$—good, $\alpha > .7$—acceptable, $\alpha > .6$—questionable, $\alpha > .5$—poor, $\alpha < .5$—unacceptable.

ALPHA IF ITEM DELETED: In reliability analysis, the resulting alpha if the variable to the left is deleted.

ANALYSIS OF VARIANCE (ANOVA): A statistical test that identifies whether there are any significant differences between three or more sample means. See Chapters 13, 14, and 15 for a more complete description.

ANOVA Command: The SPSS command that accesses two-way, three-way, or higher order analysis of variance procedures. See Chapters 14 and 15 for additional detail.

ASYMPTOTIC VALUES: Determination of parameter estimates based on asymptotic values (the value a function is never expected to exceed). This process is used in nonlinear regression and other procedures where an actual value is not possible to calculate.

B: In regression output, the B values are the regression coefficients and the constant for the regression equation. The B may be thought of as a weighted constant that describes the magnitude of influence a particular independent variable has on the dependent variable. A positive value for B indicates a corresponding increase in the value of the dependent variable, whereas a negative value for B decreases the value of the dependent variable.

BAR GRAPH: A graphical representation of the frequency of categorical data. A similar display for continuous data is called a *histogram*.

BARTLETT TEST OF SPHERICITY: This is a measure of the multivariate normality of a set of distributions. A significance value $< .05$ suggests that the data do not differ significantly from multivariate normal.

BETA (β): In regression procedures, the standardized regression coefficients. This is the B-value for standardized scores (*z*-scores) of the variables. These values will vary strictly between plus-and-minus 1.0 and may be compared directly with beta values in other analyses.

BETA IN: In multiple regression analysis, the beta values for the *excluded* variables if these variables were actually in the regression equation.

BETWEEN-GROUPS SUM OF SQUARES: The sum of squared deviations between the grand mean and each group mean weighted (multiplied) by the number of subjects in each group.

BINOMIAL TEST: A nonparametric test that measures whether a distribution of values is binomially distributed (each outcome equally likely). For instance, if you tossed a coin 100 times, you would expect a binomial distribution (approximately 50 heads and 50 tails).

BOX'S M: A measure of multivariate normality based on the similarities of determinants of the covariance matrices for two or more groups.

CANONICAL CORRELATION: In discriminant analysis, the canonical correlation is a correlation between the discriminant scores for each subject and the levels of the dependent variable for each subject. See page 215 for an example of how a canonical correlation is calculated.

CANONICAL DISCRIMINANT FUNCTIONS: The linear discriminant equation(s) calculated to maximally discriminate between levels of the dependent (or criterion) variable. This is described in detail in Chapter 23.

CHI-SQUARE ANALYSIS: A nonparametric test that makes comparisons (usually of cross-tabulated data) between two or more samples on the *observed frequency* of values with the *expected frequency* of values. Also used as a test of the goodness-of-fit of log-linear and structural models. For the latter, the question being asked is: Does the actual data differ significantly from results predicted from the model that has been created? The formula for the Pearson chi-square is:

$$\chi^2 = \Sigma[(f_o - f_e)^2/f_e]$$

CLUSTER ANALYSIS: A procedure by which subjects, cases, or variables are clustered into groups based on similar characteristics of each.

CLUSTER Command: The SPSS command that accesses cluster analysis. Please see Chapter 22 for additional detail.

COCHRAN'S C and BARTLETT-BOX F: Measure whether the variances of two or more groups differ significantly from each other (heteroschedasticity). A high probability value (for example, $p > .05$) indicates that the variances of the groups do *not* differ significantly.

COLUMN PERCENT: A term used with crosstabulated data. It is the result of dividing the frequency of values in a particular cell by the frequency of values in the entire column. Column percents sum to 100% in each column.

COLUMN TOTAL: A term used with crosstabulated data. It is the total number of subjects in each column.

COMMUNALITY: Used in factor analysis, a measure designed to show the proportion of variance that factors contribute to explaining a particular variable. In the SPSS default procedure, communalities are initially assigned a value of 1.00.

COMPUTE IF Command: The SPSS command that allows the researcher to compute new variables from mathematical manipulations of variables already in the data file. See Chapter 5 for details.

CONFIDENCE INTERVAL: The range of values within which a particular statistic is likely to fall. For instance, a 95% confidence interval for the mean indicates that there is a 95% chance that the true population mean falls within the range of values listed.

CONVERGE: To converge means that after some number of iterations, the value of a particular statistic does not change more than a prespecified amount and parameter estimates are said to have "converged" to a final estimate.

CORRECTED ITEM-TOTAL CORRELATION: In reliability analysis, correlation of the designated variable with the sum of all other variables in the analysis.

CORRELATION: A measure of the strength and direction of association between two variables. See Chapter 11 for a more complete description.

CORRELATION BETWEEN FORMS: In split-half reliability analysis, an estimate of the reliability of the measure if each half had an equal number of items.

CORRELATION COEFFICIENT: A value that measures the strength of association between two variables. This value varies between ±1.0 and is usually designated by the lowercase letter r.

COUNT: In crosstabulated data, the top number in each of the cells indicating the actual number of subjects or cases in each category.

COVARIATE: A variable that has substantial correlation with the dependent variable and is included in an experiment as an adjustment of the results for differences existing among subjects prior to the experiment.

CRAMER'S V: A measure of the strength of association between two categorical variables. Cramer's V produces a value between 0 and 1 and (except for the absence of a negative relation) may be interpreted in a manner similar to a correlation. Often used within the context of chi-square analyses. The equation follows. (Note: k is the smaller of the number of rows and columns.)

$$V = \sqrt{\chi^2 / [N(k-1)]}$$

CROSSTABS Command: The SPSS command that accesses crosstabulation and chi-square analyses. See Chapter 8 for details.

CROSSTABULATION: Usually a table of frequencies of two or more categorical variables taken together. However, crosstabulation may also be used for different *ranges* of values for continuous data. See page 60 for an example.

CTL: The three-letter code following the name of a command file (e.g., **GRADES.CTL**) that relates to a particular data set.

CUMULATIVE FREQUENCY: The total number of subjects or cases having a given score or any score lower than the given score.

CUMULATIVE PERCENT: The total percent of subjects or cases having a given score or any score lower than the given score.

DAT: The three-letter code following the name of a raw data file, such as **GRADES.DAT**.

DEGREES OF FREEDOM (DF): The number of values that are free to vary, given one or more statistical restrictions on the entire set of values. Also, a statistical compensation for the failure of a range of values to be normally distributed.

DENDOGRAM: A branching-type graph used to demonstrate the clustering procedure in cluster analysis. See page 201 for an example.

DESCRIPTIVES Command: The SPSS command that accesses means, standard deviations, skewness, kurtosis, and other descriptive information. See Chapter 7 for additional detail.

DETERMINANT OF THE VARIANCE-COVARIANCE MATRICES: The determinant provides an indication of how strong a relationship there is among the variables in a correlation matrix. The smaller the number, the more closely the variables are related to each other. This is used primarily by the computer to compute the Box's *M* test. The determinant of the *pooled* variance-covariance matrix refers to all the variance-covariance matrices present in the analysis.

DEVIATION: The distance and direction (positive or negative) of any raw score from the mean.

(DIFFERENCE) MEAN: In a *t*-test, the difference between the two means.

DISCRIMINANT ANALYSIS: A procedure that creates a regression formula to maximally discriminate between levels of a categorical dependent variable.

DISCRIMINANT SCORES: Scores for each subject, based on substitution of values for the corresponding variables into the discriminant formula.

DSCRIMINANT Command: The SPSS command that accesses the discriminant analysis procedure. See Chapter 23 for details.

EIGENVALUE: In factor analysis, the proportion of variance explained by each factor. In discriminant analysis, the between-groups sums of squares divided by within-groups sums of squares. A large eigenvalue is associated with a strong discriminant function.

EQUAL-LENGTH SPEARMAN-BROWN: Used in split-half reliability analysis when there is an unequal number of items in each portion of the analysis. It produces a correlation value that is inflated to reflect what the correlation would be if each part had an equal number of items.

ETA: A measure of correlation between two variables when one of the variables is discrete.

ETA SQUARED: The proportion of the variance in the dependent variable accounted for by an independent variable. For instance, an eta squared of .044 would indicate that 4.4% of the variance in the dependent variable is due to the influence of the independent variable.

EXP(B): In logistic regression analysis, e^B is used to help in interpreting the meaning of the regression coefficients. (Remember that the regression equation may be interpreted in terms of B or e^B.)

EXPECTED VALUE: In the crosstabulation table of a chi-square analysis, the number that would appear if the two variables were perfectly independent of each other. In regression analysis, it is the same as a *predicted value*, that is, the value obtained by substituting data from a particular subject into the regression equation.

FACTOR: In factor analysis, a factor is a combination of variables whose shared correlations explain a certain amount of the total variance. After rotation, factors are designed to demonstrate underlying similarities between groups of variables.

FACTOR ANALYSIS: A statistical procedure designed to take a larger number of constructs (measures of some sort) and reduce them to a smaller number of *factors* that describe these measures with greater parsimony.

FACTOR Command: The SPSS command that accesses factor analysis. See Chapter 21 for details.

FACTOR TRANSFORMATION MATRIX: If the original *unrotated* factor matrix is multiplied by the *factor transformation matrix*, the result will be the *rotated* factor matrix.

F-CHANGE: In multiple regression analysis, the *F*-change value is associated with the additional variance explained by a new variable.

F-RATIO: In an analysis of variance, an *F*-ratio is the between-groups mean square divided by the within-groups mean square. This value is designed to compare the between-groups variation to the within-groups variation. If the between-groups variation is substantially larger than the within-groups variation, then significant differences between groups will be demonstrated. In multiple regression analysis, the *F*-ratio is the mean square (regression) divided by the mean square (residual). It is designed to demonstrate the strength of association between variables.

FREQUENCIES: A listing of the number of times certain events take place.

FREQUENCIES Command: The SPSS command that calculates frequencies, percentiles, and several different graphical representations of frequency data. See Chapter 6.

FRIDMAN 2-WAY ANOVA: A nonparametric procedure that tests whether three or more groups differ significantly from each other, based on average rank of groups rather than comparison of means from normally distributed data.

GOODNESS-OF-FIT TEST STATISTICS: The likelihood-ratio chi-square and the Pearson chi-square statistics examine the fit of log-linear models. Large chi-square values and small *p*-values indicate that the model does *not* fit the data well. Be aware that this is the opposite of thinking in interpretation of most types of analyses. Usually one looks for a large test statistic and a small *p*-value to indicate a significant effect. In this case, a large chi-square and a small *p*-value would indicate that your data differs significantly from (or does not fit well) the model you have created.

GROUP CENTROIDS: In discriminant analysis, the average discriminant score for subjects in the two (or more) groups. More specifically, the discriminant score for each group is determined when the variable means (rather than individual values for each subject) are entered into the discriminant equation. If you are discriminating between exactly two outcomes, the two scores will be equal in absolute value but have opposite signs. The dividing line between group membership in that case will be zero (0).

GUTTMAN SPLIT-HALF: In split-half reliability, a measure of the reliability of the overall test, based on a lower-bounds procedure.

HILOGLINEAR Command: The SPSS command used to create hierarchical log-linear models. See Chapter 27 for a description of this procedure.

HYPOTHESIS SS: The between-groups sum of squares; the sum of squared deviations between the grand mean and each group mean, weighted (multiplied) by the number of subjects in each group.

ICICLE PLOT: A graphical display of the step-by-step clustering procedure in cluster analysis. See page 200 for an example.

INTERACTION: The idiosyncratic effect of two or more independent variables on a dependent variable over and above the independent variables' separate (main) effects.

INTERCEPT: In regression analysis, the point where the regression line crosses the Y-axis. The intercept is the predicted value of the vertical-axis variable when the horizontal-axis variable value is zero.

INTER-ITEM CORRELATIONS: In reliability analysis, this is descriptive information about the correlation of each variable with the sum of all the others.

ITEM MEANS: In reliability analysis (using coefficient alpha), this is descriptive information about all subjects' means for all the variables. On page 225, an example clarifies this.

ITEM VARIANCES: A construct similar to that used in *item means* (the previous entry). The first number in the SPSS output is the mean of all the variances, the second is the lowest of all the variances, and so forth. Pages 225 and 226 clarify this with an example.

ITERATION: The process of solving an equation based on preselected values, then replacing the original values with the computer-generated values and solving the equation again. This process continues until some criterion (in terms of amount of change from one iteration to the next) is achieved.

K: In hierarchical log-linear models, the order of effects for each row of the table (1 = first-order effects, 2 = second-order effects, and so on).

KAISER-MAYER-OLKIN: A measure of whether the distribution of values is adequate for conducting factor analysis. A measure > .9 is generally thought of as excellent, > .8 as good, > .7 as acceptable, > .6 as marginal, > .5 as poor, and < .5 as unacceptable.

KOLMOGOROV-SMIRNOV ONE-SAMPLE TEST: A nonparametric test that determines whether the distribution of the members of a single group differ significantly from a *normal* (or *uniform*, or *poisson*) distribution.

K-SAMPLE MEDIAN TEST: A nonparametric test that determines whether two or more groups differ on the number of instances (within each group) greater than the grand median value or less than the grand median value.

KURTOSIS: A measure of deviation from normality that measures the peakedness or flatness of a distribution of values. See page 48 for a more complete description.

LIST Command: The SPSS command that allows the researcher to list all or a portion of the raw data. See Chapter 5 for additional detail.

LOG DETERMINANT: In discriminant analysis, the natural log of the determinant of each of the two (or more) covariance matrices. This is used to test the equality of group covariance matrices using Box's M.

LOGISTIC REGRESSION Command: The SPSS procedure used to conduct logistic regression analysis. See Chapter 26 for a description.

LOGLINEAR Command: The SPSS procedure used to create nonhierarchical log-linear models. See Chapter 28 for a description.

MAIN EFFECTS: The influence of a single independent variable on a dependent variable. See Chapters 14 and 15 for examples.

MANCOVA: A MANOVA that includes one or more covariates in the analysis.

MANN-WHITNEY AND WILCOXON RANK-SUM TEST: A nonparametric alternative to the t-test that measures whether two groups differ from each other based on ranked scores.

MANOVA: Multivariate analysis of variance. A complex procedure similar to ANOVA except that it allows for more than one dependent variable in the analysis.

MANOVA Command: The SPSS command that accesses multivariate T-tests and multivariate analysis of variance and covariance. See Chapters 16, 17, and 18 for additional detail.

MANOVA REPEATED MEASURES: A multivariate analysis of variance in which the same set of subjects experiences several measurements on the variables of interest over time. Computationally, it is the same as a within-subjects MANOVA.

MANOVA WITHIN-SUBJECTS: A multivariate analysis of variance in which the same set of subjects experience all levels of the dependent variable.

MANTEL-HAENSZEL TEST FOR LINEAR ASSOCIATION: Within a chi-square analysis, this procedure tests whether the two variables correlate with each other. This measure is often meaningless unless there is some logical or numeric relation to the order of the levels of the variables.

MAUCHLY'S SPHERICITY TEST: A test of multivariate normality. SPSS computes a χ^2 approximation for this test, along with its significance level. If the significance level associated with Mauchly's sphericity test is small (i.e., $p < .05$), then the data may not be spherically distributed.

MAXIMUM: Largest observed value for a distribution.

MEAN: A measure of central tendency; the sum of a set of scores divided by the total number of scores in the set.

MEANS Command: The SPSS command that allows for describing subpopulation differences. See Chapter 9 for a description.

MEAN SQUARE: Sum of squares divided by the degrees of freedom. In ANOVA, the most frequently observed mean squares are the within-groups sum of squares divided by the corresponding degrees of freedom and the between-groups sum of squares divided by the associated degrees of freedom. In regression analysis, it is the regression sum of squares and the residual sum of squares divided by the corresponding degrees of freedom. For both ANOVA and regression, these numbers are used to determine the F-ratio.

MEDIAN: A measure of central tendency; the middle point in a distribution of values.

MEDIAN TEST: See K-Sample Median Test.

MINIMUM: Lowest observed value for a distribution.

MINIMUM EXPECTED FREQUENCY: A chi-square analysis identifies the value of the cell with the minimum expected frequency.

–2 LOG LIKELIHOOD: This is used to indicate how well a log-linear model fits the data. Smaller –2 log likelihood values mean that the model fits the data better; a perfect model has a –2 log likelihood value of zero. Significant χ^2 values indicate that the model differs significantly from the theoretically "perfect" model.

MODE: A measure of central tendency; it is the most frequently occurring value.

MODEL χ^2: In logistic regression analysis, this value tests whether or not all the variables entered in the equation have a significant effect on the dependent variable. A high χ^2 value indicates that the variables in the equation significantly impact the dependent variable. This test is functionally equivalent to the overall F-test in multiple regression.

MULTIPLE REGRESSION ANALYSIS: A statistical technique designed to predict values of a dependent (or criterion) variable from knowledge of the values of two or more independent (or predictor) variables. See Chapter 20 for a more complete description.

MULTIVARIATE TEST FOR HOMOGENEITY OF DISPERSION MATRICES: Box's M test examines whether the variance-covariance matrices are the same in all cells. To evaluate this test, SPSS calculates an F or χ^2 approximation for the M. These values, along with their associated p-values, appear in the SPSS output. Significant p-values indicate *differences* between the variance-covariance matrices for the two groups.

MULTIVARIATE TESTS OF SIGNIFICANCE: In MANOVA, there are several methods of testing for differences between the dependent variables due to the independent variables. Pillai's method is considered the best test by many, in terms of statistical power and robustness.

NATURAL RESPONSE RATE TO BE ESTIMATED: In probit or logit analysis (Chapter 29), when there are groups that have a zero dose of the independent variable, the probit procedure treats such cases as a natural response rate and notes what percent of outcomes were successful without *any* influence from the independent variable.

95% CONFIDENCE INTERVAL: See *confidence interval*.

NLR Command: The SPSS command that accesses nonlinear regression. See Chapter 25 for a description of this procedure.

NONLINEAR REGRESSION: A procedure that estimates parameter values for intrinsically nonlinear equations.

NONPARAMETRIC TESTS: A series of tests that make no assumptions about the distribution of values (usually meaning the distribution is not normally distributed) and performs statistical analyses based upon rank order of values, comparisons of paired values, or other techniques that do not require normally distributed data.

NORMAL DISTRIBUTION: A distribution of values that, when graphed, produces a smooth, symmetrical, bell-shaped distribution that has skewness and kurtosis values equal to zero.

NPAR **Command**: The SPSS command that accesses a number of different nonparametric tests. See Chapter 30 for details.

OBLIQUE ROTATIONS: A procedure of factor analysis in which rotations are allowed to deviate from orthogonal (or from perpendicular) in an effort to achieve a better simple structure.

OBSERVED VALUE **or** COUNT: In a chi-square analysis, the frequency results that are actually obtained when conducting an analysis.

ONE-SAMPLE CHI-SQUARE TEST: A nonparametric test that measures whether observed scores differ significantly from expected scores for levels of a single variable.

ONE-TAILED TEST: A test in which significance of the result is based on deviation from the null hypothesis in only *one* direction.

ONEWAY **Command**: The SPSS command that accesses one-way analysis of variance. See Chapter 13 for additional detail.

OVERLAY PLOT: A type of scatter plot that graphs two or more variables along the horizontal axis against a single variable on the vertical axis.

PARAMETER: A numerical quantity that summarizes some characteristic of a population.

PARAMETRIC TEST: A statistical test that requires that the characteristics of the data being studied be normally distributed in the population.

PARTIAL: A term frequently used in multiple regression analysis. A partial effect is the unique contribution of a new variable after variation from other variables has already been accounted for.

PARTIAL CHI-SQUARE: The chi-square value associated with the unique additional contribution of a new variable on the dependent variable.

P(D/G): In discriminant analysis, given the discriminant value for that case (*D*), what is the probability of belonging to that group (*G*)?

PEARSON PRODUCT-MOMENT CORRELATION: A measure of correlation ideally suited for determining the relationship between two continuous variables.

PERCENTILE: A single number that indicates the percent of cases in a distribution falling below that single value. See Chapter 6 for an example.

P(G/D): In discriminant analysis, given that this case belongs to a given group (*G*), how likely is the observed discriminant score (*D*)?

PHI COEFFICIENT: A measure of the strength of association between two categorical variables, usually in a chi-square analysis. Phi is computed from the formula:

$$\phi = \sqrt{\chi^2 / N}$$

PIN: In regression analysis, the probability value to enter a variable into the regression equation.

PLOT Command: The SPSS command that accesses a variety of scatter plots. See Chapter 10 for a more complete description.

POOLED WITHIN-GROUP CORRELATIONS: *Pooled within group* differs from *values for the entire (total) group* in that the pooled values are the average (mean) of the group correlations. If the *N*s are equal, then this would be the same as the value for the entire group.

POOLED WITHIN-GROUPS COVARIANCE MATRIX: In discriminant analysis, a matrix composed of the means of each corresponding value within the two (or more) matrices for each level of the dependent variable.

POPULATION: A set of individuals or cases who share some characteristic of interest. Statistical inference is based on drawing samples from populations to gain a fuller understanding of characteristics of that population.

POUT: Probability value to remove an already entered variable from the regression equation.

POWER: Statistical power refers to the ability of a statistical test to produce a significant result. Power varies as a function of the type of test (parametric tests are usually more powerful than nonparametric tests) and the size of the sample (greater statistical power is usually observed with large samples than with small samples).

PRINCIPAL-COMPONENTS ANALYSIS: The default method of factor extraction used by SPSS.

PRIOR PROBABILITY FOR EACH GROUP: The .5000 value usually observed indicates that groups are weighted equally.

PROBABILITY: Also called **SIGNIFICANCE**. A measure of the rarity of a particular statistical outcome given that there is actually no effect. A significance of $p < .05$, is the most widely accepted value by which researchers accept a certain result as statistically significant. It means that there is less than a 5% chance that the given outcome could have occurred by chance.

PROBIT Command: The SPSS command that conducts probit and logit analyses. See Chapter 29 for a description.

PROCESS IF Command: The SPSS procedure that allows the researcher to select a subset of data for analysis for a single operation. See Chapter 5 for additional detail.

QUARTILES: Percentile ranks that divide a distribution into the 25th, 50th, and 75th percentiles.

R: The multiple correlation between a dependent variable and two or more independent (or predictor) variables. It varies between ±1.0 and is interpreted in a manner similar to a bivariate correlation.

R^2: Also called the multiple coefficient of determination. The proportion of variance in the dependent (or criterion) variable that is explained by the combined influence of two or more independent (or predictor) variables.

R^2 CHANGE: This represents the unique contribution of a new variable added to the regression equation. It is calculated by simply subtracting the R^2 value for the given line from the R^2 value of the previous line.

RANGE: A measure of variability; the difference between the largest and smallest scores in a distribution.

RANK: Rank or size of a covariance matrix.

RECODE **Command**: The SPSS command that allows the researcher to recode variables or to replace missing values. See Chapter 5 for a description.

REGRESSION: In multiple regression analysis, this term is often used to indicate the amount of *explained* variation and is contrasted with **RESIDUAL**, which is *unexplained* variation.

REGRESSION ANALYSIS: A statistical technique designed to predict values of a dependent (or criterion) variable from knowledge of the values of one or more independent (or predictor) variable(s). See Chapters 19 and 20 for greater detail.

REGRESSION COEFFICIENTS: The B values. These are the coefficients of the variables within the regression equation plus the constant.

REGRESSION **Command**: The SPSS command that accesses simple linear regression, curvilinear regression, and multiple regression. See Chapters 19 and 20 for a more complete description.

REGRESSION LINE: Also called the *line of best fit*. A straight line drawn through a scatter plot that represents the best possible fit for making predictions from one variable to the other.

REGRESSION PLOT: A scatter plot that includes the intercepts for the regression line in the vertical axes.

RELIABILITY **Command**: The SPSS command that accesses the reliability procedure. See Chapter 24 for additional detail.

RESIDUAL: Statistics relating to the *un*explained portion of the variance.

RESIDUALS AND STANDARDIZED RESIDUALS: In log-linear models, the residuals are the observed counts minus the expected counts. High residuals indicate that the model is not adequate. SPSS calculates the adjusted residuals using an estimate of the standard error. The distribution of adjusted residuals is a standard normal distribution, and numbers greater than 1.96 or less than −1.96 are *not* likely to have occurred by chance ($\alpha = .05$).

ROTATION: A procedure used in factor analysis in which axes are rotated in order to yield a better simple structure and a more interpretable pattern of values.

ROW PERCENT: A term used with crosstabulated data. It is the result of dividing the frequency of values in a particular cell by the frequency of values in the entire row. Row percents sum to 100% in each row.

ROW TOTAL: The total number of subjects in a particular row.

ROY-BARGMANN STEPDOWN F: In a MANOVA analysis, the stepdown F examines the effects of the covariate on each of the dependent variables. For each succeeding dependent variable, the effects of all preceding dependent variables are removed;

they have been covaried out. The *F*-values in this printout are labeled *Stepdown F* to indicate that they refer to any new variance not accounted for by previous variables in the table.

RUNS TEST: A nonparametric test that determines whether the elements of a single dichotomous group differ from a random distribution.

SAMPLE: A set of individuals or cases taken from some population for the purpose of making inferences about characteristics of the population.

SAMPLING ERROR: The anticipated difference between a random sample and the population from which it is drawn based on chance alone.

SAVE OUTFILE **Command**: The SPSS command designed to save a formatted file for future use. See pages 24 and 25 for a more complete description.

SCALE MEAN IF ITEM DELETED: In reliability analysis, for each subject all the variables (excluding the variable to the left) are summed. The values shown are the means for all variables across all subjects.

SCALE VARIANCE IF ITEM DELETED: In reliability analysis, the variance of summed variables when the variable to the left is deleted.

SCATTER PLOT: A plot showing the relationship between two variables by marking all possible pairs of values on a bicoordinate plane. See Chapter 10 for greater detail.

SCHEFFÉ PROCEDURE: The Scheffé test allows the researcher to make pair-wise comparisons of means after a significant *F*-value has been observed in an ANOVA.

SCREE PLOT: A plot of the eigenvalues in a factor analysis that is often used to determine how many factors to retain for rotation.

SELECT IF **Command**: The SPSS command that allows the researcher to select a portion of the data for analysis for a number of different procedures. See Chapter 5 for additional detail.

SIGNIFICANCE: Frequently called PROBABILITY. A measure of the rarity of a particular statistical outcome given that there is actually no effect. A significance of $p < .05$ is the most widely accepted value by which researchers accept a certain result as statistically significant. It means that there is less than a 5% chance that the given outcome could have occurred by chance.

SIGN TEST: A nonparametric test that determines whether two distributions differ based on a comparison of paired scores.

SINGULAR VARIANCE-COVARIANCE MATRICES: Cells with only one observation or with singular variance-covariance matrices indicate that there may not be enough data to accurately compute MANOVA statistics or that there may be other problems present in the data, such as linear dependencies (where one variable is dependent on one or more of the other variables). Results from any analysis with only one observation or with singular variance-covariance matrices for some cells should be interpreted with caution.

SIZE: The number associated with an article of clothing in which the magnitude of the number typically correlates positively with the size of the associated body part.

SKEWNESS: In a distribution of values, this is a measure of deviation from symmetry. Negative skewness describes a distribution with a greater number of values above the mean; positive skewness describes a distribution with a greater number of values below the mean. See Chapter 7 for a more complete description.

SLOPE: The angle of a line in a bicoordinate plane based on the amount of change in the Y variable per unit change in the X variable. This is a term most frequently used in regression analysis and can be thought of as a weighted constant indicating the influence of the independent variable(s) on a designated dependent variable.

SORT **Command**: The SPSS command that allows the researcher to reorder data within the file. See Chapter 5 for additional detail.

SPLIT-HALF RELIABILITY: A measure of reliability in which an instrument is divided into two equivalent sections (or different forms of the same test or the same test given at different times) and then intercorrelations between these two halves are calculated as a measure of internal consistency.

SQUARED EUCLIDEAN DISTANCE: The most common method (and the SPSS default) used in cluster analysis to determine how cases or clusters differ from each other. It is the sum of squared differences between values on corresponding variables.

SQUARED MULTIPLE CORRELATION: In reliability analysis, these values are determined by creating a multiple regression equation to generate the *predicted correlation* based on the correlations for all other variables.

SSCON = **1.000E–08**: This is the default value at which iteration ceases in nonlinear regression. 1.000E–08 is the computer's version of 1.000×10^{-8}, scientific notation for .00000001 (one hundred-millionth). This criterion utilizes the residual sum of squares as the value to determine when iteration ceases.

STANDARD DEVIATION: The standard measure of variability around the mean of a distribution. The standard deviation is the square root of the variance (the sum of squared deviations from the mean divided by $N - 1$).

STANDARD ERROR: This term is most frequently applied to the *mean* of a distribution but may apply to other measures as well. It is the standard deviation of the statistic-of-interest given a large number of samples drawn from the same population. It is typically used as a measure of the stability or of the sampling error of the distribution and is based on the standard deviation of a single random sample.

STANDARDIZED ITEM ALPHA: In reliability analysis, this is the alpha produced if the included items are changed to z-scores before computing the alpha.

STATISTICS FOR SUMMED VARIABLES: In reliability analysis, there are always a number of variables being considered. This line lists descriptive information about the *sum* of all variables for the entire sample of subjects.

STEPWISE VARIABLE SELECTION: This procedure enters variables into the discriminant equation, one at a time, based on a designated criterion for inclusion ($F \geq 1.00$ is default) but will drop variables from the equation if the inclusion requirement drops below the designated level when other variables have been entered.

SUM OF SQUARES: A standard measure of variability. It is the sum of the square of each value subtracted from the mean.

SYS: The three-letter code following the name of a formatted system file, such as **GRADES.SYS**.

t-**TEST**: A procedure used for comparing exactly two sample means to see if there is sufficient evidence to infer that the means of the corresponding population distributions also differ.

T-TEST Command: The SPSS command that accesses *t*-test procedures. See Chapter 12 for a description.

t-**TEST—INDEPENDENT SAMPLES**: A *t*-test that compares the means of two distributions of some variable in which there is no overlap of membership of the two groups being measured.

t-**TEST—ONE SAMPLE**: A *t*-test in which the mean of a distribution of values is compared to a single fixed value.

t-**TEST—PAIRED SAMPLES**: A *t*-test in which the same subjects experience both levels of the variable of interest.

t-**TESTS IN REGRESSION ANALYSIS**: A test to determine the likelihood that a particular correlation is statistically significant. In the regression output, it is B divided by the standard error of B.

TOLERANCE LEVEL: The tolerance level is a measure of linear dependency between one variable and the others. In discriminant analysis, if a tolerance is less than .001, this indicates a high level of linear dependency, and SPSS will not enter that variable into the equation.

TOTAL SUM OF SQUARES: The sum of squared deviations of every raw score from the overall mean of the distribution.

TUKEY'S HSD: (Honestly Significant Difference). A value that allows the researcher to make pair-wise comparisons of means after a significant F-value has been observed in an ANOVA.

TWO-TAILED TEST: A test in which significance of the result is based on deviation from the null hypothesis in *either* direction (larger or smaller).

UNEQUAL-LENGTH SPEARMAN-BROWN: In split-half reliability, the reliability calculated when the two "halves" are not equal in size.

UNIVARIATE F-TESTS: An F-ratio showing the influence of exactly one independent variable on a dependent variable.

UNSTANDARDIZED CANONICAL DISCRIMINANT FUNCTION COEFFICIENTS: This is the list of coefficients (and the constant) of the discriminant equation.

VALID PERCENT: Percent of each value excluding missing values.

VALUE: The number associated with each level of a variable.

VALUE LABEL: Names or number codes for levels of different variables.

VARIABILITY: The way in which scores are scattered around the center of a distribution. Also known as variance, dispersion, or spread.

VARIABLE LABELS: These are labels entered when formatting the raw data file. They allow up to 40 characters for a more complete description of the variable than is possible in the 8-character name.

VARIABLES IN THE EQUATION: In regression analysis, after each step in building the equation, SPSS displays a summary of the effects of the variables that are currently in the regression equation.

VARIANCE: A measure of variability about the mean, the square of the standard deviation, used largely for computational purposes. The variance is the sum of squared deviations divided by $N - 1$.

WALD: In log-linear models, a measure of the significance of B for the given variable. Higher values, in combination with the degrees of freedom, indicate significance.

WILCOXON MATCHED-PAIRS SIGNED-RANKS TEST: A nonparametric test that is similar to the sign test except the positive and negative signs are weighted by the mean rank of positive versus negative comparisons.

WILKS' LAMBDA: The ratio of the within-groups sum of squares to the total sum of squares. This is the proportion of the total variance in the discriminant scores *not* explained by differences among groups. A lambda of 1.00 occurs when observed group means are equal (all the variance is explained by factors *other than* difference between these means), whereas a small lambda occurs when within-groups variability is small compared to the total variability. A small lambda indicates that group means appear to differ. The associated significance values indicate whether the difference is significant.

WITHIN-GROUPS SUM OF SQUARES: The sum of squared deviations between the mean for each group and the observed values of each subject within that group.

Z-SCORE: Also called *standard score*. A distribution of values that standardizes raw data to a mean of zero (0) and a standard deviation of one (1.0). A z-score is able to indicate the direction and degree that any raw score deviates from the mean of a distribution. Z-scores are also used to indicate the significant deviation from the mean of a distribution. A z-score with a magnitude greater than ± 1.96 indicates a significant difference at $p < .05$ level.

REFERENCES

The three SPSS/PC+ manuals cover (in great detail) all procedures that are included in the present book:

Norusis, Marija J. (1990). *SPSS/PC+ 4.0 Base Manual*. Chicago: SPSS Inc.

Norusis, Marija J. (1990). *SPSS/PC+ Statistics 4.0*. Chicago: SPSS Inc.

Norusis, Marija J. (1990). *SPSS/PC+ Advanced Statistics 4.0*. Chicago: SPSS Inc.

Good introductory statistics texts that cover material through Chapter 13 (one-way ANOVA), and Chapter 24 (reliability):

Fox, James; Levin, Jack; & Harkins, Stephen. (1993). *Elementary Statistics in Behavioral Research*. New York: Harper Collins College Publishers.

Hopkins, Kenneth; Glass, Gene; & Hopkins, B.R. (1987). *Basic Statistics for the Behavioral Sciences*. Boston: Allyn and Bacon.

Moore, David; & McCabe, George. (1993). *Introduction to the Practice of Statistics, Second Edition*. New York: W.H. Freeman and Company.

Welkowitz, Joan; Ewen, Robert; & Cohen, Jacob. (1991). *Introductory Statistics for the Behavioral Sciences, Fourth Edition*. New York: Harcourt Brace Jovanovich.

Witte, Robert S. (1985). *Statistics, Second Edition*. New York: Holt, Rinehart and Winston.

Comprehensive coverage of Analysis of Variance:

Keppel, Geoffrey. (1973). *Design and Analysis: A Researcher's Handbook*. Englewood Cliffs, NJ: Prentice Hall.

Lindman, Harold R. (1992). *Analysis of Variance in Experimental Design*. New York: Springer-Verlag.

Schulman, Robert S. (1992). *Statistics in Plain English with Computer Applications*. New York: Van Nostrand Reinhold.

Comprehensive coverage of MANOVA and MANCOVA:

Lindman, Harold R. (1992). *Analysis of Variance in Experimental Design*. New York: Springer-Verlag.

Comprehensive coverage of simple and multiple regression analysis:

Chatterjee, Samprit; & Price, Bertram. (1991). *Regression Analysis by Example, Second Edition*. New York: John Wiley & Sons.

Gonick, Larry; & Smith, Woolcott. (1993). *The Cartoon Guide to Statistics*. New York: Harper Perennial.

Kerlinger, Fred N.; & Pedhazur, Elazar J. (1973). *Multiple Regression in Behavioral Research*. New York: Holt, Rinehart and Winston.

Schulman, Robert S. (1992). *Statistics in Plain English with Computer Applications*. New York: Van Nostrand Reinhold.

Sen, Ashish; & Srivastava, Muni. (1990). *Regression Analysis: Theory, Methods, and Applications*. New York: Springer-Verlag.

Weisberg, Sanford. (1985). *Applied Linear Regression, Second Edition*. New York: John Wiley & Sons.

Comprehensive coverage of factor analysis:

Comrey, Andrew L.; & Lee, Howard B. (1991). *A First Course in Factor Analysis*. Hillsdale, NJ: Lawrence Erlbaum Associates.

Comprehensive coverage of cluster analysis:

Everitt, Brian S. (1993). *Cluster Analysis, Third Edition*. London: Edward Arnold.

Comprehensive coverage of discriminant analysis:

McLachlan, Geoffrey J. (1992). *Discriminant Analysis and Statistical Pattern Recognition*. New York: John Wiley & Sons.

Comprehensive coverage of nonlinear regression:

Seber, G .A . F.; & Wild, C. J. (1989). *Nonlinear Regression*. New York: John Wiley & Sons.

Comprehensive coverage of logistic regression analysis and loglinear models:

Agresti, Alan. (1990). *Categorical Data Analysis*. New York: Wiley & Sons.

McLachlan, Geoffrey J. (1992). *Discriminant Analysis and Statistical Pattern Recognition.* New York: John Wiley & Sons.

Wickens, Thomas D. (1989). *Mulltiway Contingency Tables Analysis for the Social Sciences.* Hillsdale, NJ: Lawrence Erlbaum Associates.

Comprehensive coverage of logit and probit analysis:

Agresti, Alan. (1990). *Categorical Data Analysis.* New York: Wiley & Sons.

Wickens, Thomas D. (1989). *Mulltiway Contingency Tables Analysis for the Social Sciences.* Hillsdale, NJ: Lawrence Erlbaum Associates.

Comprehensive coverage of nonparametric tests:

Siegel, Sidney; & Castellan, N. John, Jr. (1988). *Nonparametric Statistics for the Behavioral Sciences, Second Edition.* New York: McGraw-Hill.

ERROR MESSAGES

This appendix is for occasions when you get a somewhat enigmatic error message from SPSS while you are trying to run a program. This will probably happen to you frequently. You may not be sure quite what the message means, but you are sure that SPSS has not given you the output that you wanted. Instead, it reported an ERROR (in big uppercase letters) and stopped.

The bad news is that we can't tell you exactly what to type in order to fix the error message. There are far too many SPSS error messages, and a number of different problems can cause each message. The good news is that, if you have been following the step-by-step instructions throughout this book, the error will probably be easy to fix.

This appendix will first describe what error messages are and then give some general procedures that usually will fix an error. Finally, if these general procedures do not work, we give you several examples of SPSS program files with errors in them, along with the error messages that SPSS produces when the program is run. We will describe what the problem is in the program and tell you how to fix it. Most error messages that you encounter can be fixed by following either the general procedures or the examples.

WHAT ERROR MESSAGES ARE

SPSS/PC+ is an exceedingly complex program. (You probably realize that by now.) It usually does a great job in complex analysis of voluminous data. Sometimes, though, it gets confused.

If SPSS isn't confused, but only a bit concerned, it issues a "NOTE." These notes are usually worth trying to figure out; they indicate that, although SPSS isn't so confused that it can't keep going, something unusual is happening in the processing. Notes are often reported when some assumption of a statistical test is violated.

When SPSS does get confused, it issues a "WARNING." Warnings are a bigger concern than notes; they mean that SPSS has found something in the commands or in the data that might give you inaccurate results. If you get a warning, you should pay attention to it and try to figure out if your results are right.

When SPSS is very confused, it issues an "ERROR." And then it gets frustrated and stops. SPSS will tell you what it thinks the problem is. Unfortunately, SPSS doesn't always know what the problem is—but even if it isn't sure, it will tell you its best guess. Sometimes that guess is wrong. That's why it is important to go through the general procedures to try to solve the problem, no matter what SPSS says the error is.

GENERAL PROCEDURES FOR FIXING ERRORS

When an error occurs, a number of steps should always be followed to determine what the problem is. Most error messages occur because of the problems listed here, so these procedures should always be followed *no matter what error message* SPSS reports.

- First of all, don't panic. The computer has very probably not broken. Unless you see smoke, you will probably be able to fix the problem easily.
- Carefully proofread the commands that you have given SPSS. The error message will be

printed after a particular command; you should proofread the command after which SPSS has stopped *and* the two previous lines. Sometimes, SPSS thinks it understands what you are telling it to do, but it really doesn't; when this happens, it will usually get confused later. So, it is important to proofread the lines *before* the line in which the error occurred.

- As you proofread, pay special attention to punctuation marks and spaces. Be sure that your commands match our examples; if a period or slash is in the wrong place, SPSS will almost always get confused and give an error message.
- Look closely at the spelling of SPSS commands and your variable names. Your variable names must be spelled exactly the same every time you use them.
- Remember that all of the **bold** text in our examples should be typed exactly as in our examples. All of the <u>underlined</u> text in our examples should *not* be typed as in our examples (unless you want to try our examples). Instead, type information that is specific to your analysis.
- If you find an error or a typo, edit the file and run it again. It should work (unless there is another error somewhere).

SAMPLE ERRORS

SPSS/PC+ can produce a huge variety of error messages. Unfortunately, a full description of all of them is not possible here, because many different problems may produce any single error message. Instead, we describe in detail several common error messages. If your particular error message is not described in these examples, it is likely that your problem is similar to the problems described in the following examples.

Problems in Opening a File

The following example is taken from Chapter 9. The correct version of the command file is listed on page 65. Below is the incorrect version of the command file:

```
GET FILE = 'GRADES.SYS.'
MEANS TABLES = TOTAL BY SECTION BY GENDER/
STATISTICS = 1.
```

When the above command file was executed, the following error occurred immediately after the first (**GET FILE**) line:

```
ERROR, Text: GRADES.SYS.
A FILE CANNOT BE OPENED ON GET, SAVE, OR AGGREGATE COMMAND—Check for a
misspelled file name.  If the file exists, try increasing the FILES
specification in CONFIG.SYS. This command not executed.
```

SPSS tried to open file **GRADES.SYS** but could not. As discussed above, the first thing to do is carefully proofread the command file. In this case, the period at the end of the **GET FILE** line is to the left of the single quote instead of to the right of the single quote. When the period is moved to the right of the single quote, at the very end of the **GET FILE** line, the program runs correctly. Note that you might have to include an A:\ or B:\ before the file name if you want to read the file from a floppy disk.

Invalid Subcommand

This example is again taken from Chapter 9; the correct version of the command file is on page 65. An incorrect version of the file is listed below:

```
GET FILE = 'GRADES.SYS'
MEANS TABLE = TOTAL BY SECTION BY GENDER/
STATISTICS = 1.
```

When the above command file was executed, it produced the following error message after the **MEANS** line:

```
ERROR, Text: MEANS: INVALID SUBCOMMAND ON GET COMMAND—Valid
subcommands are FILE, DROP, KEEP, and RENAME.  This command not
executed.
```

The clue in the error message is that SPSS says that it is on the **GET** command. But **MEANS** is supposed to be a *new* command. SPSS didn't figure out that **MEANS** was a new command because the period was missing at the end of the **GET FILE** command. Once a period is added, the file runs properly.

Undefined Variable Name

The following command file (again taken from page 65) produced the error listed below:

```
GET FILE = 'GRADES.SYS'.
MEANS TABLE = TOTAL BY SECTION BY GENDER
STATISTICS = 1.
```

```
ERROR, Text: STATISTICS
UNDEFINED VARIABLE NAME—Check for a misspelled name.  This command not
executed.
```

In this example, a slash (/) is missing from the end of the **MEANS** line. Because the slash is missing, SPSS does not realize that we are finished listing the variables to be used in the **MEANS** command and thinks that we are continuing with more variable names on the last line of the command file. Of course, since **STATISTICS** is not a variable name, SPSS produces an error message. Upon placing the slash at the end of the **MEANS** line, the file works correctly.

Misspelled Variable Name

The following command file (from page 65) produced the following error immediately after the second (**MEANS**) line:

```
GET FILE = 'GRADES.SYS'.
MEANS TABLE = TOTAL BY SECTION BY GEDNER/
STATISTICS = 1.
```

```
ERROR, Text: GEDNER
UNDEFINED VARIABLE NAME—Check for a misspelled name.  This command
not executed.
```

In this case, SPSS produced an error message that does accurately describe the problem. Since the variable name should be **GENDER** and we typed **GEDNER**, SPSS doesn't know what the variable name should be. So, it produces an error message and stops. By fixing the spelling error, and rerunning the command file, the problem is solved.

Missing Variable List

The following command file (from page 65) produced the following error message immediately after the second (**MEANS**) line:

```
GET FILE = 'GRADES.SYS'.
MEANS TABLE = BY SECTION BY GENDER/
STATISTICS = 1.

ERROR, Text: BY
MISSING VARIABLE LIST.  This command not executed.
```

In this case, SPSS expected a list of dependent variable(s) following **TABLE** =. Instead, the word **BY** came immediately after the **TABLE** = subcommand. By putting a variable name before the word **BY**, this error is fixed.

Wrong Variable Type

The following command file produced the error message below, immediately following the second (**MEANS**) line:

```
GET FILE = 'GRADES.SYS'.
MEANS TABLE = GRADE BY SECTION BY GENDER/
STATISTICS = 1.

ERROR, Text: GRADE
INVALID STRING—A quoted string is used incorrectly.  Perhaps it has
been specified for a procedure which does not accept string variables.
This command not executed.
```

In this case, the **MEANS** command gave an error because **GRADE** is not a number. **GRADE** contains the letter grades of the students in our example, and SPSS can't calculate a mean of letters (just of numbers).

Missing Parenthesis

This example is taken from Chapter 18, page 145. The following error message was produced immediately after the **WSFACTORS** line:

```
MANOVA QUIZ1 QUIZ2 QUIZ3 QUIZ4/
WSFACTORS PAPERCOL(2 INKCOL(2)/
PRINT CELLINFO(MEANS COR) TRANSFORM.
```

```
ERROR, Text: INKCOL
INVALID MANOVA WSFACTORS SUBCOMMAND—An integer greater than 1 is
required in parentheses after each factor name.  This command not
executed.
```

In this case, SPSS directs us to the text **INKCOL** in the second line of the command file. SPSS suggests that something is needed in parentheses. Aha! After the variable **PAPERCOL**, we have a left parenthesis, followed by the number 2, but no right parenthesis. If a right parenthesis is placed immediately after the number 2, the program runs correctly.

INDEX

A

ABS (Absolute value), 32
Addition, 32
Alpha (α), 95, 218, 224-227
Alphabetic data, 10, 21
Analysis of covariance, 112, 117
Analysis of variance, 62, 92, 98-112
Analyzing only part of the data, 36
ANOVA, 62, 92, 98-112
ASCII files, 6
Asymptotic correlation matrix, 235-236
Asymptotic standard error, 236

B

B, 135, 149, 155, 161, 164, 173, 244
Backward elimination, 248, 256
Backward regression analysis, 170
Bar charts, 39
Bartlett test of sphericity, 185
Bartlett-Box F, 99
Beta, 135, 149, 161, 165, 173
Between-groups degrees of freedom, 66
Between-groups sum of squares, 66, 98
Binomial test, 277, 283
Bivariate correlation, 75
Blocks of text, 16-17
Boxes, 5
Box's M, 208, 214

C

Canonical correlation, 215
Canonical discriminant function, 214, 217
Carriage Return key, 5
Categorical data, 24, 39, 53
Cell means, 125
Centroids, 216
Chi-square
    discriminant analysis, 215
    logistic regression, 243
    logit analysis, 274
    log-linear models, 248, 252-254
    one-sample test, 285
    probit analysis, 274
    test of independence, 53-54, 60
Classification results, 217
Classification table, 243
CLUSTER (Cluster analysis), 189, 194, 197
Cochran's C, 99
Coding values, 35
Coefficient alpha, 218-219, 225

Columns, 12, 17
Command file, 20, 22, 25
Command keys, 5
Communality, 176, 185
Complete linkage, 195
COMPUTE, 27-28, 32-33
Computer networks, 1
Confidence interval, 99, 127, 135, 138, 149, 255, 265
Continuous data, 39
Continuous variables, 67
Contrasts, 96, 99
Copy blocks of text, 17
CORRELATION, 75, 79-81
Correlations, 73-75, 91, 125, 132, 146, 154-155, 227
Correlation matrices
    calculating, 75
    cluster analysis, 196
    factor analysis, 175, 183
    logistic regression analysis, 244
    MANOVA, 125, 133
    nonlinear regression, 235-236
Count, 60, 99
Covariance, 112, 117
Covariance matrix, 169, 208, 214
Covariates, 107-108, 134, 259
Cramer's V, 55, 61
Creating a data file, 2
Creating new variables from old variables, 32-34
CROSSTABS, 53, 56, 60
Crosstabulation, 53
CTL files, 24-25
CTRL key, 14
Cumulative percent, 44
Curvilinear regression, 152, 159, 162, 229
Curvilinear relationship, 155, 162, 166

D

DAT files, 24
Data
    disk, 3
    editing, 14
    entry, 9
    file, 8-9, 14, 19, 24
    management, 27
    selection, 36
DATA LIST, 7, 20-21
Decimal points, 21
Degrees of freedom
    ANOVA, 66, 98-99, 106

Chi-square, 61
  discriminant analysis, 215
  log-linear models, 252-254
  MANOVA, 119, 126, 136, 148
  regression, 161, 173
  t test, 90
Delete blocks of text, 17
Dendogram, 201
Descending sort, 38
Descriptive statistics, 42, 46
DESCRIPTIVES, 46, 50, 52
Determinant, 125, 133, 214
Deviation from normality, 46, 48, 275
DF *(see Degrees of freedom)*
Dichotomous variables, 237
Discriminant analysis, 202, 207
Discriminant functions, 208, 214
Discriminant scores, 217
Disk with data, 3
Disk drive, 8
Dispersion matrices, 125, 134
DOS, 8
DOS prompt, 1, 9
Doubly multivariate MANOVA, 144-147, 150
DSCRIMINANT, 202, 207
Duncan, 95

E

e, 33
Editing a data file, 14
Eigenvalues, 177, 182, 185, 215
EJECT subcommand, 70
ENTER key, 10
EQ (Equals), 34
Equal-length Spearman-Brown, 227
Error mean squares, 126
Error messages, 22-23, 311-315
Error sum of squares, 126, 136, 151
Eta, 66
ETHNICIT, 12
Example data file, 3, 6, 11-13

EXP, 33
Expected counts, 257, 265
Expected frequencies, 61, 274
Expected values, 54, 57, 60
Experienced users, 6-8
Exponent, 32
Extract factors, 175-176
EXTRCRED, 12

F

F

  ANOVA, 66, 90, 98, 106, 119

  change, 174
  discriminant analysis, 208, 211
  MANOVA, 135, 148, 151
  regression, 161, 173
  T, 126
F4 key, 16
F7 key, 17
FACTOR, 175, 181, 185
Factor analysis, 175, 185, 189
Factor extraction, 175-176
Factor loadings, 177
Factor matrix, 188
Factor rotation, 175-178, 182
Factor selection, 177
Files
  CTL, 24-25
  DAT, 24
  SYS, 24
FINAL, 12
FIRSTNAM, 12
Forced-entry regression analysis, 170
Forced-removal regression analysis, 171
FORMATS, 20-21
Formatting
  boxes, 5
  conventions, 6
  data file, 14, 19
  italics, 6
  numbering, 5
Forward regression analysis, 170
FREQUENCIES, 39-41, 44, 51
Fridman two-way ANOVA, 277, 286

G

GE, 34
GENDER, 12
GET FILE, 24, 29
Goodness of fit, 243, 257, 265, 274
Grades example, 4
GRADES.CTL, 24
GRADES.DAT, 9, 14, 20, 24
Grand median, 275
Greater than, 34
Greater than or equal to, 34
Greenhouse-Geisser Epsilon, 150
GT, 34
Guttman split-half, 227

H

Hierarchical log-linear models, 246, 250-252, 258
HILOGLINEAR, 246, 250, 252
Histogram, 39, 45, 208
Homogeneity of dispersion matrices, 125, 134
Homogeneity of variance, 99

Hotelling's T^2, 120
Huynh-Feldt Epsilon, 150
Hypothesis mean squares, 126
Hypothesis sum of squares, 126, 136

I

Icicle plot, 195, 200
ID, 12
IF, 27-28, 34
Independent-samples t test, 83, 86, 88
INS key, 15
Inter-item correlations, 226
Interactions, 101, 105, 113-116, 119, 147
Intercept, 74, 273
Intrinsically nonlinear regression, 229
Italics, 6
Iterations, 235, 253-254, 273

K

K, 252-253
K-sample median test, 277, 287
Kaiser-Mayer-Olkin, 185
Keyboard conventions, 5
Keys, 5, 14-17
Kolmogorov-Smirnov one-sample test, 277, 284
Kurtosis, 43, 46-48

L

LASTNAME, 12
LE, 34
Least-significant difference, 95
Less than, 34
Less than or equal to, 34
Likelihood ratio chi-square, 60, 252-253
Line of best fit, 68, 163, 269
Linear regression, 152, 156-159, 246
Liner trends, 77, 166
Lines of text, 17
LIST, 20-21, 27-29
LN, 33
Log-linear models, 246, 258, 261, 264
LOG10, 33
Logarithm, 33
LOGISTIC REGRESSION, 237-242
Logit, 266-267
Logit models, 259
LOGLINEAR, 258, 261
LOWUP, 12
LT, 34

M

Main effect, 101, 106, 113, 119, 147
Managing data, 27
MANCOVA, 128, 134, 139

Mann-Whitney and Wilcoxon rank-sum test, 277-279
MANOVA, 120-124, 128-132, 139, 142, 145
Mantel-Haeszel test for linear association, 61
Math operators, 32
Maximum, 43, 46, 49, 99
Mean, 43, 46-47, 91, 98-99, 169
Mean square, 66, 98, 106, 119, 161, 173, 236
MEANS, 62-63, 65
Measures of central tendency, 46-47
Median, 43, 46-47, 51, 287
Minimum, 43, 46, 49, 99
Minimum expected frequency, 61
Missing data, 10, 30, 208
Mixed design MANOVA, 145
Mixed-subjects designs, 147-149
MOD10, 33
Mode, 43, 46-47, 51
Model selection, 166, 248, 259
Modifying variables, 34
MORE at upper right of screen, 22-23
Move blocks of text, 17
Multiple correlations, 155, 226
Multiple linear regression models, 246
Multiple R, 161, 165, 172
Multiple regression analysis, 160, 163, 168-172, 237
Multiplication, 32
Multivariate analysis of variance, 128, 132, 139
Multivariate T^2, 120, 124-125
Multivariate test for homogeneity of dispersion
     matrices, 125, 134
Multivariate tests of significance, 126
Munchly's sphericity test, 150

N

Names in data files, 10
NE, 34
Negative correlation, 76
Negatively skewed distribution, 46
Network of computers, 1
NLR, 228, 232-233
Nonhierarchical log-linear models, 258 *(see also*
     Log-linear models)
Nonlinear regression, 228
Nonparametric tests, 275
Normal distribution, 46-48, 275, 284
Not equal, 34
NPAR, 275
Numbering
     of Lines, 5
     To Do steps, 5

O

Oblique rotations, 178
Observed count, 257, 265, 274

Observed values, 54, 57-58
One-sample chi-square test, 277-285
One-sample *t* test, 84, 87, 90
One-way analysis of variance, 92
ONEWAY, 92-94, 97
Orthogonal rotations, 178
Overlay plots, 67, 70

P

p value
    ANOVA, 66, 98, 109, 119
    chi-square, 61
    correlation, 73, 77
    discriminant analysis, 211, 215
    MANOVA, 126-127, 136-138, 148, 151
    regression, 161
    t test, 85
Paired-samples *t* test, 83-84, 87-89
Parameter estimates, 126, 137, 236, 242, 248
Parametric tests, 275
Partial
    associations, 253
    chi-square, 254
    correlation, 173
Pattern matrix, 208
Pearson chi-square, 60, 252-253
Pearson goodness-of-fit, 274
Pearson *r*, 75 *(see also Correlation)*
Percentiles, 39, 45
Perfect negative correlation, 77
Perfect positive correlation, 75
Period at end of command, 21
Phi statistic, 55, 61
PLOT, 67, 69
Plot appearance, 71
Positive correlation, 76
Positively skewed distribution, 47
Predicted probabilities, 245
Predicted values, 153-153, 164
PREVGPA, 12
Principal-components analysis, 185
Printing output, 26
PROBIT, 266-267, 270-271
PROCESS IF, 27-28, 36-37

Q

Quadratic equation, 157
QUIZ variables, 12

R

r, 75 *(see also Correlation)*
R, 155, 161, 165, 172, 244
R^2, 73, 161, 165, 172, 236
Range, 43, 46, 49

Rank of covariance matrix, 214
Ranked values, 275, 286
Rearranging data, 37
RECODE, 27-31, 35
Rectangles of text, 17
REGRESSION, 152, 161-163, 168
Regression
    analysis, 160-163, 172-174, 236-237
    coefficient, 273
    equation, 152-153, 163-164
    line, 68, 73-74, 163
    models, 246
    nonlinear, 228
    plot, 67, 70-72
RELIABILITY, 218, 221-225
Repeated measures, 139
Replacing missing values, 30
Residual, 57, 119, 153-154, 161, 236, 254, 265
RETURN key, 5, 10
REVIEW, 47
Review editor, 6, 9
RND, 32
Rotated factor matrix, 188
Rotation of factors, 175-178, 182
Rounding numbers, 32
Row total, 60
Roy-Bargmann Stepdown *F* tests, 134-136
Runs test, 277

S

Save a file, 11, 14, 18, 25
SAVE OUTFILE, 25
Scatter plot, 67, 72, 156, 208
Scheffé test, 95, 98
Scratch pad, 20
Scree plot, 182, 186
SELECT IF, 27-28, 36
Selecting data for analysis, 36
Selection rule, 211
Sign test, 277, 280
Significance
    ANOVA, 61, 66, 98, 106, 119
    correlation, 73, 77
    discriminant analysis, 211
    MANOVA, 126, 136, 148, 151
    regression, 161, 173
    t, 84
Simple linear regression, 152-154, 159
Simple structure, 177
Singular variance-covariance matrices, 134
Skewness, 43, 46-48
Slope, 74
SORT, 27-28, 37
Sorting data, 37
Spearman-Brown, 227

Split-half reliability, 218-220, 225
SPSSPC, 8
SQRT (square root), 33
Stability, 46, 49
Standard deviation, 43, 46-48, 91, 99, 169, 208
Standard error
    B, 135, 149, 161, 173, 244
    defined, 49
    kurtosis, 43, 46
    mean, 43, 46, 90, 99
    parameter estimates, 127, 138, 255,
       265, 273
    skewness, 43, 46
Standardized residual, 265
Stepdown F, 136
Stepwise regression analysis, 170
Stepwise variable selection, 211
Structure matrix, 208
Student-Newman-Keuls test, 95
Subpopulation differences, 62
Subtraction, 32
Sum, 43, 49
Sum of squares
    ANOVA, 66, 98, 105, 119
    MANOVA, 136, 148, 151
    regression, 161, 173
SYS files, 24
System file, 7, 24, 49
System-missing values, 31

T

T, 161, 173
T^2, 120, 125
t probability, 99
T-TEST, 83
t values, 90, 99, 127, 135, 138, 149
Territorial map, 208
Text manipulation, 16-17
Three-way analysis of variance, 107-108, 112
To Do steps, 5
Tolerance, 173
Transformation matrices, 146
Transformed variables, 140
True score, 153
TRUNC (truncate decimal portion of number), 32

Tukey, 95
Two-tailed probability, 90-91
Two-way analysis of variance, 100, 104
Typographical conventions, 4

U

Underlined text, 6
Unequal-length Spearman-Brown, 227
Univariate F-tests, 126
User-missing values, 31

V

Valid percent, 44
Value label, 44
VALUE LABELS, 7, 24
Variability, 46-48
VARIABLE LABELS, 7, 23
Variable names, 21
Variable transformations, 140
Variance, 43, 46-48, 154
Variance-covariance matrix, 125, 133-134

W

Wald test, 244
Wald-Wolfowitz runs test, 282
Weighted comparisons, 275
Wilcoxon matched-pairs signed-ranks test, 277, 281
Wilks' Lambda, 211, 215
Windows in SPSS, 20
Within-group
    correlations, 216
    degrees of freedom, 66, 98
    sum of squares, 66, 98
Within-subjects designs, 146
Within-subjects factors, 139, 142-143
Within-subjects MANOVA, 145

Y

YEAR, 12

Z

z value, 156, 255, 265
Windows operating system, 2, 8

Notes

Notes

Pract.deb.